APPLIED MATHEMATICS SERIES

Edited by

I. S. SOKOLNIKOFF

# ADVANCED
# ANTENNA
# THEORY

## APPLIED MATHEMATICS SERIES

THE APPLIED MATHEMATICS SERIES is devoted to
books dealing with mathematical theories underlying
physical and biological sciences, and with advanced
mathematical techniques needed for solving problems
of these sciences.

# ADVANCED ANTENNA THEORY

SERGEI A. SCHELKUNOFF

MEMBER OF THE TECHNICAL STAFF
BELL TELEPHONE LABORATORIES

NEW YORK.   JOHN WILEY & SONS, INC.
LONDON.   CHAPMAN & HALL, LIMITED
1952

Library of Congress Catalog Card Number: 52-5084

PRINTED IN THE UNITED STATES OF AMERICA

To my wife

JEAN KENNEDY SCHELKUNOFF

# PREFACE

Hertz is the founder of antenna theory. Three quarters of a century ago — only a few years after publication of Maxwell's treatise on electromagnetic theory — Hertz solved the first, the simplest, and the most basic antenna problem: the problem of a small capacitor antenna. In those days the progress of antenna theory was slow. Another quarter of a century had passed before the next significant advance was made when Pocklington showed that the current and charge on thin perfectly conducting wires are propagated approximately with the speed of light and that, between any two points of monochromatic excitation, the current distribution is approximately sinusoidal. Until recently the practical theory of antennas and antenna arrays was based on these two fundamental results. Hertz's solution enables one to calcu'ate the field and distribution of radiation for any given distribution of electric current. Jointly with Pocklington's result and with the aid of the principle of conservation of energy, it makes possible the solution of many other practical problems.

During the last ten or fifteen years, however, it has become increasingly evident that the time is here for further extension of fundamental antenna theory. This realization has stimulated work in this field, and the end of it is not in sight. For this reason a unified account of recent developments is timely. In this book I present a compact but general exposition of Hallén's method of obtaining asymptotic solutions for linear antennas, Stratton and Chu's theory of spheroidal antennas, and my theory of biconical antennas and thin antennas of arbitrary shape. I have included much hitherto unpublished work, and for reasons of space have condensed some developments which can be found in fuller form elsewhere. Perhaps needless to add, there is no routine method for solving antenna problems. At present we have to make the most of isolated solutions. Fortunately these solutions bring out different aspects of antenna behavior and together present a satisfying theory.

While my principal object in this book is to present mathematical methods for solving antenna problems, I also stress the resemblance of antennas to common circuits and transmission lines. Just as science is not a collection of unrelated facts but a body of knowledge in which facts are grouped together on the basis of their essential similarity, so applied mathematics does not consist merely of methods for solving problems but is also a way of recognizing the common features in apparently dissimilar phenomena. Mathematics helps one to evolve physical pictures which bring order into a multiplicity of facts. When the quantitative solutions of given problems are hard to find, these pictures often give qualitative answers. Maxwell's equations themselves express a physical point of view — the point of view developed by Faraday and formulated by him in geometrical terms. In Faraday's picture of electromagnetic phenomena, even a vacuum is a kind of "medium" in which electric and magnetic forces cause electric and magnetic "displacements." It is not necessary to endow these concepts with their literal meanings; the picture remains just as useful if they are thought of as expressions of what will happen when appropriate experiments are performed. Maxwell's equations are the relations between the spatial rates of change of the forces and the time rates of change of the displacements. They are reminiscent of the equations for forces and displacements in springs and at once suggest that electromagnetic disturbances are propagated from place to place. From this point of view, the arms of an antenna form the banks of a channel in which the waves excited by the source are confined before they emerge into unlimited space. In this sense antennas are similar to waveguides. This simple picture led me to a successful solution of certain antenna problems which is presented in one of the chapters in this book.

Hertz's analysis of electromagnetic waves excited by an oscillating charge gives automatically the forces existing between two such charges. From this point on, waves in the medium may be ignored. Instead one's attention may be concentrated on the currents in the various sections of the antenna as is usually done in the case of electric networks. Mathematically, Maxwell's equations with various boundary conditions become converted into integral equations. It was by this method that Pocklington obtained the important sinusoidal approximation to the current in thin antennas, and the natural frequencies and damping constants of circular loops. More recently Hallén discovered a method of deriving asymptotic solutions of integral equations for thin antennas. Still more recently Schwinger discovered variational properties of certain integrals which are very useful in approximate calculations. I have devoted two chapters to the essential features of this method of approach; but for actual applications I refer the reader to the original papers by Hallén and his followers.

An alternative to this approach is a direct solution of Maxwell's equations by the method of separating the variables. Unfortunately there are only a few coordinate systems in which these equations are separable. Of these, the important systems are Cartesian, circular-cylindrical, elliptic-cylindrical, spherical, and spheroidal. The first three are very convenient for solving waveguide problems but are not well suited to antenna problems. All their coordinate surfaces are infinite in extent whereas the boundaries of actual antennas are finite. The spheroidal system (and the spherical as its special case) is the only system that contains coordinate surfaces of finite dimensions. For this reason spheroidal antennas received considerable attention in theory. As far back as 1897, Abraham analyzed free oscillations on thin spheroids. Spheroidal functions, however, turned out to be very complex, and it was only in 1941 that Stratton and Chu succeeded in obtaining and interpreting the complete solution in the case of forced oscillations. Although spheroidal antennas are not used in practice, their theory is important because it exhibits one aspect of antennas: the resemblance to leaky resonators. The impressed electromotive force excites various modes of oscillation of current in the antenna. In each mode the current excites waves in surrounding space, and energy is lost by radiation.

In the middle '30's I considered several possible methods of dealing with cylindrical antennas. It was then that I recognized the possibility of developing a method that would conform to one outstanding physical characteristic of all thin antennas regardless of their shape: The waves excited in the center of such an antenna are guided by its arms and are almost totally reflected from the ends. Spherical coordinates were clearly indicated for expressing radial propagation from a point. To simplify the boundary conditions I assumed at first that the antenna arms were conical. The surface of the antenna was divided into the major conical part and the small complementary ends. The boundary conditions over the major part were to be satisfied first. In fact, for sufficiently thin antennas the end surfaces could be neglected. Subsequently the conical boundary was deformed into an arbitrary shape. The effect of such deformation happened to be easily calculable. Thus it was no longer necessary to rely on spheroidal coordinates as sole coordinates suitable for analysis of thin antennas by the method of separating the variables. I have assigned a long chapter to this method because my early papers were too sketchy.

Many years passed before Hertz's and Pocklington's theoretical results became fully exploited. It may take as many years again for full exploitation of the new results, although even now there is ample evidence that recent theoretical work has not been in vain. Practical engineers are skillful in squeezing the most from a new idea or from a particularly significant solution. I take no chances in recommending antenna theory to applied mathematicians as a fertile field, abundant in problems requiring imagination, ingenuity, and analytic prowess. I hope that this book will interest them as well as radio engineers. Mathematicians need not fear that they may fail to understand it for lack of specialized engineering knowledge. And the type of mathematics needed in advanced antenna theory is beginning to look less fearsome to the new generation of engineers than it did to their predecessors.

I am very grateful to Miss Marion C. Gray who has checked the text and equations in the original manuscript and in proof, and who has prepared the index. I thank Miss Dorothy T. Angell for her assistance in proofreading. Mr. B. A. Clarke made many helpful suggestions in connection with illustrations, and Mr. H. P. Gridley did the drawings.

S. A. S.

*New York, December 1951*

# CONTENTS

## 1 SPHERICAL WAVES

# 1

# SPHERICAL WAVES

## 1.1 Classification of antenna theories

Passive electric structures are usually divided into circuits, transmission lines, waveguides, resonators, and antennas; but structurally there are no sharp dividing lines among these subdivisions. Any electric circuit (of practical dimensions) will radiate some power and thus will act as an antenna, although unintentionally. At low frequencies the power radiated by an ordinary circuit is negligibly small; at high frequencies special precautions (shielding, for instance) must be taken to reduce the radiated power, or else the circuit will not have the intended performance. Structurally some antennas are merely sections of transmission lines, short or long; they are also resonators. As resonators antennas are naturally poor; and, since in antennas the resonant properties are usually undesirable, efforts are often made to eliminate these properties as much as physically possible.

From the point of view of electromagnetic theory, there are also no sharp criteria which enable one to distinguish among circuits, transmission lines, waveguides, resonators, and antennas. Mathematically we are confronted with the same general problem: that of solving Maxwell's equations; but the most convenient method of solution depends on the type of structure and the most significant characteristics of the solutions that are being sought. For instance, the most significant characteristic of the field associated with a capacitor is that the electric intensity at a typical point is substantially in phase with the electric charge on one of the plates. Similarly, the magnetic intensity of the field of an inductor is substantially in phase with the electric current. To derive "circuit equations" from Maxwell's equations most directly, we should express the solutions of the latter in terms of the electric charge and the current in the conductors of the circuit. On the other hand, in a waveguide it is usually more convenient to concentrate first on finding the field, and from it the current and charge in the walls. Then in calculating the field the walls are considered merely as boundaries of the field.

In these examples it is possible to interchange the methods of solution; but only at the price of making simple solutions unwieldy. Linear antennas, however, have equal affinity to circuits, to cavity resonators, and to waveguides. On the one hand, they may be considered as radiating circuits, or rather as radiating transmission lines; on the other hand, they, *and* the surrounding space, may be thought of either as cavity resonators or as waveguides. Antenna theories may thus be classified broadly into two types: (1) *circuit theories*, in which the emphasis is on the current and charge in the conductors; and (2) *field theories*, in which the emphasis is on the fields, and the conductors appear only as the boundaries. Field theories may further be subdivided into *resonator theories* depending on the affinity between antennas and cavity resonators, and into *mode theories* exhibiting the resemblance of antennas to waveguides.

## 1.2  Maxwell's electromagnetic laws, differential equations, and boundary conditions

In their most general form, the laws of interaction between electric and magnetic fields, discovered by Ampère and Faraday and generalized by Maxwell, may be stated as follows:

1. *Ampère-Maxwell law.* The total electric current (the sum of conduction, convection, and displacement currents) passing through a given surface equals the magnetomotive force (the line integral of the magnetic intensity $H$) round the edge of the surface.

2. *Faraday-Maxwell law.* The total magnetic current (the sum of the magnetic displacement current and the convection current, when the condition of magnetized bodies is expressed in terms of equivalent magnetic charge) passing through a given surface equals the negative electromotive force (the line integral of the electric intensity $E$) round the edge of the surface.

It is assumed that, when the handle of a right-handed screw is turned in the positive direction of integration round the edge of the surface of integration, the screw advances in the positive direction of the normal to the surface.

In antenna theory we are not concerned with the internal structure of electric generators. Each generator is enclosed by some surface on which the electric field is assumed to be given. Under some conditions the details of this "impressed" field distribution are either unimportant or relatively unimportant, and it is sufficient to know only the voltage across the terminals of the generator. In any region in which free electrons are confined to conductors with no moving parts, and in which the electric intensity $E$ and the magnetic intensity $H$ are differentiable functions of time and position, the electromagnetic laws of interaction between $E$ and $H$ may be expressed by partial differential equations,

$$\text{curl } E = -\mu \frac{\partial H}{\partial t}, \qquad \text{curl } H = gE + \varepsilon \frac{\partial E}{\partial t}, \qquad (1)$$

where $g$, $\varepsilon$, $\mu$ are, respectively, the conductivity, the dielectric constant, and the permeability of the medium.

If $E$ and $H$ are of the form $E(x, y, z) \exp(pt)$ and $H(x, y, z) \exp(pt)$, where the oscillation constant

$$p = \xi + j\omega \qquad (2)$$

may be any complex number, equations 1 become

$$\text{curl } E = -p\mu H, \qquad \text{curl } H = (g + p\varepsilon)E. \qquad (3)$$

If $p = j\omega$, we have the steady-state equations. Equations 3 are Laplace transforms of equations 1, and hence are equally general. In antenna theory, however, we are interested mostly in the steady-state case, and occasionally in transient oscillations in which the growth constant $\xi$ is negative. Taking the divergence of equations 3, we have

$$\text{div } H = 0, \qquad \text{div } E = 0. \qquad (4)$$

At a boundary between two media with different electromagnetic properties, the *tangential components of E and H are continuous.* These conditions enable us to connect solutions of equations 3 across a surface of discontinuity in the medium. At a perfectly conducting surface the tangential component of $E$ (and, hence, the normal component of $H$) vanishes by definition. Across such a surface the tangential component of $H$ is discontinuous. Let $n$ be a unit normal to that side of the surface on which the tangential component $H_t$ is positive in the direction $C \times n$, where $C$ is the linear electric current density; then,

$$H_t{}^+ - H_t{}^- = C \times n. \qquad (5)$$

The normal component of the electric displacement density is also discontinuous; thus,

$$\varepsilon^+ E_n{}^+ - \varepsilon^- E_n{}^- = \sigma, \qquad (6)$$

where $\sigma$ is the surface density of electric charge.

At a surface of discontinuity moving in a homogeneous dielectric medium, the boundary conditions are

$$E_t^+ - \eta H_t^+ = E_t^- - \eta H_t^-, \qquad H_n^+ = H_n^-, \qquad E_n^+ = E_n^-, \quad (7)$$

where

$$\eta = \left(\frac{\mu}{\varepsilon}\right)^{1/2} \qquad (8)$$

is the intrinsic impedance of the medium. The positive directions of $E_t$ and $H_t$ (which are perpendicular to each other) have been chosen so that the surface of discontinuity is moving in that direction in which a right-handed screw advances when its handle is turned through 90° from $E_t$ to $H_t$. Equations 7, 8, and the following expression for the velocity with which the surface of discontinuity is expanding normally to itself,

$$v = (\mu\varepsilon)^{-1/2}, \qquad (9)$$

are obtained directly from Maxwell's electromagnetic laws.

## 1.3 Maxwell's equations in orthogonal coordinates

Antenna problems are considerably simplified if all conductors are assumed to be perfect. This assumption does not detract from the practical value of the results. In the first place, the effect of the conductivity of good conductors on the field distribution is small. In the second place, the principal part of this effect can be evaluated *a posteriori* from the solutions of idealized problems. When the conductors are perfect, they become merely the boundaries of fields in dielectric media where $g = 0$. The steady-state case is the one of principal interest, and in most subsequent equations we shall assume that $p = j\omega$. In some cases, however, we shall consider transient fields, and then we shall replace $j\omega$ by the more general parameter $p$. As far as algebraic details are concerned, there is little difference between $p$ and $j\omega$.

In orthogonal coordinates $(u, v, w)$ Maxwell's equations become

$$\frac{\partial(e_3 E_w)}{\partial v} - \frac{\partial(e_2 E_v)}{\partial w} = -j\omega\mu e_2 e_3 H_u,$$

$$\frac{\partial(e_3 H_w)}{\partial v} - \frac{\partial(e_2 H_v)}{\partial w} = j\omega\varepsilon e_2 e_3 E_u,$$

$$\frac{\partial(e_1 E_u)}{\partial w} - \frac{\partial(e_3 E_w)}{\partial u} = -j\omega\mu e_3 e_1 H_v,$$

$$\frac{\partial(e_1 H_u)}{\partial w} - \frac{\partial(e_3 H_w)}{\partial u} = j\omega\varepsilon e_3 e_1 E_v,$$

$$(10)$$

$$\frac{\partial (e_2 E_v)}{\partial u} - \frac{\partial (e_1 E_u)}{\partial v} = -j\omega\mu e_1 e_2 H_w,$$

$$\frac{\partial (e_2 H_v)}{\partial u} - \frac{\partial (e_1 H_u)}{\partial v} = j\omega\varepsilon e_1 e_2 E_w.$$

To these it is often convenient to add the divergence equations 4, even though they follow from equations 10 and do not constitute independent equations,

$$\frac{\partial}{\partial u} (e_2 e_3 E_u) + \frac{\partial}{\partial v} (e_3 e_1 E_v) + \frac{\partial}{\partial w} (e_1 e_2 E_w) = 0,$$

$$\frac{\partial}{\partial u} (e_2 e_3 H_u) + \frac{\partial}{\partial v} (e_3 e_1 H_v) + \frac{\partial}{\partial w} (e_1 e_2 H_w) = 0.$$

(11)

The coefficients, $e_1$, $e_2$, $e_3$, are defined by the metrical form

$$ds^2 = e_1{}^2 \, du^2 + e_2{}^2 \, dv^2 + e_3{}^2 \, dw^2. \tag{12}$$

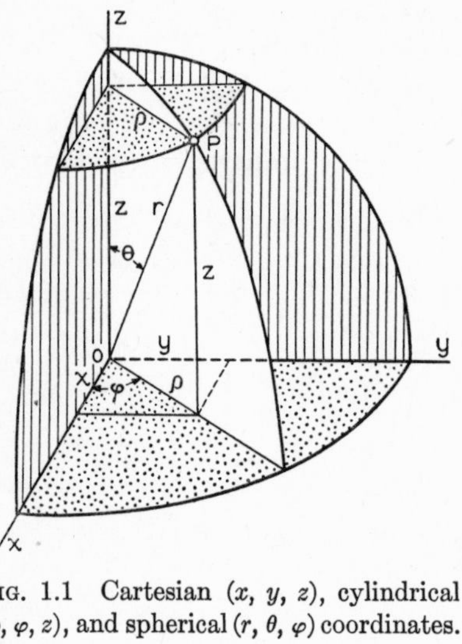

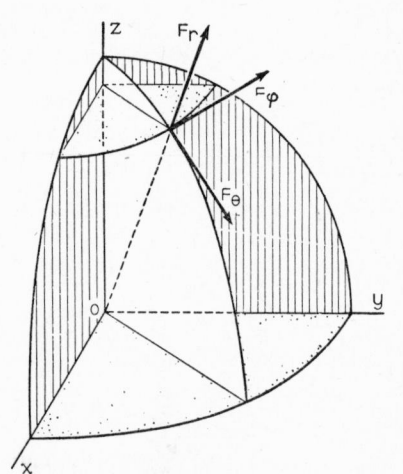

FIG. 1.1   Cartesian $(x, y, z)$, cylindrical $(\rho, \varphi, z)$, and spherical $(r, \theta, \varphi)$ coordinates.

FIG. 1.2   Vector components in spherical coordinates.

In antenna theory the most important coordinates are spherical and spheroidal. In this chapter we shall consider spherical wave functions.

## 1.4   Maxwell's equations in spherical coordinates

In spherical coordinates (Figs. 1.1 and 1.2),

$$ds^2 = dr^2 + r^2 \, d\theta^2 + r^2 \sin^2 \theta \, d\varphi^2. \tag{13}$$

Hence,

$$\frac{\partial}{\partial\theta}(\sin\theta\, E_\varphi) - \frac{\partial E_\theta}{\partial\varphi} = -j\omega\mu r\sin\theta\, H_r, \qquad \frac{\partial}{\partial r}(rE_\theta) - \frac{\partial E_r}{\partial\theta} = -j\omega\mu r H_\varphi,$$

$$\frac{\partial}{\partial\theta}(\sin\theta\, H_\varphi) - \frac{\partial H_\theta}{\partial\varphi} = j\omega\varepsilon r\sin\theta\, E_r, \qquad \frac{\partial}{\partial r}(rH_\theta) - \frac{\partial H_r}{\partial\theta} = j\omega\varepsilon r E_\varphi,$$

$$\tag{14}$$

$$\frac{\partial E_r}{\partial\varphi} - \sin\theta\frac{\partial}{\partial r}(rE_\varphi) = -j\omega\mu r\sin\theta\, H_\theta,$$

$$\frac{\partial H_r}{\partial\varphi} - \sin\theta\frac{\partial}{\partial r}(rH_\varphi) = j\omega\varepsilon r\sin\theta\, E_\theta.$$

The divergence equations are

$$\sin\theta\frac{\partial}{\partial r}(r^2 E_r) + r\frac{\partial}{\partial\theta}(\sin\theta\, E_\theta) + r\frac{\partial E_\varphi}{\partial\varphi} = 0,$$

$$\tag{15}$$

$$\sin\theta\frac{\partial}{\partial r}(r^2 H_r) + r\frac{\partial}{\partial\theta}(\sin\theta\, H_\theta) + r\frac{\partial H_\varphi}{\partial\varphi} = 0.$$

## 1.5 Transverse magnetic waves

Spherical waves are said to be *transverse magnetic* (TM) if the radial component of magnetic intensity is zero. In this case we conclude from the second divergence equation that the transverse components of $H$ are derivable from a stream function $\Pi$; thus,

$$r\sin\theta\, H_\theta = \frac{\partial\Pi}{\partial\varphi}\;; \qquad rH_\varphi = -\frac{\partial\Pi}{\partial\theta}\cdot \tag{16}$$

Similarly, from the first equation in the set 14, we conclude that the transverse components of $E$ are derivable from a potential function $V$,

$$rE_\theta = -\frac{\partial V}{\partial\theta}, \qquad r\sin\theta\, E_\varphi = -\frac{\partial V}{\partial\varphi}\cdot \tag{17}$$

Substituting from equations 16 and 17 in the fourth and sixth equations of the set 14, we have

$$\frac{\partial\Pi}{\partial r} = -j\omega\varepsilon V. \tag{18}$$

The radial electric intensity may be expressed from the remaining three equations in either of the following two forms,

$$E_r = -\frac{1}{j\omega\varepsilon r^2}\left[\frac{1}{\sin\theta}\frac{\partial}{\partial\theta}\left(\sin\theta\frac{\partial\Pi}{\partial\theta}\right) + \frac{1}{\sin^2\theta}\frac{\partial^2\Pi}{\partial\varphi^2}\right],$$

$$E_r = -j\omega\mu\Pi - \frac{\partial V}{\partial r} = \frac{1}{j\omega\varepsilon}\left(\frac{\partial^2\Pi}{\partial r^2} + \beta^2\Pi\right), \tag{19}$$

where

$$\beta = \omega(\mu\varepsilon)^{1/2} = \frac{\omega}{v} \tag{20}$$

is the phase constant. Comparing the two expressions for $E_r$, we find that the stream function satisfies the following equation:

$$r^2 \frac{\partial^2 \Pi}{\partial r^2} + \frac{1}{\sin\theta} \frac{\partial}{\partial\theta}\left(\sin\theta \frac{\partial\Pi}{\partial\theta}\right) + \frac{1}{\sin^2\theta} \frac{\partial^2\Pi}{\partial\varphi^2} = -\beta^2 r^2 \Pi. \tag{21}$$

The complete field has thus been expressed in terms of a single scalar function.

Consider now fields for which

$$\Pi(r, \theta, \varphi) = R(r)\, T(\theta, \varphi) \tag{22}$$

so that the field pattern is the same on all spheres concentric with the origin. Substituting in equation 21, we have

$$\sin\theta \frac{\partial}{\partial\theta}\left(\sin\theta \frac{\partial T}{\partial\theta}\right) + \frac{\partial^2 T}{\partial\varphi^2} = -\nu(\nu+1)\sin^2\theta\, T, \tag{23}$$

$$\frac{d^2 R}{dr^2} = \left[-\beta^2 + \frac{\nu(\nu+1)}{r^2}\right] R, \tag{24}$$

where $\nu$ is the separation constant. From equations 22 and 24, we have

$$\frac{\partial^2 \Pi}{\partial r^2} = \left[-\beta^2 + \frac{\nu(\nu+1)}{r^2}\right] \Pi. \tag{25}$$

From equations 18 and 25, we obtain

$$\frac{\partial V}{\partial r} = -\left[j\omega\mu + \frac{\nu(\nu+1)}{j\omega\varepsilon r^2}\right]\Pi, \qquad \frac{\partial \Pi}{\partial r} = -j\omega\varepsilon V. \tag{26}$$

Hence, $V$ and $\Pi$ vary as the voltage and current in a transmission line with a distributed series inductance $\mu$ henrys per meter, series capacitance $\varepsilon r^2/\nu(\nu+1)$ farad-meters, and shunt capacitance $\varepsilon$ farads per meter. The corresponding transmission line diagram is shown in Fig. 1.3$a$. If we differentiate equations 26 with respect to $\theta$ and substitute from equations 16 and 17, we find that $rE_\theta$ and $rH_\varphi$ satisfy equations 26. Likewise, $rE_\varphi$ and $-rH_\theta$ satisfy these equations.

When the stream function may be expressed as in equation 22, the ratios $E_\theta/H_\varphi$ and $E_\varphi/H_\theta$ are independent of $\theta$ and $\varphi$. These ratios are called *radial wave impedances*. The algebraic signs are chosen so that the transverse components $E_t$, $H_t$, and the direction in which the impedance is taken, form a right-handed triplet of orthogonal directions.

Hence, the radial wave impedances in the directions of increasing and decreasing $r$ are, respectively,

$$Z^+ = \frac{E_\theta}{H_\varphi} = -\frac{E_\varphi}{H_\theta}, \qquad Z^- = -\frac{E_\theta}{H_\varphi} = \frac{E_\varphi}{H_\theta}. \qquad (27)$$

The reciprocals of the wave impedances are called the *wave admittances* and denoted by $Y$.

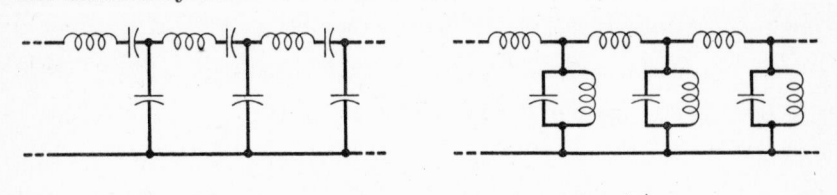

(a)                                    (b)

Fig. 1.3   Transmission-line diagrams representing radial propagation: (*a*) TM waves, (*b*) TE waves.

From equations 16, 17, 19, and 22, we have the following expressions for the field components:

$$r \sin \theta \, H_\theta = R \frac{\partial T}{\partial \varphi}, \qquad rH_\varphi = -R \frac{\partial T}{\partial \theta}, \qquad (28)$$

$$E_\theta = Z^+ H_\varphi, \qquad E_\varphi = -Z^+ H_\theta, \qquad j\omega\varepsilon r^2 E_r = \nu(\nu + 1)RT,$$

where

$$Z^+ = -\frac{1}{j\omega\varepsilon R} \frac{dR}{dr}. \qquad (29)$$

Solutions of equation 24 may be expressed in terms of the *normalized Bessel functions* defined in terms of regular Bessel functions as follows:*

$$Jn_\nu(x) = (\tfrac{1}{2}\pi x)^{\frac{1}{2}} J_{\nu+\frac{1}{2}}(x), \qquad Nn_\nu(x) = (\tfrac{1}{2}\pi x)^{\frac{1}{2}} N_{\nu+\frac{1}{2}}(x),$$

$$Kn_\nu(x) = \left(\frac{2x}{\pi}\right)^{\frac{1}{2}} K_{\nu+\frac{1}{2}}(x), \qquad In_\nu(x) = (\tfrac{1}{2}\pi x)^{\frac{1}{2}} I_{\nu+\frac{1}{2}}(x). \qquad (30)$$

These functions are related as follows:

$$In_\nu(jx) = j^{\nu+1} Jn_\nu(x),$$
$$Kn_\nu(jx) = (-j)^{\nu+1}[Jn_\nu(x) - j\,Nn_\nu(x)]. \qquad (31)$$

* In the reference texts by the author, *Electromagnetic Waves* and *Applied Mathematics* (D. Van Nostrand, New York), the normalized functions were distinguished from the corresponding regular functions by the addition of a circumflex accent. The notation introduced here now seems preferable.

In particular, for integral values of $\nu$,

$$Kn_0(x) = e^{-x}, \qquad Kn_1(x) = e^{-x}(1 + x^{-1}),$$

$$Kn_2(x) = e^{-x}(1 + 3x^{-1} + 3x^{-2}), \tag{32}$$

$$Kn_n(x) = e^{-x} \sum_{m=0}^{n} \frac{(n + m)!}{m!(n - m)!(2x)^m} \cdot$$

When $n$ is not an integer, the series for $Kn$ is asymptotic. The $In$ function is given by

$$In_\nu(x) = \tfrac{1}{2}[Kn_\nu(-x) + (-)^{\nu+1}Kn_\nu(x)]. \tag{33}$$

The general solution of equation 24 is

$$R = A\,Jn_\nu(\beta r) + B\,Nn_\nu(\beta r) = A'\,Kn_\nu(j\beta r) + B'\,In_\nu(j\beta r). \tag{34}$$

The first form is particularly convenient in the steady-state case and the second in the transient case (and also for waves in dissipative media). In the transient case, for instance, $j\beta = j\omega(\mu\varepsilon)^{1/2}$ is replaced by a more general expression $p(\mu\varepsilon)^{1/2}$ where $p$ is complex, and

$$R = A'\,Kn_\nu(pr\sqrt{\mu\varepsilon}) + B'\,In_\nu(pr\sqrt{\mu\varepsilon}). \tag{35}$$

Separating the variables in equation 23, we obtain

$$T(\theta, \varphi) = \Theta(\theta)\,\Phi(\varphi), \tag{36}$$

where

$$\sin\theta\,\frac{d}{d\theta}\left(\sin\theta\,\frac{d\Theta}{d\theta}\right) + [\nu(\nu + 1)\sin^2\theta - \mu^2]\Theta = 0, \tag{37}$$

$$\frac{d^2\Phi}{d\varphi^2} = -\mu^2\Phi. \tag{38}$$

Equation 37 is the associated Legendre equation. In most cases general solutions of equations 37 and 38 are*

$$\Theta = C\,P_\nu{}^\mu(\cos\theta) + D\,P_\nu{}^\mu(-\cos\theta),$$
$$\Phi = E\cos\mu\varphi + F\sin\mu\varphi. \tag{39}$$

But, when $\nu + \mu$ is an integer, $P_\nu{}^\mu(\cos\theta)$ and $P_\nu{}^\mu(-\cos\theta)$ are not linearly independent, and, for the second solution, we may use the limit of

$$Q_\nu{}^\mu(\cos\theta) = \frac{\pi}{2}\,\frac{P_\nu{}^\mu(\cos\theta)\cos(\nu + \mu)\pi - P_\nu{}^\mu(-\cos\theta)}{\sin(\nu + \mu)\pi}, \tag{40}$$

as $\nu + \mu$ approaches an integral value.

If $\nu = 0$, we introduce a new independent variable,

$$\rho = \cot\tfrac{1}{2}\theta, \tag{41}$$

---

* We do not expect any confusion between the separation constant $\mu$ and the permeability $\mu$.

in equation 37 and obtain

$$\rho \frac{d}{d\rho} \left( \rho \frac{d\Theta}{d\rho} \right) - \mu^2 \Theta = 0. \tag{42}$$

The solution of this equation is

$$\Theta = C\rho^\mu + D\rho^{-\mu} = C \cot^\mu \tfrac{1}{2}\theta + D \tan^\mu \tfrac{1}{2}\theta, \qquad \mu \neq 0,$$
$$= C \log \rho + D = C \log \cot \tfrac{1}{2}\theta + D, \qquad \mu = 0. \tag{43}$$

In this case $E_r$, as well as $H_r$, vanishes, and the waves are *transverse electromagnetic* (TEM).

### 1.6 Transverse electric waves

Spherical waves are said to be *transverse electric* (TE) if the radial component of $E$ vanishes. The field expressions are similar to those for TM waves, with the parts played by $E$ and $H$ interchanged. Thus, $E$ is derivable from a stream function $\Psi$, and the transverse component of $H$ from a potential function $U$. Omitting the details of the derivation, we have

$$r \sin \theta \, E_\theta = - \frac{\partial \Psi}{\partial \varphi}, \qquad\qquad rE_\varphi = \frac{\partial \Psi}{\partial \theta},$$

$$rH_\theta = - \frac{\partial U}{\partial \theta}, \qquad r \sin \theta \, H_\varphi = - \frac{\partial U}{\partial \varphi}, \tag{44}$$

$$H_r = \frac{1}{j\omega\mu} \left( \frac{\partial^2 \Psi}{\partial r^2} + \beta^2 \Psi \right).$$

The stream function satisfies equation 21. When $\Psi$ is of the form 22,

$$r \sin \theta \, E_\theta = -R \frac{\partial T}{\partial \varphi}, \qquad rE_\varphi = R \frac{\partial T}{\partial \theta},$$

$$H_\theta = -Y^+E_\varphi, \qquad H_\varphi = Y^+E_\theta, \qquad j\omega\mu r^2 H_r = \nu(\nu+1)RT, \tag{45}$$

where the radial wave admittance in the direction of increasing $r$ is

$$Y^+ = - \frac{1}{j\omega\mu R} \frac{dR}{dr}. \tag{46}$$

The stream function $\Psi$ and the potential function $U$ satisfy the following equations:

$$\frac{\partial \Psi}{\partial r} = -j\omega\mu U, \qquad \frac{\partial U}{\partial r} = - \left[ j\omega\varepsilon + \frac{\nu(\nu+1)}{j\omega\mu r^2} \right] \Psi. \tag{47}$$

Likewise $rE_\theta$, $rH_\varphi$, and $-rE_\varphi$, $rH_\theta$ satisfy equations 47. Hence, these three pairs of functions vary with $r$ as the voltage and current in a transmission line with a distributed series inductance $\mu$, shunt capacitance $\varepsilon$, and shunt inductance $\mu r^2/\nu(\nu+1)$ all per unit length. The corresponding transmission line diagram is shown in Fig. 1.3$b$.

## 1.7　General expressions for spherical wave functions

The most general spherical wave is the sum of transverse magnetic and transverse electric waves. Hence,

$$E_r = \frac{1}{j\omega\varepsilon}\left(\frac{\partial^2\Psi_1}{\partial r^2} + \beta^2\Psi_1\right), \quad H_r = \frac{1}{j\omega\mu}\left(\frac{\partial^2\Psi_2}{\partial r^2} + \beta^2\Psi_2\right),$$

$$rE_\theta = \frac{1}{j\omega\varepsilon}\frac{\partial^2\Psi_1}{\partial r\,\partial\theta} - \frac{1}{\sin\theta}\frac{\partial\Psi_2}{\partial\varphi},$$

$$rH_\theta = \frac{1}{\sin\theta}\frac{\partial\Psi_1}{\partial\varphi} + \frac{1}{j\omega\mu}\frac{\partial^2\Psi_2}{\partial r\,\partial\theta},$$

$$rE_\varphi = \frac{1}{j\omega\varepsilon\sin\theta}\frac{\partial^2\Psi_1}{\partial r\,\partial\varphi} + \frac{\partial\Psi_2}{\partial\theta}, \quad rH_\varphi = -\frac{\partial\Psi_1}{\partial\theta} + \frac{1}{j\omega\mu\sin\theta}\frac{\partial^2\Psi_2}{\partial r\,\partial\varphi},$$

$$\text{(48)}$$

where both $\Psi$ functions satisfy equation 21. To prove the generality of equations 48, consider any given field. From $E_r$ we can determine $\Psi_1$ and the corresponding part of the total field. Subtracting this part from the total field, we obtain a field for which $E_r = 0$.

## 1.8　Waves in free space

If all sources of waves are confined within a shell bounded by concentric spheres $r = r_1$ and $r = r_2 > r_1$, the field intensities outside the shell must satisfy the homogeneous Maxwell's equations 14 and the following boundary conditions: (1) All wave functions must be regular, (2) they must be periodic functions of $\varphi$, and (3) at infinity they must represent waves traveling *from* the origin. The periodicity condition requires $\mu$ in the expressions 39 to be an integer. When $\nu$ is not an integer, the associated Legendre functions in equations 39 become infinite, the first at $\theta = \pi$ and the second at $\theta = 0$. Hence, for waves in free space $\nu$ must be an integer, and the characteristic $T$ function is of the form

$$T = P_n{}^m(\cos\theta)(E\cos m\varphi + F\sin m\varphi). \quad \text{(49)}$$

If $n = 0$, the only regular $T$ function is a constant. The corresponding field vanishes identically. Hence, in free space there can be no transverse electromagnetic waves.

Since $Nn_n(x)$ becomes infinite at $x = 0$, in the region $0 \leq r < r_1$ the coefficient $B$ in equation 34 must vanish. In the region $r_2 < r < \infty$, we must have $B = -jA$ in order to obtain a progressive wave traveling from the origin. In the second form of the solution, $A' = 0$ in the region $r < r_1$, and $B' = 0$ in the region extending to infinity. If there is another surface of discontinuity, at $r = r_3 > r_2$, for instance, than in the region $r_2 < r < r_3$ we must retain both $A$ and $B$.

## 1.9 Waves in regions bounded by perfectly conducting conical surfaces with the apices at the origin

Consider now a region bounded by one or more perfectly conducting surfaces

$$\theta = f(\varphi). \tag{50}$$

At each surface the tangential component of $E$ (and, therefore, the normal component of $H$) must vanish. In the case of TM waves, the radial and transverse components of $E$ are given by equations 28, and $E_r$ will vanish if either $\nu = 0$ or $T$ vanishes on the boundary,

$$T[f(\varphi), \varphi] = 0. \tag{51}$$

The transverse component $E_t$ is derivable from a potential function which is proportional to $T$. Hence, the tangential component of $E_t$ will vanish if $T$ is constant on the boundary, and, in particular, if it vanishes. Thus, equation 51 is the boundary condition for TM waves, when $\nu \neq 0$.

For TE waves the transverse component of $H$ is derivable from a potential function $U$. Its component normal to the boundary is $-\partial U/\partial n$. Since $U$ is proportional to $T$, the boundary condition is

$$\frac{\partial T}{\partial n} = 0. \tag{52}$$

These boundary conditions define a set of characteristic values and functions for any given set of perfectly conducting conical surfaces.

If $\nu = 0$, the waves are transverse electromagnetic. Such waves can exist only in the presence of at least two perfectly conducting cones. In this case we express the electric intensity as the gradient of a potential function, and the boundary condition is

$$T = \text{constant} \tag{53}$$

on the surface of each cone.

## 1.10 Orthogonality

Green's theorems for a spherical surface are

$$\iint \text{grad } U \cdot \text{grad } V \, d\Omega = \int U \frac{\partial V}{\partial n} \, ds - \iint U \, \Delta V \, d\Omega, \tag{54}$$

$$\iint (U \, \Delta V - V \, \Delta U) \, d\Omega = \int \left( U \frac{\partial V}{\partial n} - V \frac{\partial U}{\partial n} \right) ds, \tag{55}$$

where $d\Omega = \sin\theta\, d\theta\, d\varphi$ is a differential solid angle, the line integrals are taken over the boundary of the area of integration, and the normal derivatives are taken along the *outward* normals. On the surface of a unit sphere, the gradient of a scalar function $T$ and the divergence of a vector function $F$ are

$$\operatorname{grad} T = \left( \frac{\partial T}{\partial \theta} \,,\, \frac{1}{\sin\theta}\,\frac{\partial T}{\partial \varphi} \right), \tag{56}$$

$$\operatorname{div} F = \frac{1}{\sin\theta}\,\frac{\partial}{\partial\theta}(\sin\theta\, F_\theta) + \frac{1}{\sin\theta}\,\frac{\partial F_\varphi}{\partial\varphi}. \tag{57}$$

Hence, the Laplacian is

$$\Delta T = \operatorname{div}\operatorname{grad} T = \frac{1}{\sin\theta}\,\frac{\partial}{\partial\theta}\left(\sin\theta\,\frac{\partial T}{\partial\theta}\right) + \frac{1}{\sin^2\theta}\,\frac{\partial^2 T}{\partial\varphi^2}. \tag{58}$$

When $T$ is a solution of equation 23,

$$\Delta T = -\nu(\nu + 1)T. \tag{59}$$

For a pair $T_1$, $T_2$ of such solutions, equations 54 and 55 become

$$\iint \operatorname{grad} T_1 \cdot \operatorname{grad} T_2\, d\Omega = \int T_1 \frac{\partial T_2}{\partial n}\, ds + \nu_2(\nu_2 + 1)\iint T_1 T_2\, d\Omega, \tag{60}$$

$$[\nu_1(\nu_1 + 1) - \nu_2(\nu_2 + 1)]\iint T_1 T_2\, d\Omega = \int \left( T_1 \frac{\partial T_2}{\partial n} - T_2 \frac{\partial T_1}{\partial n} \right) d\Omega. \tag{61}$$

If neither $\nu_1$ nor $\nu_2$ vanishes, the line integrals vanish on the boundary of each perfectly conducting cone. If there are no perfectly conducting cones, the line integrals vanish when the surface integration is extended over the entire unit sphere, because $T_1$ and $T_2$ are regular. Therefore, if $\nu_1 \neq \nu_2$,

$$\iint T_1 T_2\, d\Omega = 0, \qquad \iint \operatorname{grad} T_1 \cdot \operatorname{grad} T_2\, d\Omega = 0, \tag{62}$$

and $T_1$, $T_2$, as well as their gradients, are orthogonal. If $\nu_1 = \nu_2 = \nu \neq 0$ and $T_1 = T_2 = T$,

$$\iint |\operatorname{grad} T|^2\, d\Omega = \nu(\nu + 1)\iint T^2\, d\Omega. \tag{63}$$

If there are two or more linearly independent $T$ functions for the same $\nu$, they may or may not be orthogonal. If they are not, we can always obtain linear combinations of these functions which are orthogonal. Let $T_1$ and $T_2$ be nonorthogonal functions, and let

$$T_3 = T_1 + kT_2. \tag{64}$$

This function is orthogonal to $T_1$ if

$$\iint T_1 T_3 \, d\Omega = \iint T_1{}^2 \, d\Omega + k \iint T_1 T_2 \, d\Omega = 0, \qquad (65)$$

that is, if

$$k = -\frac{\iint T_1{}^2 \, d\Omega}{\iint T_1 T_2 \, d\Omega}. \qquad (66)$$

By our assumption the denominator does not vanish and $k$ is well defined. Similarly, if there is a third solution which is not orthogonal to either of two orthogonal solutions, we form a linear combination of the three and determine the coefficients to make it orthogonal to the first two.

If $T_1$ belongs to $\nu_1 \neq 0$ and vanishes on the boundary, while $T_2$ belongs to $\nu_2 = 0$, then, from equation 60, we obtain

$$\iint \operatorname{grad} T_1 \cdot \operatorname{grad} T_2 \, d\Omega = 0. \qquad (67)$$

These orthogonality conditions enable us to determine the field when the components of either the electric or the magnetic intensity tangential to a given sphere $r = a$ are given.* Suppose that we know $E_\theta(a, \theta, \varphi)$ and $E_\varphi(a, \theta, \varphi)$. From the first equation in the set 14, we find

$$H_r(a, \theta, \varphi) = \frac{1}{j\omega\mu a \sin\theta} \left[ \frac{\partial E_\theta}{\partial \varphi} - \frac{\partial}{\partial \theta} (\sin\theta \, E_\varphi) \right]. \qquad (68)$$

From $H_r$ we can determine the transverse electric component of the entire field. We take the general flux function,

$$\Psi = \sum_\nu a_\nu R_\nu(r) \, T_\nu(\theta, \varphi), \qquad (69)$$

where the summation extends over a complete orthogonal set of characteristic functions appropriate to the region under consideration. Using equations 45, we have

$$j\omega\mu r^2 H_r(r, \theta, \varphi) = \sum_\nu \nu(\nu + 1)a_\nu R_\nu(r) \, T_\nu(\theta, \varphi). \qquad (70)$$

Let

$$H_r(a, \theta, \varphi) = \sum_\nu A_\nu T_\nu(\theta, \varphi). \qquad (71)$$

By virtue of the orthogonality,

$$A_\nu = N_\nu{}^{-1} \iint H_r(a, \theta, \varphi) \, T_\nu(\theta, \varphi) \, d\Omega,$$

$$N_\nu = \iint [T_\nu(\theta, \varphi)]^2 \, d\Omega. \qquad (72)$$

* Another solution of this problem is given in Problem 34 at the end of the book.

From equations 70 and 71, we have

$$a_\nu = \frac{j\omega\mu a^2 A_\nu}{\nu(\nu + 1) R_\nu(a)}.$$  (73)

Hence, we have the flux and the complete TE component of the field. Incidentally we have also $E_{\theta,\mathrm{TE}}(a, \theta, \varphi)$ and $E_{\varphi,\mathrm{TE}}(a, \theta, \varphi)$. We subtract these functions from the given functions $E_\theta(a, \theta, \varphi)$ and $E_\varphi(a, \theta, \varphi)$ and obtain $E_{\theta,\mathrm{TM}}(a, \theta, \varphi)$ and $E_{\varphi,\mathrm{TM}}(a, \theta, \varphi)$.

Now, if we take a complete set of stream functions appropriate for TM waves (including the TEM wave corresponding to $\nu = 0$), then,

$$\Pi = \sum_\nu a_\nu R_\nu(r) T_\nu(\theta, \varphi),$$

$$j\omega\varepsilon r E_t = \sum_\nu a_\nu R_\nu'(r) \,\mathrm{grad}\, T_\nu(\theta, \varphi).$$  (74)

Using again the orthogonality properties, we have

$$a_\nu R_\nu'(a) \iint |\mathrm{grad}\, T_\nu|^2 \, d\Omega = j\omega\varepsilon a \iint E_t \cdot \mathrm{grad}\, T_\nu \, d\Omega.$$  (75)

When $\nu$ is different from zero, we can use equation 63 to simplify the calculation of the square of the gradient. When $\nu = 0$, we can use equation 60 to reduce the surface integral to a line integral. From equation 61 we can obtain the integral of $T^2$ by letting $\nu_1 \to \nu_2 = \nu$.

### 1.11  Transverse electromagnetic waves

We shall now consider TEM waves in greater detail. If we start with TM waves and assume that $E_r$ vanishes, we find that $\nu = 0$, and equations 26 for the potential and stream functions become

$$\frac{\partial V}{\partial r} = -j\omega\mu\Pi, \qquad \frac{\partial \Pi}{\partial r} = -j\omega\varepsilon V.$$  (76)

Hence, $V$ and $\Pi$ are sinusoidal functions of $\beta r$. Equation 23 for the $T$ function becomes

$$\sin\theta \frac{\partial}{\partial\theta}\left(\sin\theta \frac{\partial T}{\partial\theta}\right) + \frac{\partial^2 T}{\partial\varphi^2} = 0.$$  (77)

Both $V$ and $\Pi$ also satisfy this equation. On the surface of each perfectly conducting cone emerging from the origin, we must have

$$T = \mathrm{constant}.$$  (78)

The field components are given by equations 16 and 17. Since $V$ and $\Pi$ are sinusoidal functions of $\beta r$, the amplitudes of all field components vary as $1/r$. Hence, the transverse voltages (the line integrals of $E$ along curves in spherical surfaces concentric with the origin) remain finite as $r$ approaches zero. TEM waves are the only waves for which this is true; for any other spherical wave whose source is at the origin, the electric intensity approaches zero more rapidly than $1/r$, and the voltages become infinite. Hence, an *electric generator of infinitesimal dimensions with a finite internal electromotive force produces no external field in free space; and, in the presence of two or more cones connected to its terminals, it produces a field which depends on the voltages between the terminals of the generator but not on the details of the internal field distribution.* These ideal generators are approximated by small generators, where the term "small" signifies that, if $a$ is the radius of the smallest sphere that can enclose the generator, then, $\beta a \ll 1$.

Introducing a new independent variable

$$\rho = \tan \tfrac{1}{2}\theta \tag{79}$$

in equation 77, we obtain Laplace's equation in plane polar coordinates,

$$\rho \frac{\partial}{\partial \rho} \left( \rho \frac{\partial T}{\partial \rho} \right) + \frac{\partial^2 T}{\partial \varphi^2} = 0. \tag{80}$$

If we imagine a plane tangent at the north pole, $\theta = 0$, to a sphere of unit diameter, then equation 79 gives a correspondence between points $(\theta, \varphi)$ on this *Neumann sphere** and points $(\rho, \varphi)$ in the plane. The corresponding points lie on the radii drawn from the south pole, $\theta = \pi$. The corresponding solutions are given by typical functions of a complex variable $z$, where

$$z = \rho e^{j\varphi} = e^{j\varphi} \tan \tfrac{1}{2}\theta. \tag{81}$$

Hence, we have a correspondence between two-dimensional electrostatic fields for planes and spheres, and for systems of parallel cylinders and systems of cones emerging from a common apex. Likewise, for every TEM wave on a system of parallel cylinders, we have a corresponding TEM wave on a system of cones. In particular, circles on the Neumann sphere correspond to circles in the tangent plane.

The potential $V$ of a line charge of linear density $q$ and passing through a point $z = z_1$, and the stream function $\Pi$ of the current $I$ are

$$V = \frac{-q}{2\pi\varepsilon} \log|z - z_1|, \qquad \Pi = \frac{-I}{2\pi} \log|z - z_1|. \tag{82}$$

These functions are also the potential and the stream function of the radial filaments of charge and current passing through $z = z_1$. The point $z = \infty$, which is the point at infinity in the plane and the south

* *Applied Mathematics*, p. 29.

pole $\theta = \pi$ on the Neumann sphere, is also a singular point.   For every straight filament of charge or current, there exists an equal and opposite parallel filament at infinity, and, for every radial filament of charge or current, there exists an equal and opposite filament along the radius $\theta = \pi$.   For a charge $q$ and current $I$ on the radius $(\theta_1, \varphi_1)$ and the opposite charge $-q$ and current $-I$ on $(\theta_2, \varphi_2)$, we have

$$V = \frac{q}{2\pi\varepsilon} \log \frac{d_2}{d_1}, \qquad \Pi = \frac{I}{2\pi} \log \frac{d_2}{d_1}, \qquad (83)$$

where

$$d_1 = |z - z_1| = [\rho^2 - 2\rho_1\rho \cos(\varphi - \varphi_1) + \rho_1{}^2]^{\frac{1}{2}}$$
$$= [\tan^2 \tfrac{1}{2}\theta - 2 \tan \tfrac{1}{2}\theta \tan \tfrac{1}{2}\theta_1 \cos(\varphi - \varphi_1) + \tan^2 \tfrac{1}{2}\theta_1]^{\frac{1}{2}}. \qquad (84)$$

The expression for $d_2$ is similar.   In the present case, the charge and current filaments along $\theta = \pi$ cancel.

Consider now $n + 1$ perfectly conducting conical surfaces emerging from the origin.   Let $I_1, I_2, \cdots, I_n$, and $-I_1 - I_2 \cdots - I_n$ be the currents in these conductors.   The last conductor may be called the "ground cone."   We are free to choose $\Pi$ so that it (and, hence, $V$) vanishes on the ground cone.   The stream functions on the remaining conductors will be linear functions of the currents,

$$\Pi_1 = p_{11}I_1 + p_{12}I_2 + \cdots + p_{1n}I_n,$$
$$\Pi_2 = p_{21}I_1 + p_{22}I_2 + \cdots + p_{2n}I_n, \qquad (85)$$
$$- - - - - - - - - - - - - - - -$$
$$\Pi_n = p_{n1}I_1 + p_{n2}I_2 + \cdots + p_{nn}I_n.$$

Equations 76 are satisfied on a typical radius $(\theta, \varphi)$, and, hence, on each conductor.   Substituting from equations 85 and calling the corresponding potentials of the cones $V_1, V_2, \cdots, V_n$, we obtain the equations for the voltages and currents.

In particular, for two cones, we have

$$\frac{dV}{dr} = -j\omega LI, \qquad \frac{dI}{dr} = -j\omega CV, \qquad (86)$$

where $I$ is the current in one cone and $V$ is the transverse voltage from this conductor to the other.   The series inductance $L$ and the shunt capacitance $C$, per unit length, are

$$L = \mu p_{11}, \qquad C = \frac{\varepsilon}{p_{11}}. \qquad (87)$$

More generally the inductances and the potential coefficients of a system of conical conductors are proportional to the corresponding $p$'s.

To calculate $L$ and $C$, consider current $I$ along the radius $(\gamma, 0)$ and $-I$ along the radius $(\gamma, \pi)$. The stream function $\Pi$ is given by equation 83, where

$$d_1 = (\rho^2 - 2c\rho \cos \varphi + c^2)^{\frac{1}{2}}, \qquad c = \tan \tfrac{1}{2}\gamma,$$
$$d_2 = (\rho^2 + 2c\rho \cos \varphi + c^2)^{\frac{1}{2}}, \qquad \rho = \tan \tfrac{1}{2}\theta. \tag{88}$$

Let $u = \log(d_2/d_1)$; then,

$$\rho^2 - 2c\rho \coth u \cos \varphi + c^2 = 0 \tag{89}$$

is the equation of the cone $u = $ constant. It is also the equation of its trace on the Neumann sphere and of the projection of the trace on the tangent plane. If $u = u_1$ and $u = u_2$ are two such conductors, then,

$$L = \frac{\mu}{2\pi}(u_1 - u_2), \qquad C = \frac{2\pi\varepsilon}{u_1 - u_2}. \tag{90}$$

Next we have to express $u_1 - u_2$ in terms of the dimensions of the cones.

The cones $u = u_1$ and $u = u_2$ are circular. To show this, let us start with two circular cones whose axes are $(\vartheta_1, 0)$ and $(\vartheta_2, \pi)$. Let $\alpha$ and $\beta$ be the cone angles (the angles between the axes and the generators of the corresponding cones). Then, the equations of the cones are

$$\cos \theta \cos \vartheta_1 + \sin \theta \sin \vartheta_1 \cos \varphi = \cos \alpha,$$
$$\cos \theta \cos \vartheta_2 - \sin \theta \sin \vartheta_2 \cos \varphi = \cos \beta. \tag{91}$$

Since

$$\cos \theta = \frac{1 - \rho^2}{1 + \rho^2}, \qquad \sin \theta = \frac{2\rho}{1 + \rho^2}, \tag{92}$$

equations 91 are readily transformed into the form 89, and reciprocally equations of the form 89 may be transformed into the form 91. Thus, we find

$$c \coth u_1 = (\cos \alpha + \cos \vartheta_1)^{-1} \sin \vartheta_1,$$
$$c \coth u_2 = -(\cos \beta + \cos \vartheta_2)^{-1} \sin \vartheta_2,$$
$$c = (\cos \alpha - \cos \vartheta_1)^{\frac{1}{2}}(\cos \alpha + \cos \vartheta_1)^{-\frac{1}{2}}$$
$$= (\cos \beta - \cos \vartheta_2)^{\frac{1}{2}}(\cos \beta + \cos \vartheta_2)^{-\frac{1}{2}}. \tag{93}$$

The last equation shows that, when $\gamma$ is assigned, the angles $\alpha$, $\beta$, $\vartheta_1$, $\vartheta_2$ are not independent. Simplifying the relationship between them, we have

$$\frac{\cos \vartheta_1}{\cos \vartheta_2} = \frac{\cos \alpha}{\cos \beta}. \tag{94}$$

From this equation we can obtain the ratios of the differences between the numerators and denominators to the corresponding sums, and then we find

$$\tan \tfrac{1}{2}(\vartheta_1 - \vartheta_2) = \tan \tfrac{1}{2}(\alpha - \beta) \tan \tfrac{1}{2}(\alpha + \beta) \cot \tfrac{1}{2}\vartheta, \qquad (95)$$

where $\vartheta = \vartheta_1 + \vartheta_2$ is the angle between the axes of the cones.

Hence, if we know the cone angles $\alpha$, $\beta$ and the angle $\vartheta$ between their axes, we can find the angles $\vartheta_1$, $\vartheta_2$ that these axes must make with the bisector of the angle between the focal lines $(\gamma, 0)$ and $(\gamma, \pi)$, which is in the present case the $z$ axis.  From equation 93 we obtain, successively, coth $u_1$, coth $u_2$, sinh $u_1$, sinh $u_2$, cosh $u_1$, cosh $u_2$, cosh $(u_1 - u_2)$, and, finally,

$$u_1 - u_2 = \cosh^{-1} \frac{\cos \alpha \cos \beta - \cos \vartheta}{\sin \alpha \sin \beta}. \qquad (96)$$

It should be noted that each cone has two axes: $(\vartheta_1, 0)$, $(\pi - \vartheta_1, \pi)$, for example.  A particular choice of the axis defines the interior of the cone, in the sense that the axis itself is in the interior.  In the foregoing discussion we have chosen the axes and, hence, the cone angles so that *one cone is in the exterior of the other*.  If we choose the axes and the radii so that one cone is in the interior of the other, then, in equation 96 we should replace $\alpha$ and $\vartheta$ by $\pi - \alpha$ and $\pi - \vartheta$.

For coaxial cones, $\vartheta = \pi$, and

$$u_1 - u_2 = \log(\cot \tfrac{1}{2}\alpha \cot \tfrac{1}{2}\beta). \qquad (97)$$

This expression, however, is more readily obtained directly from equations 82 if we let $z_1 = 0$.

If $\alpha$ and $\beta$ are small,

$$u_1 - u_2 \simeq \cosh^{-1} \frac{2 \sin^2 \tfrac{1}{2}\vartheta}{\alpha\beta} \simeq 2 \log \frac{2 \sin \tfrac{1}{2}\vartheta}{(\alpha\beta)^{\frac{1}{2}}}. \qquad (98)$$

## 1.12   Dipoles and solenoids; capacitors and loops

As the frequency of oscillations approaches zero, electromagnetic fields approach either static electric or static magnetic fields.  Reciprocally, we can start with static fields and determine the corresponding electromagnetic fields.  A simple pole, that is, a point charge $Q$, generates the simplest electrostatic field: $E_r = Q/4\pi\varepsilon r^2$, $E_\theta = E_\varphi = 0$.  The corresponding electromagnetic field is not simple, however, since the law of conservation of electric charge requires an infinite electric current filament supplying charge to the pole or abstracting charge from it.  In fact, the simple pole in the nonstatic case may be considered as one end of a semi-infinite chain of dipoles, with the other end at infinity.

The electrostatic field of two point charges, $Q$ and $-Q$, an infinitesimal distance $l$ apart and situated at points whose Cartesian coordinates are $(0, 0, \frac{1}{2}l)$ and $(0, 0, -\frac{1}{2}l)$ is

$$E_r = \frac{Ql \cos \theta}{2\pi\varepsilon r^3}, \qquad E_\theta = \frac{Ql \sin \theta}{4\pi\varepsilon r^3}, \qquad E_\varphi = 0. \tag{99}$$

The product $Ql$ is the moment of the dipole. This field is independent of the $\varphi$ coordinate. When $Q$ varies with time (by passing from one pole to the other), there are radial displacement currents which, in accordance with the Ampère-Maxwell law, generate magnetomotive forces in circles coaxial with the dipole. Hence, we have the component $H_\varphi$ of the magnetic intensity. The variable field is thus a transverse magnetic field. From equations 28 we see that $T(\theta, \varphi) = \Theta(\theta)$ must equal $\cos \theta$, at least when $\omega = 0$, if we are to obtain equation 99. From equation 37 we find that $T$ is independent of $\omega$ and that $\Theta(\theta) = \cos \theta$ satisfies equation 37 if $\nu = 1$. This, together with the boundary condition at infinity, gives $R(r)$, except for an arbitrary constant. In this way we obtain

$$E_r = \frac{\eta A}{2\pi r^2}\left(1 + \frac{1}{j\beta r}\right) e^{-j\beta r + j\omega t} \cos \theta,$$

$$E_\theta = \frac{j\omega\mu A}{4\pi r}\left(1 + \frac{1}{j\beta r} - \frac{1}{\beta^2 r^2}\right) e^{-j\beta r + j\omega t} \sin \theta, \tag{100}$$

$$H_\varphi = \frac{j\beta A}{4\pi r}\left(1 + \frac{1}{j\beta r}\right) e^{-j\beta r + j\omega t} \sin \theta.$$

As $\beta r \to 0$, equations 100 approach equations 99 if

$$A e^{j\omega t} = j\omega Ql = Il, \tag{101}$$

where $I$ is the current passing between the poles.

A point source of magnetostatic field is provided by one end of an infinitely thin and infinitely long solenoid whose other end is at infinity. If $\Phi$ is the magnetic displacement (or "flux") issuing from the open end at the origin, then, $H_r = \Phi/4\pi\mu r^2$, $H_\theta = H_\varphi = 0$. We have seen that, except in the limiting case $\omega = 0$, there are no solutions of Maxwell's equations that are independent of the angular coordinates. Next in the order of complexity is the field of a magnetic dipole formed by an infinitely thin solenoid of infinitesimal length $l$,

$$H_r = \frac{\Phi l \cos \theta}{2\pi\mu r^3}, \qquad H_\theta = \frac{\Phi l \sin \theta}{4\pi\mu r^3}, \qquad H_\varphi = 0. \tag{102}$$

This is the magnetic counterpart of the electrostatic field defined by equations 99. The corresponding field at all frequencies may be obtained from equations 100 if we note that Maxwell's equations remain invariant when we interchange $\mu$ and $\varepsilon$, and $E$ and $-H$. Hence,

$$H_r = \frac{\eta^{-1}A}{2\pi r^2} \left( 1 + \frac{1}{j\beta r} \right) e^{-j\beta r + j\omega t} \cos \theta,$$

$$H_\theta = \frac{j\omega\varepsilon A}{4\pi r} \left( 1 + \frac{1}{j\beta r} - \frac{1}{\beta^2 r^2} \right) e^{-j\beta r + j\omega t} \sin \theta, \qquad (103)$$

$$E_\varphi = - \frac{j\beta A}{4\pi r} \left( 1 + \frac{1}{j\beta r} \right) e^{-j\beta r + j\omega t} \sin \theta.$$

As $\beta r \to 0$, equations 103 approach equations 102, if

$$A e^{j\omega t} = j\omega\Phi l = Vl, \qquad (104)$$

where $V = j\omega\Phi = \partial\Phi/\partial t$ is the magnetic displacement current through the solenoid.

The dimensions of a three-dimensional structure may be made to approach zero in different ways. In the electric dipole we start with point charges: that is, with one limiting process already completed. We can also start with charged particles of radius $a$, much smaller than the distance $l$ between them, and let both $a$ and $l$ approach zero, either keeping their ratio constant or permitting $a/l$ to approach zero. In the first case the voltage between the charges is infinite, and in the second it approaches infinity. But suppose we start with a capacitor formed by two parallel plates of area $S$, an infinitesimal distance $l$ apart. If $V$ is the voltage across the capacitor, the charge on the positive plate is

$$Q = CV, \qquad C = \frac{\varepsilon S}{l}. \qquad (105)$$

The dipole moment of the capacitor is

$$Ql = \varepsilon SV, \qquad (106)$$

and equations 99 become

$$E_r = \frac{SV \cos \theta}{2\pi r^3}, \qquad E_\theta = \frac{SV \sin \theta}{4\pi r^3}, \qquad E_\varphi = 0. \qquad (107)$$

We shall call the product $SV$ the *area moment* of the capacitor. Equation 106 gives the moment of the dipole producing the same external field as the capacitor whose area moment is $SV$. Suppose now that, starting with finite values of $S$ and $l$, we let them approach zero in such a way that the capacitance $C$ remains constant. The external field of the capacitor will approach zero with $S$ at all frequencies. Thus, we have one ideal element of electric circuit theory. For finite values of $S$ we have a "capacitor antenna."

The inductance of a thin solenoid is $L = \mu n^2 S/l$, where $n$ is the number of turns, $l$ the length of the solenoid, and $S$ the area of the cross section. This can be kept finite as $S$ and $l$ are allowed to approach zero by increasing $n$. Since $\Phi = \mu I n S/l = LI/n$, the *magnetic dipole moment* $\Phi l = LIl/n$ approaches zero. Hence, the external field of an infinitesimal solenoid of finite inductance vanishes. Thus, we obtain another ideal element of circuit theory, an "inductor."

The field of steady electric current $I$ flowing round the edge of an infinitesimal area $S$, situated in the $xy$ plane at the origin, is

$$H_r = \frac{SI \cos \theta}{2\pi r^3}, \qquad H_\theta = \frac{SI \sin \theta}{4\pi r^3}, \qquad H_\varphi = 0. \quad (108)$$

We shall call the product $SI$ the *area moment* of the current loop. If $Q$ is a charged particle revolving in a circular orbit with frequency $f$, the area moment is $QfS$. The external field of the current loop with area moment $IS$ is the same as that of the magnetic dipole (the solenoid) with moment

$$\Phi l = \mu S I. \quad (109)$$

Although the external fields of the solenoid and the loop are the same, the internal fields are very different. The quantities that determine the intensity of the field are also different. Thus, the magnetic flux through a loop formed by an infinitely thin wire is infinite; it depends on the radius of the wire if the radius is finite. The external field depends on the current and not on the flux. In an infinitely thin solenoid the current is infinite and the flux is finite. If the cross section of the solenoid is finite but small, the flux depends on the current, the number of turns, and the area of the cross section; but it is the flux and not the internal details that determines the external field. Of course, if the solenoid is not infinitely thin, we have to make a correction for the leakage of magnetic flux in the vicinity of the ends. This leakage makes the solenoid effectively shorter, and it alters the field in the immediate vicinity of the ends or "poles" of the solenoid. Similar corrections have to be made in the case of a loop if the wire is not infinitely thin. The effective area is reduced, and the field near the loop is altered somewhat.

We should also mention toroidal coils. In the static case the field is confined to the interior of the coil. In the a-c case there is an external field. If the toroid is thin, its external field equals the external field of a capacitor of area moment $VS$, where $V$ is the magnetic current in the toroid and $S$ is the area of the loop.

## 1.13   Infinitesimal electric circuits, small antennas, and transmission lines

In the preceding section we have considered ideal circuit elements, capacitors and inductors, from the point of view of Maxwell's theory. They are obtained in the limit as the dimensions of the corresponding physical structures become vanishingly small. Infinitesimal capacitors and inductors (and resistors as well) possess *at all frequencies* the electrical properties ascribed to them in ordinary circuit theory. A more detailed study would show that actual physical structures approximate the ideal structures when their dimensions are very small compared with the wavelength $\lambda = c/f$ corresponding to the highest frequency $f$ under consideration.

Infinitesimal circuit elements may be connected by infinitesimal leads into circuits and networks which obey Kirchhoff's equations provided the approach to the limit satisfies certain conditions. In deriving Kirchhoff's equations from Maxwell's equations, we have to make two assumptions: (1) The charge on each connecting lead is negligible, and (2) the magnetic flux linked with each closed mesh is negligible. Whether these requirements are satisfied or not depends on the manner in which the dimensions of the leads approach zero. If we let the radius of each lead approach zero while keeping the length finite, the charge on each lead will approach zero, while the magnetic flux linked with each mesh will *increase* indefinitely. If we keep the radii finite and let the distances between the leads shrink, the magnetic flux linked with each mesh will approach zero, but the charge on each lead will increase indefinitely. We can realize intermediate cases by imposing certain conditions on the ratios of various dimensions. In order to satisfy both of the above-mentioned requirements, it is necessary to maintain finite ratios between the radii of the leads and the distances between the leads while letting all dimensions approach zero. In this case the terminals of the various circuit elements and the leads connecting them disappear from the equations, and Maxwell's equations become Kirchhoff's circuit equations. Thus, if we pass to the limit properly, the physical dimensions of generators, circuit elements, and circuits themselves are eliminated, and we have to deal only with the electrical properties: impressed voltages, currents in the various branches, resistances, inductances, and capacitances.

At low frequencies most practical circuits satisfy the assumptions implied in Kirchhoff's equations to a high degree of approximation; but at high frequencies this is not necessarily the case. In theory, where for the purposes of mathematical simplification some dimensions are assumed to be vanishingly small, it is particularly necessary to inquire whether the assumptions constitute a reasonable approximation or a radical modification of the problem.

Small antennas are essentially small circuits in which the external field of one element may dominate the field of the others. In a capacitor antenna the capacitance may be tuned out by an inductance whose external field is negligible. The external field of such an antenna is given by equation 96. To obtain the free oscillations of the capacitor antenna, we replace $j\omega$ by $p = \xi + j\omega$,

$$E_r = \frac{\eta A}{2\pi r^2} \left( 1 + \frac{c}{pr} \right) \exp\left( pt - \frac{pr}{c} \right) \cos\theta,$$

$$E_\theta = \frac{p\mu A}{4\pi r} \left( 1 + \frac{c}{pr} + \frac{c^2}{p^2 r^2} \right) \exp\left( pt - \frac{pr}{c} \right) \sin\theta, \qquad (110)$$

$$H_\varphi = \frac{pA}{4\pi cr} \left( 1 + \frac{c}{pr} \right) \exp\left( pt - \frac{pr}{c} \right) \sin\theta.$$

At great distances from the antenna, $E_\theta = \eta H_\varphi$. By integrating the Poynting vector over a large sphere, we express the radiated power in terms of the moment $A$ of the current in the capacitor. The damping constant $(-\xi)$ may be obtained by successive approximations. First we obtain $\omega$ from the internal field of the antenna; then we calculate the average loss of energy per second $W$ on the assumption that $\xi = 0$. If $\mathcal{E}$ is the total stored energy, then $\xi = -W/2\mathcal{E}$.

Similarly, small loop antennas are loops tuned with capacitors whose external fields are negligible.

Electric generators may be located either in the immediate vicinity of antenna terminals or at some distance from them. In the latter case the energy is brought to the antennas by transmission lines. These feeders and antennas form integrated radiating systems. After considering antennas separately from transmission lines, we must consider the interaction between them. For this reason it is important to know the ideal conditions under which the interaction between the local circuits and transmission lines on the one hand and the antennas on the other vanishes. We have already seen that infinitesimal circuits have no external fields, and, therefore, do not interact with antennas. Similarly, transmission lines with infinitesimal transverse dimensions do not affect the behavior of antennas, and reciprocally are not affected by antennas. First, let us consider a coaxial line formed by perfectly conducting coaxial cylinders. It is a limiting case of two coaxial cones,

with vanishingly small internal angles.  The characteristic impedance
for TEM waves is

$$K = \frac{\eta}{2\pi} \log \frac{b}{a} , \tag{111}$$

where $a$ and $b > a$ are the radii of the cylinders.  This impedance
remains constant if $a$ and $b$ approach zero while $b/a$ is constant.  Theoretically, it is possible to maintain any impedance; but, practically,
there are severe limitations.  In the process of passing to the limit all
the higher modes disappear, and we have an ideal single-mode transmission line of the elementary transmission line theory.  No energy can
pass through a perfect conductor; hence, the energy guided by the
coaxial line can escape it only through a hole, such as the hole at the
end of the line where the inner conductor is connected to one arm of the
antenna and the outer conductor to the other arm.  The voltage across
the conductors of the coaxial line is impressed on the antenna.  The
same voltage is also impressed between the antenna arm connected to
the inner conductor and the outer surface of the outer conductor.  However, in the limit there can be no current on the outer surface, assuming
of course that the energy delivered by the coaxial line to the antenna
is finite.  Thus, if $I$ is the current on the outer surface, the magnetic
intensity in the vicinity of the surface is $H_\varphi = I/2\pi\rho$, where $\rho$ is the
distance from the axis.  The energy density is proportional to the
square of $H_\varphi$.  Hence, the energy stored in the vicinity of the conductor
is proportional to $\log \rho$ and becomes infinite as $\rho$ approaches zero unless $I$
also approaches zero.  Thus, in the limit the coaxial pair impresses
a voltage on the antenna; but, otherwise, it has no effect on its performance.

   In practice, there is always some interaction between antennas and
transmission lines feeding them, although it is customary to reduce
this interaction by means of specially designed "wave traps."

   Another important type of transmission line is represented by a
pair of parallel wires.  It is a limiting case of two diverging cones with
vanishingly small internal angles and vanishingly small angle between
the axes.  In the case of equal wires, the characteristic impedance is

$$K = \frac{\eta}{2\pi} \cosh^{-1}\left( \frac{l^2}{2a^2} - 1 \right), \tag{112}$$

where $a$ is the radius and $l$ the distance between the axes of the wires.
The impedance remains constant as long as the ratio $l/a$ is kept constant
while $a$ and $l$ approach zero.  In the limit the field at any finite distance

from the line vanishes. Such lines can be bent without affecting their internal fields.

If $l$ remains constant while $a$ approaches zero, then $K$ becomes infinite. Such a line can serve as a source of infinite impedance supplying a given current to a given structure. It is also possible to imagine a parallel-wire transmission line in which both "wires" are cylindrical cages consisting of an infinite number of infinitely thin wires, and choose the infinities in such a way that the characteristic impedance of the line is infinite and yet the fields external to the cages are equal to the fields of smooth cylinders. The current in such lines is not affected by the antennas which they may feed.

### 1.14 Biconical transmission lines

We have already noted the importance of transverse electromagnetic waves for producing radiation. Without them an infinitesimal generator cannot radiate, and a small generator can radiate very little energy unless the internal fields are permitted to become very large. Antennas guide the energy from the generator, or from the junction with the feeder transmission line, into free space. In the vicinity of the generator (or the junction), TEM waves are the only ones of importance. All other waves are generated when the antenna wires connected to the generator are suddenly discontinued at some distance from the generator. The effect of these waves on the voltage and current at the antenna terminals manifests itself through their effect on the TEM waves. In the case of two (or more) infinitely long cones, the waves must be progressive waves moving away from the generator. When the cones are discontinued, there will appear a TEM wave moving toward the generator, the wave "reflected" from the discontinuity. As far as TEM waves are concerned, the discontinuity behaves as an impedance discontinuity in transmission lines, and we can speak of the "impedance (or admittance) of space as seen from the outer antenna terminals."

Consider now TEM waves in a pair of cones diverging from the origin. The current $I_0(r)$ in one of the cones and the transverse voltage $V_0(r)$ from this cone to the other obey equations 86, where the subscript zero is used as a reference to TEM waves. The general solution may be expressed in terms of $V_0$ and $I_0$ at $r = 0$ or at some other distance $r = l$. Thus, it is easy to show that

$$V_0(r) = V_0(l) \cos \beta(l - r) + jK\,I_0(l) \sin \beta(l - r),$$
$$I_0(r) = I_0(l) \cos \beta(l - r) + jK^{-1} V_0(l) \sin \beta(l - r),$$
(113)

where $K$ is the characteristic impedance, and is found from equations 90 and 96,

$$K = \left(\frac{L}{C}\right)^{\frac{1}{2}} = \frac{\eta}{2\pi} \cosh^{-1} \frac{\cos\alpha\cos\beta - \cos\vartheta}{\sin\alpha\sin\beta} \, . \tag{114}$$

If the outer ends of the cones happen to be at $r = l$, the admittance

$$Y_t = \frac{I_0(l)}{V_0(l)} \tag{115}$$

is called the *terminal admittance*. It is the admittance of free space as seen from the ends of the biconical transmission line. However, we can always define an effective admittance (equation 115) at $r = l$, irrespective of the location of the discontinuity. Substituting $I_0(l)$ from equation 115 in equation 113, we obtain

$$K I_0(r) = V(l)[j\sin\beta(l - r) + KY_t\cos\beta(l - r)],$$
$$V_0(r) = V(l)[\cos\beta(l - r) + jKY_t\sin\beta(l - r)]. \tag{116}$$

The *input admittance* at $r = 0$ is, then,

$$Y_i = \frac{I_0(0)}{V_0(0)} = K^{-1}\frac{KY_t\cos\beta l + j\sin\beta l}{\cos\beta l + jKY_t\sin\beta l} \, . \tag{117}$$

It is also the input admittance $Y_i(r_i)$ at any other input sphere $r = r_i$, provided we interpret $l$ as the difference $l - r_i$. The *input impedance* is $Z_i = 1/Y_i$.

The electric and magnetic intensity may be expressed in terms of the voltage and current. If the cones are coaxial with the $z$ axis, the most direct method for obtaining the required expression is to use the Ampère-Maxwell equation for a typical circle coaxial with the $z$ axis and the segment of the sphere with the center at the origin and passing through this circle,

$$2\pi r \sin\theta \, H_\varphi(r, \theta) = I_0(r), \qquad H_\varphi = \frac{I_0(r)}{2\pi r \sin\theta} \, . \tag{118}$$

Since $E_\theta$ is the same function of $\theta$ as $H_\varphi$, we assume $E_\theta = A/\sin\theta$ and integrate it along a typical meridian from one cone to the other to obtain $V(r)$. The quantity $A$ is thus expressed in terms of $V(r)$, and we find

$$E_\theta = \frac{\eta V(r)}{2\pi K r \sin\theta} \, . \tag{119}$$

In the more general case of noncoaxial cones, the field is obtained from the stream function (equation 83).

### 1.15 Quasibiconical transmission lines

In the case of two thin cones, equation 98 may be expressed in terms of the radii $a$ and $b$ of the cones at distance $r$ from the apex and the distance $d = 2r \sin \frac{1}{2}\vartheta$ between the corresponding elements on the axes of the cones. Hence, we have the following expressions for the distributed parameters of the biconical transmission line:

$$L = \frac{\mu}{\pi} \log\{d(r)[a(r) \, b(r)]^{-\frac{1}{2}}\}, \qquad C = \frac{\mu\varepsilon}{L} \cdot \qquad (120)$$

Both $L$ and $C$ are independent of $r$, even though $a$, $b$, $d$ are functions of $r$.

Let us now distort the cones into some other surfaces of revolution: cylinders or spheroids, for instance. The magnetic lines will remain circular, and the electric lines will approximately follow the meridians except where $r$ is comparable to $a$ and $b$. In this region we shall assume correspondingly smaller deformations to keep the electric lines close to the meridians. Then the field will vary with $\theta$ approximately in accordance with equations 117 and 118, and, after appropriate integration with respect to $\theta$, we obtain the transmission equations 86 for our "quasibiconical" line in which $L$ and $C$ are still given by equations 120. Both $L$ and $C$ are now functions of $r$.

The approximate solutions may be obtained by the wave perturbation method.* We shall summarize the results. There are two types of approximation, depending on the rapidity with which $L$ and $C$ vary with $x = r - r_i$, where $r_i$ is the radius of the input region. First let

$$\beta(x) = \omega[L(x) \, C(x)]^{\frac{1}{2}}, \qquad K(x) = \left[\frac{L(x)}{C(x)}\right]^{\frac{1}{2}},$$

$$\vartheta(x) = \int_0^x \beta(x) \, dx, \qquad (121)$$

$$V(\vartheta) = [K(\vartheta)]^{\frac{1}{2}} v(\vartheta), \qquad I(\vartheta) = [K(\vartheta)]^{-\frac{1}{2}} i(\vartheta),$$

where $V(\vartheta)$, $I(\vartheta)$, $K(\vartheta)$ are $V(x)$, $I(x)$, $K(x)$ expressed as functions of $\vartheta$; that is, $V(\vartheta) = V[x(\vartheta)]$, etc. Choosing $v$ and $i$ as the new dependent variables and $\vartheta$ as the independent variable, we have

$$\frac{dv}{d\vartheta} = -ji - \frac{K'}{2K} v, \qquad \frac{di}{d\vartheta} = -jv + \frac{K'}{2K} i. \qquad (122)$$

If $K'/2K$ is smaller, or at least not much larger, than unity, then,

$$v(\vartheta) = v_0(\vartheta) + v_1(\vartheta) + v_2(\vartheta) + \cdots,$$

$$i(\vartheta) = i_0(\vartheta) + i_1(\vartheta) + i_2(\vartheta) + \cdots, \qquad (123)$$

* *Applied Mathematics*, pp. 212–220.

where

$$v_0(\vartheta) = Ae^{-j\vartheta} - Be^{j\vartheta}, \qquad i_0(\vartheta) = Ae^{-j\vartheta} + Be^{j\vartheta},$$

$$v_n(\vartheta) = -\int_0^{\vartheta} \frac{K'(\varphi)}{2K(\varphi)} \left[ v_{n-1}(\varphi) \cos(\vartheta - \varphi) + j\, i_{n-1}(\varphi) \sin(\vartheta - \varphi) \right] d\varphi,$$

$$\tag{124}$$

$$i_n(\vartheta) = \int_0^{\vartheta} \frac{K'(\varphi)}{2K(\varphi)} \left[ i_{n-1}(\varphi) \cos(\vartheta - \varphi) + j\, v_{n-1}(\varphi) \sin(\vartheta - \varphi) \right] d\varphi.$$

In particular, the functions,

$$i_0(\vartheta) = e^{-j\vartheta}, \qquad\qquad\qquad v_0(\vartheta) = e^{-j\vartheta},$$

$$i_1(\vartheta) = e^{j\vartheta} \int_0^{\vartheta} \frac{K'(\varphi)}{2K(\varphi)} e^{-2j\varphi}\, d\varphi, \qquad v_1(\vartheta) = -i_1(\vartheta), \tag{125}$$

give one pair of approximate solutions $i(\vartheta)$, $v(\vartheta)$. The other pair is given by $i^*(\vartheta)$, $-v^*(\vartheta)$. If $K'/2K$ is small compared with unity and if $\beta$ is constant, we find the following approximate wave functions:

$$I^+(x) = \left[ \frac{K(0)}{K(x)} \right]^{\frac{1}{2}} [1 + j\,k(x)]e^{-j\beta x}, \qquad k(x) = \frac{K'(x)}{4\beta\,K(x)},$$

$$I^-(x) = -\left[ \frac{K(0)}{K(x)} \right]^{\frac{1}{2}} [1 - j\,k(x)]e^{j\beta x}, \tag{126}$$

$$V^+(x) = [K(0)\,K(x)]^{\frac{1}{2}}[1 - j\,k(x)]e^{-j\beta x},$$

$$V^-(x) = [K(0)\,K(x)]^{\frac{1}{2}}[1 + j\,k(x)]e^{j\beta x}.$$

The impedance $Z(0)$ in terms of $Z(l)$ is

$$Z(0) = K(0)\,\frac{Z(l)\,P_1(\beta l) + j\,K(l)\,P_2(\beta l)}{K(l)\,P_3(\beta l) + j\,Z(l)\,P_4(\beta l)}, \tag{127}$$

where

$$P_1(\beta l) = \cos \beta l + [k(l) + k(0)] \sin \beta l,$$

$$P_2(\beta l) = \sin \beta l + [k(l) - k(0)] \cos \beta l,$$

$$\tag{128}$$

$$P_3(\beta l) = \cos \beta l - [k(l) + k(0)] \sin \beta l,$$

$$P_4(\beta l) = \sin \beta l - [k(l) - k(0)] \cos \beta l.$$

If $k(x)$ is not small compared with unity, it is best to write equations 86 in the form,

$$\frac{dV}{dx} = -j\omega L_0 I - j\omega[L(x) - L_0]I,$$

$$\tag{129}$$

$$\frac{dI}{dx} = -j\omega C_0 V - j\omega[C(x) - C_0]V,$$

where $L_0$, $C_0$ are some mean values of $L(x)$ and $C(x)$ in the interval $(0, l)$ under consideration. Introducing new variables,

$$\vartheta = \omega(L_0 C_0)^{\frac{1}{2}} x, \qquad K_0 = \left(\frac{L_0}{C_0}\right)^{\frac{1}{2}}, \tag{130}$$

$$V = K_0^{\frac{1}{2}} v, \qquad I = K_0^{-\frac{1}{2}} i,$$

we have

$$\frac{dv}{d\vartheta} = -ji - j f(\vartheta)i, \qquad \frac{di}{d\vartheta} = -jv - j g(\vartheta)v, \tag{131}$$

$$f(\vartheta) = \frac{L(\vartheta) - L_0}{L_0}, \qquad g(\vartheta) = \frac{C(\vartheta) - C_0}{C_0}.$$

If $i_0(\vartheta) = \exp(-j\vartheta)$, $v_0(\vartheta) = \exp(-j\vartheta)$, then the second terms in the series 123 are

$$i_1(\vartheta) = -\tfrac{1}{2}je^{-j\vartheta} \int_0^\vartheta [f(\varphi) + g(\varphi)] \, d\varphi +$$

$$\tfrac{1}{2}je^{j\vartheta} \int_0^\vartheta [f(\varphi) - g(\varphi)]e^{-2j\varphi} \, d\varphi,$$

$$v_1(\vartheta) = -\tfrac{1}{2}je^{-j\vartheta} \int_0^\vartheta [f(\varphi) + g(\varphi)] \, d\varphi - \tag{132}$$

$$\tfrac{1}{2}je^{j\vartheta} \int_0^\vartheta [f(\varphi) - g(\varphi)]e^{-2j\varphi} \, d\varphi.$$

In particular, the mean values $L_0$, $C_0$ may be taken as the average values $L_a$, $C_a$ of $L(x)$, $C(x)$ in the interval $(0, l)$. If $L(x) \, C(x) = \text{const.}$ and the variations in $L$ and $C$ are relatively small, then $f(\varphi) + g(\varphi)$ is a small quantity of the second order. In such a case, we have approximately

$$Z(0) = K_a \frac{Z(l) \, P_1(\beta l) + j K_a \, P_2(\beta l)}{K_a \, P_3(\beta l) + j \, Z(l) \, P_4(\beta l)}, \tag{133}$$

where

$$P_1(\beta l) = \cos \beta l - K_a^{-1} M(\beta l) \cos \beta l + K_a^{-1} N(\beta l) \sin \beta l,$$

$$P_2(\beta l) = \sin \beta l - K_a^{-1} M(\beta l) \sin \beta l - K_a^{-1} N(\beta l) \cos \beta l,$$

$$P_3(\beta l) = \cos \beta l + K_a^{-1} M(\beta l) \cos \beta l - K_a^{-1} N(\beta l) \sin \beta l,$$

$$P_4(\beta l) = \sin \beta l + K_a^{-1} M(\beta l) \sin \beta l + K_a^{-1} N(\beta l) \cos \beta l, \tag{134}$$

where

$$K_a = \frac{1}{l}\int_0^l K(x)\,dx, \qquad K(x) = \left[\frac{L(x)}{C(x)}\right]^{1/2},$$

$$M(\beta l) = \beta\int_0^l [K_a - K(x)]\sin 2\beta x\,dx, \qquad (135)$$

$$N(\beta l) = \beta\int_0^l [K_a - K(x)]\cos 2\beta x\,dx.$$

In the case of thin antennas, $K_a$ is large, and $Z(l) \simeq K_a{}^2/Z_a$, where $Z_a = R_a + jX_a$ is a function depending on $\beta l$. Neglecting the products of $M/K_a$, $N/K_a$, $R_a/K_a$, $X_a/K_a$, we obtain, from equation 133,

$$Z(0) = K_a\frac{R_a\sin\beta l + j[(X_a - N)\sin\beta l - (K_a - M)\cos\beta l]}{[(K_a + M)\sin\beta l + (X_a + N)\cos\beta l] - jR_a\cos\beta l}. \qquad (136)$$

## REFERENCES

1. Julius Adams Stratton, *Electromagnetic Theory*, McGraw-Hill, New York, 1941
2. S. A. Schelkunoff, *Electromagnetic Waves*, D. Van Nostrand, New York, 1943.

# 2

# MODE THEORY OF ANTENNAS

## 2.1  General mathematical formulation of the antenna problem

The simplicity of the mathematical formulation of the antenna problem contrasts sharply with the complexity of its solutions.  Figure 2.1 shows an antenna;  the dotted line indicates an input boundary $S_i$ which, in the case of a transmitting antenna, is a somewhat arbitrary surface separating the source of power from the rest of space.  Outside this boundary we have an electromagnetic field satisfying Maxwell's equations.  Inside the boundary we may have moving conductors, clouds of interacting electrons, sources of heat, etc., and Maxwell's equations have to be supplemented by dynamical and thermodynamical equations.  In the case of a

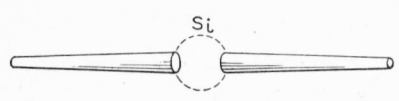

FIG. 2.1  An antenna; the "input boundary" $S_i$ encloses a source of power in the case of a transmitting antenna and a sink of power in the case of a receiving antenna.

receiving antenna, $S_i$ encloses a sink of power; this "load" may also be complex.  The electromagnetic field problem concerns only the region outside the input boundary; the conditions inside $S_i$ are replaced by the boundary conditions over $S_i$.

The problem of the transmitting antenna in free space may be formulated as follows:

1.  Outside the input boundary the field in the antenna and around it must satisfy Maxwell's equations.

2.  The components of the electric and magnetic intensity tangential to the surface of the antenna must be continuous.

3.  The field must be finite everywhere except under certain limit conditions.  If the input region is infinitesimal or if the antenna is perfectly conducting and its radius is zero, certain infinities are permissible;

the nature of these infinities is derived from the conditions existing under normal circumstances by passing to the limit.

4. At infinity the field must represent a wave moving away from the antenna; that is, the field must vary as $r^{-1}f(ct - r)$, where $r$ is the distance from some point around the antenna. In the monochromatic case the field should vary as $r^{-1} \exp j(\omega t - \beta r)$.

5. At the input boundary the tangential component of the electric intensity is given.

The second condition is necessary because, owing to the difference in the electromagnetic constants of the antenna and free space, Maxwell's equations are discontinuous at the surface of the antenna. The equations have to be solved separately for the region occupied by the antenna and for free space; the solutions must then be connected. The second boundary condition gives the connecting equations, and it may be derived either from the integral form of Maxwell's equations or from the differential form. In the latter case we should start with an assumption of a rapid but continuous change in the medium in the "boundary layer" separating the antenna from free space, and then pass to the limit of a boundary layer of zero thickness.

In the case of the receiving antenna the fifth condition is replaced by

5. The ratio of the tangential components of electric and magnetic intensity at the input boundary is given.

Sometimes it is assumed for mathematical convenience that the wave impressed on the antenna is a plane wave. In such a case the fourth boundary condition should be replaced by

4. At infinity the difference between the total field and the primary or impressed field must represent a wave moving away from the antenna.

That is, only that part of the total field must satisfy the original boundary condition at infinity which is produced by the currents and charges in the receiving antenna.

A substantial simplification occurs in the idealized case in which the antenna is assumed to be perfectly conducting. In this case the second boundary condition becomes

2. The tangential component of the electric intensity must vanish at the surface of the antenna.

From the practical point of view, this idealization is not objectionable. Antennas are made from good conductors, and the *effect of their finite conductivity can be evaluated from the solution of the idealized case.*

## 2.2 Two general methods of approach to the solution of the antenna problem

The antenna problem is primarily a "boundary value problem." To obtain the most general solution of Maxwell's equations is easy; to find that particular solution which satisfies the various supplementary conditions is far more difficult. The problem is greatly simplified when the surface of the antenna happens to coincide with a coordinate surface in a coordinate system in which Maxwell's partial differential equations are "separable" into ordinary differential equations. The "separation of variables" is possible in only a few coordinate systems, and there is only one such coordinate system, the spheroidal, in which there is a family of coordinate surfaces with finite dimensions. For this reason electric oscillations on spheroidal conductors have been widely studied; as we shall see in the next chapter, the major problem in this case is the evaluation of the appropriate spheroidal functions.

The method of separation of variables is applicable to other than spheroidal antennas if we relax the requirement that the antenna surface coincide with an *entire* coordinate surface, and require only that it can be subdivided into parts coinciding with parts of coordinate surfaces. For example, conical antennas are bounded by portions of cones and spheres. In this case we look for solutions which individually satisfy only some of the boundary conditions, but which can be combined so as to satisfy all the boundary conditions.

Both the spheroidal and the conical boundaries may be "perturbed" into other shapes, cylindrical for instance. The solution can be perturbed correspondingly, and the variety of shapes that can be treated by the method of separation of variables is thus greatly increased. The functions associated with conical boundaries are much simpler than those associated with spheroids, and in their case the method of perturbation is more practical.

We have already stated that the complete solution may be expressed as the sum of solutions satisfying some, but not all, of the boundary conditions. In spherical coordinates each term happens to represent a relatively simple wave, a *mode of propagation* consistent with the electromagnetic laws and certain boundaries. The entire analysis is very similar to that used in the case of waveguides. Thus, we find a mathematical justification of an intuitively evident connection between antennas and transmission lines, for a waveguide differs from an ordinary transmission line only in that it permits many modes of propagation instead of just one mode. Waveguides, antennas, and even free space may be described as multiple transmission lines. In the preceding chapter we have found that each mode of propagation may be described by a simple conventional transmission line diagram.   For this reason the antenna theory that uses these concepts may conveniently be called the *mode theory of antennas*.*   On the other hand, in spheroidal coordinates the various terms represent certain modes of forced oscillations and exhibit an affinity between antennas and resonators.   Thus, the theory of spheroidal antennas, as developed in the next chapter, is an example of the *resonator theory of antennas*.

Another approach to the solution of the antenna problem is based on the fact that a differential equation together with the boundary conditions may often be converted into an integral equation, that is, an equation containing the unknown function under the integral sign. In the case of antennas the unknown function represents the antenna current, or more generally the density of the current.   Some integral equations for antennas are obvious generalizations of the Kirchhoff equations for electric networks, and for this reason the antenna theory based on them may conveniently be called the *circuit theory of antennas*. In this theory our attention is concentrated on the current at various points of the antenna, and the field around the antenna is kept in the background, whereas in the mode theory the field is prominent, and the antenna current is in the background.   The mode theory of antennas clarifies the relationship between antennas and ordinary transmission lines; the circuit theory of antennas clarifies the relationship between antennas and ordinary electric networks.   Physically both theories present the same facts from different points of view.   The circuit theory of antennas as developed by Hallén will be presented in Chapter 4.

## 2.3   Antenna analysis in terms of spherical coordinates

If the dimensions of the source of power are small compared with λ, the waves excited by it will be spherical or substantially spherical.   Hence, it is particularly convenient to formulate the antenna problem in terms of spherical coordinates.   Consider, for example, a symmetric antenna (Fig. 2.2) with a source of power at the center.   We surround this

---

* In the first paper expounding this theory, the author called it " transmission theory " to stress the clarity with which this theory explains transmission of energy from the source along the antenna into free space.   Subsequently, some authors called it "transmission line theory."   The inclusion of the word "line" altered the intended meaning of the phrase and tended to create an impression that this theory treated antennas from the point of view of ordinary transmission line theory.   To avoid this possible implication Aharoni in his book *Antennae* suggested the name " wave guide theory of antennae " (p. 86), which is a good name for the present theory.   Our new name " mode theory of antennas " has the virtue of being somewhat shorter.

source by a spherical input boundary $S_i$. We assume that we know the electric intensity tangential to $S_i$. Eventually we shall find that, for sufficiently small sources, we need not know the precise distribution of this intensity but only the voltage impressed by the generator on the input boundary. If $\lambda$ is large, say, of the order of 50 or 100 meters, the *source* or *generator region* may be taken large enough to include the tuning coils or capacitors and even more elaborate matching networks. Since the dimensions of these networks are small compared with $\lambda$, their effect on the antenna input voltage may best be calculated from elementary quasistatic theory. Later we shall see how these methods fit into the framework of electromagnetic theory.

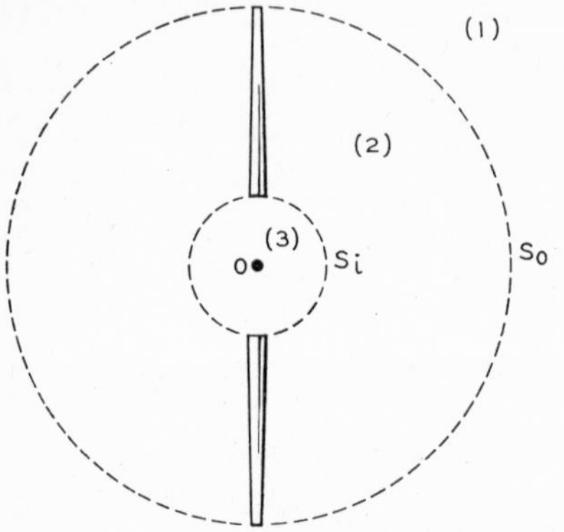

Next we introduce the *antenna output boundary sphere* $S_0$ passing through the outer ends of the antenna arms. This boundary sphere separates the *free space region* 1 from the *antenna region* 2 which is bounded in the interior by the input boundary sphere $S_i$. Our terminology implies that we shall consider specifically transmitting antennas. In view of reciprocity theorems, the results will be general.

Fig. 2.2 Subdivision of the space around a symmetric antenna into (1) the free-space region, (2) the antenna region, and (3) the generator region.

When the medium surrounding the antenna is divided into regions as in Fig. 2.2, we automatically separate the lateral surface of the antenna, which is in the antenna region 2, from the ends, which are parts of the output boundary surface $S_0$. Hence, the boundary condition at the surface of the antenna is now replaced by three separate boundary conditions:

1. In the antenna region the tangential $E$ must vanish at the surface of the antenna.
2. The field in the antenna region must join continuously the field in the free space region.
3. The field tangential to the ends of the antenna must vanish.

The second and third conditions are really parts of one condition at the complete closed surface $S_0$. If the antenna is circularly symmetric and is so energized that the currents flow along its length, the only nonvanishing components of the field are $E_r$, $E_\theta$, $H_\varphi$. When the transverse dimensions of the antenna are small, these components are still the most important ones, irrespective of antenna symmetry.

For a biconical antenna (Fig. 2.3) the boundary conditions may be expressed as follows:

1. At infinity,

$$E_\theta, H_\varphi \propto \frac{e^{-j\beta r}}{r}. \tag{1}$$

2. In the antenna region,

$$E_r(\psi) = 0, \qquad E_r(\pi - \psi) = 0, \tag{2}$$

where $\theta = \Psi$ is the equation for the surface of the upper cone.*

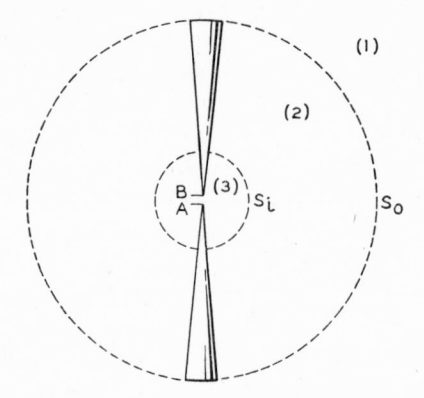

Fig. 2.3  A symmetric biconical antenna.

3. At the output boundary $S_0$ the field is continuous:

$$
\begin{aligned}
E_\theta(l + 0) &= E_\theta(l - 0), & \psi < \theta < \pi - \psi, \\
H_\varphi(l + 0) &= H_\varphi(l - 0), & \psi < \theta < \pi - \psi, \\
E_r(l + 0) &= E_r(l - 0), & \psi < \theta < \pi - \psi, \\
E_\theta(l + 0) &= 0, & 0 \le \theta \le \psi, \quad \text{and} \quad \pi - \psi < \theta \le \pi.
\end{aligned}
\tag{3}
$$

The second and third of these equations are not independent, and we may use either, as suits our convenience.

4. At the input boundary $E_\theta$ is given.
5. In the free space region 1, the field must be finite.

The need for the fifth condition does not become obvious until we actually study solutions of Maxwell's equations, and find that the

* If the lower cone angle is different from the upper, the second equation becomes $E_r(\pi - \psi_2) = 0$, with corresponding changes in conditions 3.

general solution in region 1 involves more arbitrary constants than can be determined from the first four boundary conditions. The analysis of these solutions shows that all except those in a certain set become infinite for one or more values of $\theta$, and for that reason have to be rejected.

Condition 4 implies that the transverse voltage in the input boundary between the cones is given,

$$V_i = \int_\psi^{\pi-\psi} E_\theta r \, d\theta. \tag{4}$$

This "input voltage" is not sufficient to define completely the field around the antenna. We must know its distribution over the input boundary. The study of solutions brings out, however, the following facts: (1) If the dimensions of the input boundary are very small compared with the wavelength, the details of the voltage distribution do not affect the antenna field significantly except near the input boundary; (2) the effect may always be associated with the generators and networks in the input region; (3) because of the small dimensions of the input region, this effect may be calculated by solving appropriate electrostatic and magnetostatic problems; (4) under many practical conditions, the effect is negligible.

No difficulties are encountered if the dimensions of the input region are assumed to be infinitely small, in which case equation 4 represents the fourth boundary condition completely. This enables us to separate the antenna problem from the local circuit problem. This separation is possible even if the system is such that the interaction between the circuits and the antenna is substantial. It is only when the dimensions of the input region become large that no useful purpose is served by the separation between the antenna and the local circuits; the interaction becomes so great, the various parts of the system become so well integrated, that a recognition of these facts can only simplify the problem.

The preceding formulation of the antenna problem applies specifically to forced oscillations. The boundary conditions for natural oscillations differ from the foregoing conditions only in equation 4. Thus, if the apices of the cones are short-circuited, this particular boundary condition becomes

$$\int_\psi^{\pi-\psi} E_\theta r \, d\theta \to 0 \quad \text{as} \quad r \to 0. \tag{5}$$

On the other hand, if the apices are insulated, then the current vanishes at $A$, $B$, and

$$r H_\varphi(\psi) \to 0, \quad \text{as} \quad r \to 0. \tag{6}$$

The main difference between thin biconical antennas and thin antennas of other shapes is expressed in the principal wave, which constitutes only one term in the general expression for the field in the antenna region. Inasmuch as we have already developed a theory of principal waves (Chapter 1), our main problem in this chapter is the development of a theory for biconical antennas. Having solved this problem, we can readily generalize the results (Section 15 of this chapter) for antennas of arbitrary shape.

## 2.4   General expressions for the field around a biconical antenna

When the field is independent of the $\varphi$ coordinate, Maxwell's equations, which normally involve six interdependent components of $E$ and $H$, break up into two separate sets of three equations each. One of these sets involves $E_r$, $E_\theta$, $H_\varphi$, and the other contains only $H_r$, $H_\theta$, $E_\varphi$. In the first case the currents in the conical surfaces are strictly radial since they must be perpendicular to $H_\varphi$; for the same reason the currents in the end caps flow along the meridians. In the second case the currents circulate around the conical surfaces. We are interested in the first case, which is a special case of the TM waves considered in Section 1.5. Thus,

$$E_r = - \frac{n(n+1)\, R(r)\, \Theta(\theta)}{j\omega\varepsilon r^2}\,,$$

$$E_\theta = - \frac{1}{j\omega\varepsilon r}\frac{dR}{dr}\frac{d\Theta}{d\theta}\,, \qquad H_\varphi = \frac{R}{r}\frac{d\Theta}{d\theta}\,, \tag{7}$$

where $n$ is an arbitrary parameter and $R(r)$, $\Theta(\theta)$ are solutions of the following differential equations,

$$\sin\theta\,\frac{d^2\Theta}{d\theta^2} + \cos\theta\,\frac{d\Theta}{d\theta} + n(n+1)\sin\theta\,\Theta = 0, \tag{8}$$

$$\frac{d^2R}{dr^2} = \left[ -\beta^2 + \frac{n(n+1)}{r^2} \right] R. \tag{9}$$

The general solution of equation 9 is

$$R(r) = A_n\, Jn_n(\beta r) + B_n\, Nn_n(\beta r), \tag{10}$$

where $Jn_n(\beta r)$ and $Nn_n(\beta r)$ are the normalized Bessel functions of order $n$ defined by*

$$Jn_n(\beta r) = (\tfrac{1}{2}\pi\beta r)^{\frac{1}{2}} J_{n+\frac{1}{2}}(\beta r), \qquad Nn_n(\beta r) = (\tfrac{1}{2}\pi\beta r)^{\frac{1}{2}} N_{n+\frac{1}{2}}(\beta r). \tag{11}$$

If $n$ is not an integer, the general solution of equation 8 is†

$$\Theta(\theta) = C_n\, P_n(\cos\theta) + D_n\, P_n(-\cos\theta). \tag{12}$$

* *Applied Mathematics*, pp. 396–397.
† *Ibid.*, p. 418.

The first solution reduces to unity when $\theta = 0$ and is logarithmically infinite when $\theta = \pi$; the second reduces to unity at $\theta = \pi$ and is logarithmically infinite when $\theta = 0$. If $n$ is an integer, the two solutions differ only by a constant factor $(-)^n$ and are finite for all values of $\theta$. In this case the second independent solution is $Q_n(\cos\theta)$; this solution is logarithmically infinite at $\theta = 0, \pi$.

In the antenna region $E_r$ must vanish on the conical boundaries $\theta = \theta_1$ and $\theta = \theta_2$. In view of equations 7, this condition is satisfied either when

$$n = 0 \tag{13}$$

or when

$$\Theta(\theta_1) = 0, \qquad \Theta(\theta_2) = 0. \tag{14}$$

When $n = 0$, the radial component vanishes for all $\theta$, and the waves are transverse electromagnetic. This case has been fully considered in Chapter 1.

From equations 12 and 14, we have

$$C_n P_n(\cos\theta_1) + D_n P_n(-\cos\theta_1) = 0,$$
$$C_n P_n(\cos\theta_2) + D_n P_n(-\cos\theta_2) = 0. \tag{15}$$

Solving for the ratio $D_n/C_n$, we find

$$\frac{D_n}{C_n} = -\frac{P_n(\cos\theta_1)}{P_n(-\cos\theta_1)} = -\frac{P_n(\cos\theta_2)}{P_n(-\cos\theta_2)} ; \tag{16}$$

hence, $n$ must be a root of the following characteristic equation:

$$P_n(\cos\theta_1) P_n(-\cos\theta_2) = P_n(\cos\theta_2) P_n(-\cos\theta_1). \tag{17}$$

In the case of a single cone $\theta = \theta_1$, we have to satisfy only the first condition 14; the second condition is then replaced by the requirement that the field must be finite. Thus, if the field is in the region $\theta < \theta_1$,

$$\Theta(\theta) = C_n P_n(\cos\theta), \tag{18}$$

since $P_n(-\cos\theta)$ is infinite at $\theta = 0$. Similarly, if the field is in the region $\theta > \theta_1$,

$$\Theta(\theta) = D_n P_n(-\cos\theta). \tag{19}$$

In the first case (equation 18) $n$ must be a root of

$$P_n(\cos\theta_1) = 0; \tag{20}$$

and in the second case (equation 19) we have

$$P_n(-\cos\theta_1) = 0. \tag{21}$$

In free space the field must be finite at $\theta = 0, \pi$. This condition is not satisfied by any solution when $n$ is not an integer; hence, $n$ must be an integer, and

$$\Theta(\theta) = C_n P_n(\cos \theta), \qquad n = 1, 2, 3, \cdots, \qquad (22)$$

since $Q_n(\theta)$ is infinite at $\theta = 0, \pi$.

In the case of two equal cones (Fig. 2.3), $\theta_1 = \psi$, and $\theta_2 = \pi - \psi$. Equation 17 becomes

$$[P_n(\cos \psi)]^2 = [P_n(-\cos \psi)]^2; \qquad (23)$$

therefore, we have either

$$P_n(\cos \psi) = P_n(-\cos \psi) \qquad (24)$$

or

$$P_n(\cos \psi) = -P_n(-\cos \psi). \qquad (25)$$

In the last case $D_n = C_n$, and

$$\Theta(\theta) = C_n' L_n(\cos \theta), \qquad (26)$$

where $L_n(\cos \theta)$ is an even Legendre function of order $n$ defined by*

$$L_n(\cos \theta) = \tfrac{1}{2}[P_n(\cos \theta) + P_n(-\cos \theta)]. \qquad (27)$$

In the first case $D_n = -C_n$, and

$$\Theta(\theta) = C_n' M_n(\cos \theta), \qquad (28)$$

where $M_n(\cos \theta)$ is an odd Legendre function*

$$M_n(\cos \theta) = \tfrac{1}{2}[P_n(\cos \theta) - P_n(-\cos \theta)]. \qquad (29)$$

The derivatives,

$$\frac{d}{d\theta} L_n(\cos \theta) = -\tfrac{1}{2}[P_n'(\cos \theta) - P_n'(-\cos \theta)] \sin \theta,$$

$$\frac{d}{d\theta} M_n(\cos \theta) = -\tfrac{1}{2}[P_n'(\cos \theta) + P_n'(-\cos \theta)] \sin \theta, \qquad (30)$$

are, respectively, odd and even functions. Hence, if the tangential electric intensity impressed at the input boundary is a symmetric (even) function of $\theta$, the field in the antenna region will be given by a series of odd $\Theta$ functions (equation 28). The even functions (equation 27) will appear in the case of an unbalanced or shunt type of feed.

---

* *Applied Mathematics*, p. 420. In the first paper on antennas by the author (*IRE Proc.*, September 1941), and in the paper by P. D. P. Smith (*Jour. Appl. Phys.*, January 1948), $L_n(\cos \theta)$ was used to denote the odd function now called $M_n(\cos \theta)$. It is hoped that the subsequent change in notation will not cause misunderstanding.

The balanced type of feed is the most important case from the practical point of view, and will be used in the subsequent details of the solution. The general method, however, is equally applicable to other cases. In all cases we can write general solutions in various regions bounded by concentric spheres as infinite series of solutions of the form given in equations 7, in which the $\Theta$ functions are the characteristic functions obtained from the boundary conditions. With each $\Theta$ function there will be associated an $R$ function (equation 10). The additional arbitrary constants are determined from the boundary conditions at the spherical boundaries separating the various regions. Thus, for the symmetric biconical antenna (Fig. 2.3) so energized that the currents in its arms are equal and similarly directed at points equidistant from $r = 0$, the field in the antenna region is given by

$$r^2 E_r = -\frac{1}{2\pi j\omega\varepsilon} \sum_n a_n \frac{S_n(\beta r)}{S_n(\beta l)} M_n(\cos\theta), \tag{31}$$

$$rH_\varphi = \frac{I_0(r)}{2\pi\sin\theta} + \frac{1}{2\pi}\sum_n \frac{a_n}{n(n+1)} \frac{S_n(\beta r)}{S_n(\beta l)} \frac{d}{d\theta} M_n(\cos\theta), \tag{32}$$

$$rE_\theta = \frac{\eta V(r)}{2\pi K\sin\theta} + j\frac{\eta}{2\pi}\sum_n \frac{a_n}{n(n+1)} \frac{S_n'(\beta r)}{S_n(\beta l)} \frac{d}{d\theta} M_n(\cos\theta), \tag{33}$$

$$K\,I_0(r) = V(l)[j\sin\beta(l-r) + KY_t\cos\beta(l-r)], \tag{34}$$

$$V(r) = V(l)[\cos\beta(l-r) + jKY_t\sin\beta(l-r)], \tag{35}$$

$$K = \frac{\eta}{\pi}\log\cot\tfrac{1}{2}\psi, \qquad S_n(\beta r) = Jn_n(\beta r) + p_n Nn_n(\beta r), \tag{36}$$

where the summations are extended over all the zeros of $M_n(\cos\psi)$. Equations 34 and 35 are general expressions for the conduction current in the cones and the transverse voltage (the integral of $E_\theta$ between the cones along a typical meridian) associated with the TEM waves (Section 1.14). In anticipation of the forthcoming proof that the complementary waves contribute nothing to the transverse voltage, the subscript 0 indicating the TEM wave is not used in connection with this voltage. The constants of integration in equations 34 and 35 are the voltage $V(l)$ at the output boundary $S_0$ and the *terminating admittance*

$$Y_t = \frac{I_0(l)}{V(l)}. \tag{37}$$

This is the admittance "seen by the TEM wave" at the output boundary. The factors $S_n(\beta l)$ in the denominators have been included for convenience in satisfying the boundary conditions at $r = l$. In the general expression 10 for the radial wave function we have substituted $A_n = a_n$ and $B_n = p_n a_n$ in order to separate one set of constants $a_n$, which will be determined from the boundary conditions at the output boundary sphere $r = l$, from the other set $p_n$, which will be determined from the conditions at the input boundary. If the radius of the input boundary is zero, we must have

$$p_n = 0; \tag{38}$$

otherwise, not only the field intensities $H_\varphi$, $E_\theta$ would tend to infinity as $r$ approaches zero but also their integrals. The latter represent currents and voltages and should be finite.

In the space outside the output boundary, we have a similar set of equations, except that there are no terms corresponding to TEM waves. Thus,

$$r^2 E_r = - \frac{1}{2\pi j \omega \varepsilon} \sum_{k=1,3,5,\ldots} b_k \frac{R_k(\beta r)}{R_k(\beta l)} P_k(\cos \theta), \tag{39}$$

$$rH_\varphi = \frac{1}{2\pi} \sum_{k=1,3,5,\ldots} \frac{b_k}{k(k+1)} \frac{R_k(\beta r)}{R_k(\beta l)} \frac{d}{d\theta} P_k(\cos \theta), \tag{40}$$

$$rE_\theta = j \frac{\eta}{2\pi} \sum_{k=1,3,5,\ldots} \frac{b_k}{k(k+1)} \frac{R_k'(\beta r)}{R_k(\beta l)} \frac{d}{d\theta} P_k(\cos \theta), \tag{41}$$

$$R_k(\beta r) = Jn_k(\beta r) + q_k Nn_k(\beta r). \tag{42}$$

When the medium outside the output boundary is homogeneous, $q_k = -j$, and

$$R_k(\beta r) = Hn_k(\beta r) = Jn_k(\beta r) - j Nn_k(\beta r). \tag{43}$$

These radial functions become proportional to $\exp(-j\beta r)$ as $r$ increases indefinitely.

### 2.5  Antenna current and transverse voltage

The current in the upper antenna arm is

$$I(r) = 2\pi r \sin \psi \, H_\varphi(r, \psi). \tag{44}$$

We shall represent this current as the sum of the *principal current* $I_0(r)$ associated with the TEM waves and the *complementary current* $\bar{I}(r)$ associated with all other waves,

$$I(r) = I_0(r) + \bar{I}(r). \tag{45}$$

The principal current is given by equation 34; the complementary current is found from equation 32,

$$\bar{I}(r) = \sum_n \frac{a_n}{n(n+1)} \frac{S_n(\beta r)}{S_n(\beta l)} \sin \psi \frac{d}{d\psi} M_n(\cos \psi). \tag{46}$$

We define the *transverse voltage* $V(r)$ as the line integral along a typical meridian from the upper antenna arm to the lower,

$$V(r) = \int_\psi^{\pi-\psi} rE_\theta \, d\theta. \tag{47}$$

This integral vanishes for every term in equation 33 except the first. Hence, *only the TEM waves contribute to the transverse voltage*, and this voltage is given by equation 35.

It should be noted that the transverse voltage as here defined is not equal to the difference of the scalar electric potentials at the two ends of the meridian; it includes a contribution from the dynamic component of the electric intensity (that is, from the vector potential). In the case of the biconical antenna, the transverse voltage is seen to be sinusoidally distributed; hence, for other antennas, including the cylindrical antenna, it is *not* distributed sinusoidally. On the other hand, the scalar potential is distributed sinusoidally on the cylindrical antenna but not on others.

## 2.6 Fundamental theorem

The input admittance of the antenna is

$$Y_i = \frac{I(r_i)}{V(r_i)} = \frac{I_0(r_i)}{V(r_i)} + \frac{\bar{I}(r_i)}{V(r_i)}. \tag{48}$$

Thus, we have a fundamental theorem: *The input admittance of a symmetric biconical antenna equals the sum of two admittances. The first of these admittances equals the admittance of a uniform transmission line terminated into an appropriate admittance $Y_t$. The second admittance represents the local effect at the input terminals, and it vanishes as the dimensions of the input region vanish.*

From equations 34 and 35, we have          •

$$KY_i = \frac{KY_t \cos \beta(l-r_i) + j \sin \beta(l-r_i)}{\cos \beta(l-r_i) + jKY_t \sin \beta(l-r_i)} + \frac{\bar{I}(r_i)}{V(r_i)}. \tag{49}$$

If $r_i = 0$, then,

$$KY_i = \frac{KY_t \cos \beta l + j \sin \beta l}{\cos \beta l + jKY_t \sin \beta l}. \tag{50}$$

Introducing in equation 50 the impedance $Z_a$ seen at the distance $\lambda/4$ from the end of the line (this impedance is called the *inverse radiation impedance*),

$$Z_a = K^2 Y_t, \tag{51}$$

and taking the reciprocal, we find

$$Z_i = K \frac{K \cos \beta l + jZ_a \sin \beta l}{Z_a \cos \beta l + jK \sin \beta l} = K \frac{Z_a \sin \beta l - jK \cos \beta l}{K \sin \beta l - jZ_a \cos \beta l}. \tag{52}$$

## 2.7   General formula for the terminating admittance

When $r = l$, equation 32 becomes

$$l\, H_\varphi(l, \theta) = \frac{Y_t\, V(l)}{2\pi \sin \theta} + \frac{1}{2\pi} \sum_n \frac{a_n}{n(n+1)} \frac{d}{d\theta} M_n(\cos \theta). \tag{53}$$

Integrating from $\theta = \psi$ to $\theta = \pi - \psi$, we find that all terms on the right except the first disappear. Thus, we find

$$KY_t = \frac{\eta}{V(l)} \int_\psi^{\pi-\psi} l\, H_\varphi(l, \theta)\, d\theta. \tag{54}$$

Since $H_\varphi$ must be continuous at the output boundary sphere, it is also given by equation 40. Substituting in equation 54 and integrating, we find

$$KY_t = - \frac{\eta}{\pi\, V(l)} \sum_{k=1,3,5,\ldots} \frac{b_k}{k(k+1)} P_k(\cos \psi). \tag{55}$$

## 2.8   Auxiliary formulas for calculating the terminating admittance

The terminating admittance, normalized with respect to the characteristic admittance $1/K$, has thus been expressed in terms of an infinite sequence of coefficients $b_1, b_3, b_5, \cdots$. The $a_n$'s do not enter equation 55 directly, but in general they also have to be determined since the two sets of constants are interdependent. Notable exceptions are two extreme cases: (1) thin biconical antennas in which $\psi$ is very small, (2) spherical antennas in which $\psi$ is nearly equal to $\pi/2$. In these cases the limits approached by the $b$'s can be found rather easily. In fact, in the case of thin antennas there are two methods by which we can find $Y_t$ even *without* obtaining the $b$'s. The solutions in the two extreme cases may be taken as the first terms in sequences of successive approximations to the solution of the problem for intermediate values of the half cone angle $\psi$. Thus, starting with the already determined limits of the $b_k$'s, we may use one of the boundary conditions at the output boundary sphere to evaluate the $a_n$'s and then the other boundary condition to re-evaluate the $b_k$'s; then the cycle is repeated. In order to carry out these successive approximations, we need certain auxiliary formulas which we shall now derive.

Substituting $r = l$ in equation 32, we obtain

$$lH_\varphi = \frac{Y_t \, V(l)}{2\pi \sin \theta} + \frac{1}{2\pi} \sum_n \frac{a_n}{n(n+1)} \frac{d}{d\theta} M_n(\cos \theta),$$
$$\psi < \theta < \pi - \psi, \tag{56}$$

where $n$ is a typical zero of $M_n(\cos \psi)$. Similarly, from equation 40,

$$lH_\varphi = \frac{1}{2\pi} \sum_{k=1,3,5,\ldots} \frac{b_k}{k(k+1)} \frac{d}{d\theta} P_k(\cos \theta), \qquad 0 \leq \theta \leq \pi. \tag{57}$$

To simplify the form of the corresponding expressions for $E_\theta(l, \theta)$, we introduce the *radial wave impedances* at the output boundary for the various modes of propagation,

$$Z_k{}^+ = \frac{E_{\theta,k}(l)}{H_{\varphi,k}(l)} = j\eta \, \frac{R_k{}'(\beta l)}{R_k(\beta l)} = j\eta \, \frac{Jn_k{}'(\beta l) + q_k \, Nn_k{}'(\beta l)}{Jn_k(\beta l) + q_k \, Nn_k(\beta l)} , \tag{58}$$

$$Z_n{}^- = - \frac{E_{\theta,n}(l)}{H_{\varphi,n}(l)} = -j\eta \, \frac{S_n{}'(\beta l)}{S_n(\beta l)}$$

$$= -j\eta \, \frac{Jn_n{}'(\beta l) + p_n \, Nn_n{}'(\beta l)}{Jn_n(\beta l) + p_n \, Nn_n(\beta l)} . \tag{59}$$

In particular, when region 1 is homogeneous, $q_k = -j$, and

$$Z_k{}^+ = j\eta \, \frac{Jn_k{}'(\beta l) - j \, Nn_k{}'(\beta l)}{Jn_k(\beta l) - j \, Nn_k(\beta l)} . \tag{60}$$

Similarly, if the input region is infinitesimal, $p_n = 0$, and

$$Z_n{}^- = -j\eta \, \frac{Jn_n{}'(\beta l)}{Jn_n(\beta l)} . \tag{61}$$

At the output boundary $E_\theta$ may thus be expressed either as

$$lE_\theta = \frac{1}{2\pi} \sum_{k=1,3,5,\ldots} \frac{b_k}{k(k+1)} Z_k{}^+ \frac{d}{d\theta} P_k(\cos \theta), \qquad 0 \leq \theta \leq \pi; \tag{62}$$

or as

$$lE_\theta = \frac{\eta \, V(l)}{2\pi K \sin \theta} - \frac{1}{2\pi} \sum_n \frac{a_n}{n(n+1)} Z_n{}^- \frac{d}{d\theta} M_n(\cos \theta),$$
$$\psi < \theta < \pi - \psi;$$

$$= 0, \qquad\qquad 0 < \theta < \psi \quad \text{or} \quad \pi - \psi < \theta < \pi; \tag{63}$$

and the two expressions must be equivalent.

Using equation 56 and the orthogonal properties of Legendre functions and their derivatives,* we can express the $a_n$'s in terms of $lH_\varphi$ and, therefore, in terms of the $b_n$'s.  Thus,

$$a_n = \frac{2\pi n(n+1) \int_\psi^{\pi-\psi} (lH_\varphi) \sin\theta \frac{d}{d\theta} M_n(\cos\theta)\, d\theta}{\int_\psi^{\pi-\psi} \left[ \frac{d}{d\theta} M_n(\cos\theta) \right]^2 \sin\theta\, d\theta} \cdot \tag{64}$$

Substituting the expression for $lH_\varphi$ in terms of the $b$'s, we have

$$a_n = \sum_{k=1,3,5,\ldots} u_{nk} b_k,$$

$$u_{nk} = \frac{n(n+1) \int_\psi^{\pi-\psi} \sin\theta \frac{d}{d\theta} M_n(\cos\theta) \frac{d}{d\theta} P_k(\cos\theta)\, d\theta}{k(k+1) \int_\psi^{\pi-\psi} \left[ \frac{d}{d\theta} M_n(\cos\theta) \right]^2 \sin\theta\, d\theta} \cdot \tag{65}$$

Integrating the integral in the numerator of equation 65 by parts, we have

$$\int_\psi^{\pi-\psi} \sin\theta \frac{d}{d\theta} M_n(\cos\theta) \frac{d}{d\theta} P_k(\cos\theta)\, d\theta$$

$$= \sin\theta\, M_n(\cos\theta) \frac{d}{d\theta} P_k(\cos\theta) \Big|_\psi^{\pi-\psi} -$$

$$\int_\psi^{\pi-\psi} M_n(\cos\theta) \frac{d}{d\theta} \left[ \sin\theta \frac{d}{d\theta} P_k(\cos\theta) \right] d\theta. \tag{66}$$

The integrated term vanishes because $M_n(\cos\psi)$ and $M_n(-\cos\psi)$ vanish.  The second term may be simplified since equation 8 is equivalent to

$$\frac{d}{d\theta}\left( \sin\theta \frac{d\Theta}{d\theta} \right) = -n(n+1) \sin\theta\, \Theta, \tag{67}$$

and $P_k(\cos\theta)$ is its solution when $n = k$.  Thus,

$$\int_\psi^{\pi-\psi} \sin\theta \frac{d}{d\theta} M_n(\cos\theta) \frac{d}{d\theta} P_k(\cos\theta)\, d\theta$$

$$= k(k+1) \int_\psi^{\pi-\psi} M_n(\cos\theta)\, P_k(\cos\theta) \sin\theta\, d\theta. \tag{68}$$

* *Applied Mathematics*, p. 431.

The value of the last integral may be found elsewhere,*

$$\int_{\psi}^{\pi-\psi} M_n(\cos\theta)\,P_k(\cos\theta)\sin\theta\,d\theta = \frac{\sin\theta\left[M_n\dfrac{dP_k}{d\theta} - P_k\dfrac{dM_n}{d\theta}\right]_{\psi}^{\pi-\psi}}{n(n+1) - k(k+1)}$$

$$= \frac{2}{n(n+1) - k(k+1)}\sin\psi\,P_k(\cos\psi)\frac{d\,M_n(\cos\psi)}{d\psi}. \quad (69)$$

Similarly, for the integral in the denominator, we find

$$\int_{\psi}^{\pi-\psi}\left[\frac{d}{d\theta}M_n(\cos\theta)\right]^2\sin\theta\,d\theta = n(n+1)\int_{\psi}^{\pi-\psi}[M_n(\cos\theta)]^2\sin\theta\,d\theta, \quad (70)$$

$$\int_{\psi}^{\pi-\psi}[M_n(\cos\theta)]^2\sin\theta\,d\theta = \frac{\sin\theta}{2n+1}\left(\frac{\partial M_n}{\partial\theta}\frac{\partial M_n}{\partial n} - M_n\frac{\partial^2 M_n}{\partial\theta\,\partial n}\right)\Bigg|_{\psi}^{\pi-\psi}$$

$$= -\frac{2}{2n+1}\sin\psi\,\frac{\partial\,M_n(\cos\psi)}{\partial\psi}\frac{\partial\,M_n(\cos\psi)}{\partial n}. \quad (71)$$

If $\psi$ is not too small, the last integral may be evaluated more simply by substituting an approximate expression for $M_n(\cos\theta)$. Thus, we have evaluated the $u$ coefficients in equation 65,

$$u_{nk} = \frac{2n+1}{k(k+1) - n(n+1)}\frac{P_k(\cos\psi)}{\partial\,M_n(\cos\psi)/\partial n}. \quad (72)$$

Using equation 62 and the orthogonal properties of the Legendre functions, we can express the $b$'s in terms of $lE_\theta$; then, by substituting from equation 63, we can find the $b$'s in terms of the $a$'s and $V(l)$. Thus,

$$b_k = \frac{\pi(2k+1)}{Z_k^+}\int_0^{\pi}(lE_\theta)\sin\theta\,\frac{d}{d\theta}P_k(\cos\theta)\,d\theta. \quad (73)$$

Substituting from equation 63, we have

$$Z_k^+ b_k = -\frac{(2k+1)\eta\,V(l)}{K}P_k(\cos\psi) + \sum_n Z_n^- v_{kn}a_n,$$

$$v_{kn} = \frac{k(k+1)}{n(n+1)}\frac{2k+1}{k(k+1) - n(n+1)}\times \quad (74)$$

$$\sin\psi\,P_k(\cos\psi)\frac{d\,M_n(\cos\psi)}{d\psi}.$$

Equations 65 and 74 are linear algebraic equations defining the coefficients $a_n$, $b_k$ in terms of $V(l)$. If these equations are solved, the

* *Applied Mathematics*, p. 425, eq. 39.

$b$'s can be substituted in the expression 55 for the terminating admittance normalized with respect to $K$; $V(l)$ cancels out.

The number of equations may be reduced in half by eliminating the $a$'s from equations 74 with the aid of equation 65,

$$b_k = - \frac{(2k + 1)\eta\, V(l)}{KZ_k{}^+} P_k(\cos \psi) + \sum_{n,} \sum_{\alpha=1,3,\ldots} \frac{Z_n{}^-}{Z_k{}^+} v_{kn} u_{n\alpha} b_\alpha. \quad (75)$$

## 2.9   Symmetric spherical antennas

The symmetric spherical antenna is a special case of a biconical antenna with $\psi$ nearly equal to $\pi/2$; it is also a spheroidal antenna of zero eccentricity. As we shall presently see, the complementary waves in the antenna region may be neglected when the length of the gap between the hemispheres, $s = l(\pi - 2\psi)$, is small compared with $\lambda/2$. Setting the $a_n$'s equal to zero in equation 74, we have

$$b_k = - \frac{(2k + 1)\eta\, V(l)}{KZ_k{}^+} P_k(\cos \psi), \quad (76)$$

where the radial wave impedances are given by equation 60. Substituting in equation 55 and then in equation 51, we have

$$Z_a = K^2 Y_t \doteq \frac{\eta^2}{\pi} \sum_{k=1,3,5,\ldots} \frac{2k + 1}{k(k + 1)} [P_k(\cos \psi)]^2\, Y_k{}^+,$$

$$Y_k{}^+ = \frac{1}{Z_k{}^+} . \qquad\qquad (77)$$

The normalized values of the radial wave conductances and susceptances for the first seven modes of propagation are shown in Figs. 2.4 and 2.5.

If the length of the gap between the hemispheres is small compared with $\lambda/2$, all the higher order waves in the antenna region are highly attenuated because, even near the gap which is the widest part of the region, the cutoff wavelengths for these modes are $2s$, $2s/3$, $2s/5$, etc., and hence much smaller than $\lambda$. Consequently, these waves are concentrated in the vicinity of the gap, the reactive energy associated with them is small, and their effect on $Y_t$ must be small.

This is an intuitive deduction from our knowledge of waveguide theory. We may also use a more detailed mathematical analysis to arrive at the same conclusion. When $\psi$ is not too small and not too near $\pi$, we have the following approximate formulas for the Legendre functions,*

* *Applied Mathematics*, p. 419.

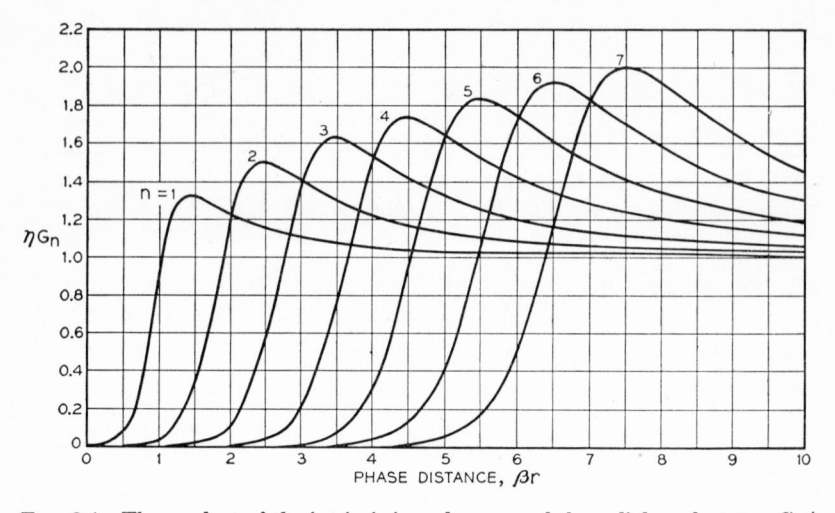

FIG. 2.4    The product of the intrinsic impedance $\eta$ and the radial conductance $G_n{}^+$ of progressive spherical waves in free space as a function of the phase radius $\beta r$.

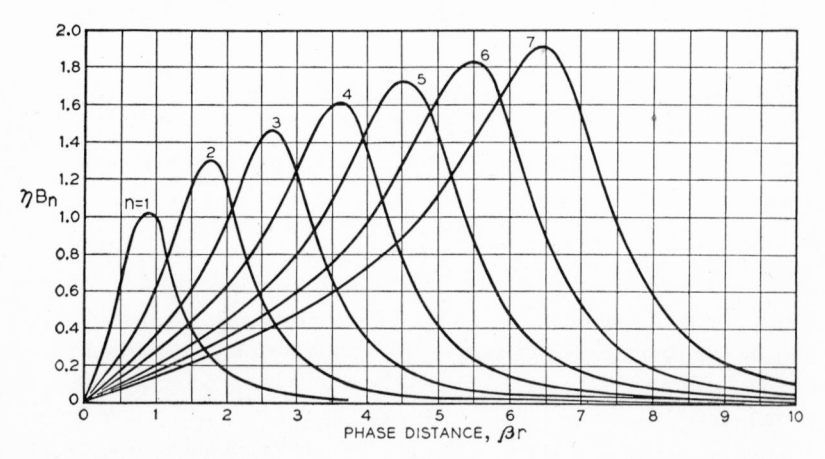

FIG. 2.5    The product of the intrinsic impedance $\eta$ and the radial susceptance $B_n{}^+$ of progressive spherical waves in free space as a function of the phase radius $\beta r$.

$$P_n(\cos\psi) = \frac{\cos(q\psi - \tfrac{1}{4}\pi)}{(\tfrac{1}{2}\pi p \sin\psi)^{1/2}}, \qquad P_n(-\cos\psi) = \frac{\cos(q\pi - q\psi - \tfrac{1}{4}\pi)}{(\tfrac{1}{2}\pi p \sin\psi)^{1/2}},$$

$$\tag{78}$$

$$q = [(n + \tfrac{1}{2})^2 + \tfrac{1}{4}]^{1/2}, \qquad p = [(n + \tfrac{1}{2})^2 - \tfrac{1}{4}]^{1/2} = [n(n+1)]^{1/2}.$$

Therefore,

$$M_n(\cos\psi) = \frac{\sin(\tfrac{1}{2}q\pi - \tfrac{1}{4}\pi)\sin q(\tfrac{1}{2}\pi - \psi)}{(\tfrac{1}{2}\pi p \sin\psi)^{1/2}}. \tag{79}$$

The roots of this equation are

$$q(\tfrac{1}{2}\pi - \psi) = m\pi, \qquad m = 1, 2, 3, \cdots,$$

$$q = \frac{2m\pi}{\pi - 2\psi}. \tag{80}$$

These roots approach infinity as $\psi$ approaches $\pi/2$. For $n$ we have

$$n = -\tfrac{1}{2} + \sqrt{q^2 - \tfrac{1}{4}} = -\frac{1}{2} + q - \frac{1}{8q} - \frac{1}{128q^3} - \cdots. \tag{81}$$

Since $\pi - 2\psi = s/l$, we can express $q$ and therefore $n$ in terms of the length of the gap between the hemispheres,

$$q = \frac{2m\pi l}{s}, \qquad n = \frac{2m\pi l}{s} - \frac{1}{2} - \frac{s}{16m\pi l} - \cdots. \tag{82}$$

For large $n$,

$$Jn_n(\beta l) = \frac{\sqrt{\pi}(\tfrac{1}{2}\beta l)^{n+1}}{(n+0.5)!}, \qquad Jn_n{}'(\beta l) = \frac{\sqrt{\pi}(n+1)(\tfrac{1}{2}\beta l)^n}{(n+0.5)!\,2},$$

$$Z_n{}^- = -j\eta\,\frac{Jn_n{}'(\beta l)}{Jn_n(\beta l)} = -\frac{j\eta(n+1)}{\beta l} \tag{83}$$

$$= \frac{n+1}{j\omega\varepsilon l} = \frac{2m\pi}{j\omega\varepsilon s} + \frac{1}{j\omega\varepsilon l} - \cdots.$$

From these equations we conclude that the coefficients $v_{kn}$ in equations 74 for the $b$'s decrease rapidly as $n$ increases and $s$ decreases; hence, the influence of the $a$'s on the $b$'s decreases.

As the frequency approaches zero, $\beta$ approaches zero and

$$Nn_k(\beta l) = -\frac{(k-0.5)!}{\sqrt{\pi}(\tfrac{1}{2}\beta l)^k}, \qquad Nn_k{}'(\beta l) = \frac{(k-0.5)!\,k}{2\sqrt{\pi}(\tfrac{1}{2}\beta l)^{k+1}}, \tag{84}$$

$$Z_k{}^+ = -\frac{j\eta k}{\beta l} = \frac{k}{j\omega\varepsilon l}.$$

The terminating admittance will approach the admittance of the capacitor formed by the hemispheres, and we may write

$$Y_t = j\omega C_t,$$

$$C_t = \frac{\varepsilon l\eta^2}{\pi K^2} \sum_{k=1,3,5,\ldots} \frac{2k+1}{k^2(k+1)} [P_k(\cos\psi)]^2. \tag{85}$$

As $\psi$ approaches $\pi/2$,

$$K \rightarrow \frac{\eta}{2\pi} (\pi - 2\psi) = \frac{\eta}{\pi} \left( \frac{\pi}{2} - \psi \right). \tag{86}$$

Since $P_k(\cos \psi)$ also approaches zero, we need a finer approximation than equation 78 in order to evaluate equation 85. To obtain this approximation (for the case of general $n$) we shall use the exact values of $P_n(\cos \psi)$ and its derivative at $\psi = \pi/2$,

$$P_n(0) = \frac{\left( \dfrac{n-1}{2} \right)!}{\left( \dfrac{n}{2} \right)! \sqrt{\pi}} \cos \frac{n\pi}{2},$$

$$P_n'(0) = - \frac{dP_n(\cos \psi)}{d\psi} \bigg|_{\psi = \pi/2} = \frac{\left( \dfrac{n}{2} \right)! \, 2}{\left( \dfrac{n-1}{2} \right)! \sqrt{\pi}} \sin \frac{n\pi}{2}. \tag{87}$$

If $\psi$ is not too near 0 or $\pi$, the approximate solution of Legendre's equation is

$$P_n(\cos \psi) = \frac{A \cos q\psi + B \sin q\psi}{\sqrt{\sin \psi}}, \qquad q = [(n + \tfrac{1}{2})^2 + \tfrac{1}{4}]^{\frac{1}{2}}. \tag{88}$$

Hence,

$$A \cos \frac{q\pi}{2} + B \sin \frac{q\pi}{2} = P_n(0),$$

$$-A \sin \frac{q\pi}{2} + B \cos \frac{q\pi}{2} = - \frac{1}{q} P_n'(0). \tag{89}$$

Solving for $A$, $B$ and substituting in equation 88, we find

$$P_n(\cos \psi) = \frac{P_n(0) \cos q \left( \psi - \dfrac{\pi}{2} \right) - q^{-1} P_n'(0) \sin q \left( \psi - \dfrac{\pi}{2} \right)}{\sqrt{\sin \psi}} . \tag{90}$$

For large $n$,

$$\frac{\left( \dfrac{n}{2} \right)!}{\left( \dfrac{n-1}{2} \right)!} = \sqrt{\frac{n}{2}}, \tag{91}$$

and equation 90 becomes

$$P_n(\cos\psi) = \frac{\cos\left[\left(n+\frac{1}{2}\right)\psi - \frac{\pi}{4}\right]}{\sqrt{\frac{1}{2}n\pi \sin\psi}}.\tag{92}$$

Let

$$\vartheta = \pi - 2\psi = \frac{s}{l}.\tag{93}$$

Substituting from equation 92 in equation 85 and noting that $k$ is an odd integer, we have (for small $\vartheta$)

$$C_t = \frac{4\varepsilon l}{\vartheta^2} \sum_{k=1,3,\dots} \frac{(2k+1)[1-\cos(k+\frac{1}{2})\vartheta]}{k^3(k+1)}.\tag{94}$$

Introducing a new variable of summation,

$$t = (k+\tfrac{1}{2})\vartheta, \qquad \Delta t = 2\vartheta,\tag{95}$$

we have

$$C_t = 4\varepsilon l \sum_{\frac{3}{2}\vartheta,\frac{5}{2}\vartheta,\dots} \left(1+\frac{\Delta t}{4t}\right)^{-1}\left(1-\frac{\Delta t}{4t}\right)^{-3}\frac{1-\cos t}{t^3}\,\Delta t.\tag{96}$$

We shall now neglect $\Delta t/4t$ in the parentheses and replace the sum by an integral,

$$C_t = 4\varepsilon l \int_{\frac{3}{2}\vartheta}^{\infty} \frac{1-\cos t}{t^3}\,dt.\tag{97}$$

Evaluating,

$$C_t = 2\varepsilon l\left[\frac{1-\cos\frac{3}{2}\vartheta}{(\frac{3}{2}\vartheta)^2} + \frac{\sin\frac{3}{2}\vartheta}{\frac{3}{2}\vartheta} - \mathrm{Ci}\,\tfrac{3}{2}\vartheta\right]$$

$$= 2\varepsilon l\left(\log\frac{1}{\vartheta} + 0.52\right).\tag{98}$$

To increase the accuracy we should evaluate the initial terms of the series 94 and replace the remainder by an integral.

For small $\vartheta$ the series 94 converges slowly; so does the imaginary part of the series in equation 77 since, when $k$ is large, the approximation for $Y_k^+$ is the same as for small $\omega$. Since we have evaluated $C_t$, we can subtract $j\omega C_t$ from $Y_t$ and thus increase the rapidity of convergence of the remainder:

$$Y_t = j\omega C_t + \frac{4\pi}{\vartheta^2} \sum_{k=1,3,\dots} \frac{2k+1}{k(k+1)}\,[P_k(\cos\psi)]^2\left[Y_k^+ - \frac{j\omega\varepsilon l}{k}\right].\tag{99}$$

In fact, this series approaches a limit as $\vartheta$ approaches zero. Thus,

$$P_k(\cos\psi) = P_k\left[\cos\left(\frac{\pi}{2} - \frac{\vartheta}{2}\right)\right]$$

$$= P_k\left(\cos\frac{\pi}{2}\right) - \frac{\vartheta}{2}\frac{d}{d\psi}P_k(\cos\psi)\bigg|_{\psi=\pi/2}$$

$$= \vartheta\sin\frac{k\pi}{2}\frac{\left(\dfrac{k}{2}\right)!}{\left(\dfrac{k-1}{2}\right)!\sqrt{\pi}}, \tag{100}$$

and

$$Y_t = j\omega C_t + 4\sum_{k=1,3,\ldots}\frac{(2k+1)\left[\left(\dfrac{k}{2}\right)!\right]^2}{k(k+1)\left[\left(\dfrac{k-1}{2}\right)!\right]^2}\left[Y_k{}^+ - \frac{j\omega\varepsilon l}{k}\right]. \tag{101}$$

## 2.10   Thin biconical antennas

As $\psi$ approaches zero, the inverse radiation impedance, $Z_a = K^2 Y_t$, approaches a limit which can be expressed either as a series,

$$Z_a = K^2 Y_t = \frac{\eta}{\pi}\sum_{k=1,3,5,\ldots}\frac{2k+1}{k(k+1)}Jn_k(\beta l)[Jn_k(\beta l) - j\,Nn_k(\beta l)]$$

$$= \tfrac{1}{2}\eta(\beta l)\sum_{k=1,3,5,\ldots}\frac{2k+1}{k(k+1)}J_{k+\frac{1}{2}}(\beta l)[J_{k+\frac{1}{2}}(\beta l) - j\,N_{k+\frac{1}{2}}(\beta l)], \tag{102}$$

or in terms of the sine and cosine integrals,

$$Z_a = R_a + jX_a,$$

$$R_a = \frac{\eta}{2\pi}\,\mathrm{Cin}\,2\beta l + \frac{\eta}{4\pi}\,(2\,\mathrm{Cin}\,2\beta l - \mathrm{Cin}\,4\beta l)\cos 2\beta l +$$

$$\frac{\eta}{4\pi}\,(\mathrm{Si}\,4\beta l - 2\,\mathrm{Si}\,2\beta l)\sin 2\beta l, \tag{103}$$

$$X_a = \frac{\eta}{2\pi}\,\mathrm{Si}\,2\beta l - \frac{\eta}{4\pi}\,(\mathrm{Cin}\,4\beta l - 2\log 2)\sin 2\beta l -$$

$$\frac{\eta}{4\pi}\,\mathrm{Si}\,4\beta l\cos 2\beta l.$$

These limits can be found in various ways. One method follows from the fundamental theorem in Section 2.6, and from the earlier theorem to the effect that, as the radius of the antenna approaches zero, the current distribution approaches a sinusoidal form with the nodes at the ends. Thus, as $\psi \to 0$,

$$I(r) \to jK^{-1} V(l) \sin \beta(l - r) \equiv I_0 \sin \beta(l - r). \tag{104}$$

At the same time $K$ approaches infinity, and from equation 52 we find

$$Z_i = -jK \cot \beta l + \frac{Z_a}{\sin^2 \beta l} + O\left(\frac{1}{K}\right). \tag{105}$$

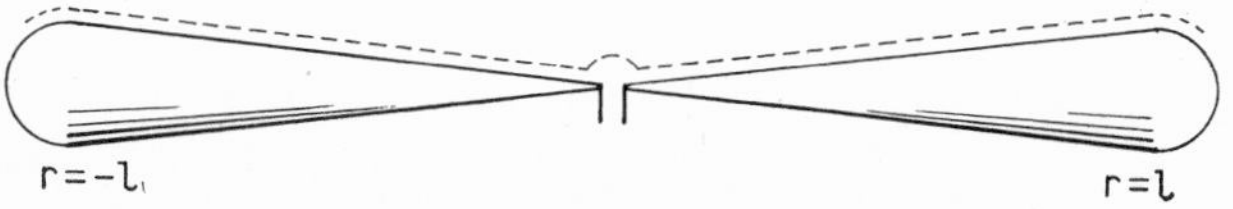

FIG. 2.6　Contour of integration (the broken line) used to obtain the complex radiated power from a biconical antenna.

For the complex power input to the antenna we find

$$\Psi = \tfrac{1}{2} Z_i I_i I_i^* = \tfrac{1}{2} Z_i I_0 I_0^* \sin^2 \beta l$$

$$= \tfrac{1}{2}\left[ -jK \sin \beta l \cos \beta l + Z_a + O\left(\frac{1}{K}\right)\right] I_0 I_0^*. \tag{106}$$

This must equal the complex radiated power,

$$\Psi = -\tfrac{1}{2} \int E_s I^*(r)\, ds$$

$$= -\tfrac{1}{2} I_0^* \int E_s \sin \beta(l - r)\, ds, \tag{107}$$

where the integration is extended along the broken line in Fig. 2.6 and $E_s$ is the tangential component of the electric intensity. This line is parallel to a typical generator of the cone, with an infinitesimal, semicircular indentation around the apex. We are interested, of course, in the limit approached by $\Psi$ as $\psi$ approaches 0. Then the current is distributed on the axis of the cone and extends from $z = -l$ to $z = l$. The field is*
(Fig. 2.7)

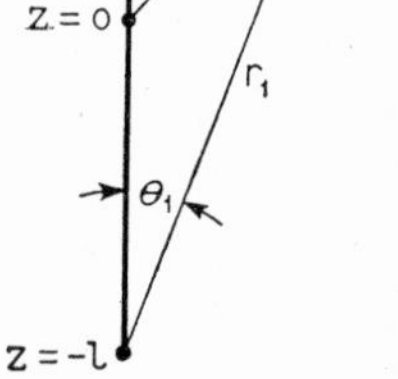

FIG. 2.7　Explaining equations 108.

$$E_z = \frac{\eta}{4\pi} jI_0 \left( 2\, \frac{e^{-j\beta r}}{r} \cos \beta l - \frac{e^{-j\beta r_1}}{r_1} - \frac{e^{-j\beta r_2}}{r_2} \right),$$

* *Electromagnetic Waves*, p. 371.

$$\rho E_\rho = \frac{\eta}{4\pi} jI_0(e^{-j\beta r_1}\cos\theta_1 + e^{-j\beta r_2}\cos\theta_2 - 2\cos\beta le^{-j\beta r}\cos\theta),$$

$$\tag{108}$$

$$\rho H_\varphi = \frac{jI_0}{4\pi}\ (e^{-j\beta r_1} + e^{-j\beta r_2} - 2e^{-j\beta r}\cos\beta l).$$

The spherical components of $E$ are

$$E_r = E_z\cos\theta + E_\rho\sin\theta, \qquad E_\theta = -E_z\sin\theta + E_\rho\cos\theta. \tag{109}$$

On the surface of the infinitely thin cone $\theta = \psi$,

$$E_r = E_z + E_\rho\psi$$
$$= \frac{j\eta I_0}{4\pi}\left[\frac{e^{-j\beta(l+r)} - e^{-j\beta(l-r)}}{r} - \frac{e^{-j\beta(l+r)}}{l+r} - \frac{e^{-j\beta(l-r)}}{l-r}\right]. \tag{110}$$

On the surface of the circle of infinitesimal radius $r = \varepsilon$, centered at $z = 0$,

$$\varepsilon E_\theta = -\frac{j\eta I_0\cos\beta l}{2\pi\sin\theta}. \tag{111}$$

Because of symmetry, the integral in equation 107 can be evaluated along one half of the contour shown in Fig. 2.6 and the result doubled,

$$\Psi = -I_0{}^*\int_0^l E_r\sin\beta(l-r)\,dr + I_0{}^*\int_\psi^{\pi/2}\varepsilon E_\theta\sin\beta l\,d\theta$$

$$= -I_0{}^*\int_0^l E_r\sin\beta(l-r)\,dr - \tfrac{1}{2}jK\sin\beta l\cos\beta l\,I_0 I_0{}^*. \tag{112}$$

Comparing with equation 106, we find

$$Z_a = -\frac{2}{I_0}\int_0^l E_r\sin\beta(l-r)\,dr$$

$$= \frac{j\eta}{2\pi}\int_0^l\left[\frac{e^{-j\beta(l-r)} - e^{-j\beta(l+r)}}{r} + \frac{e^{-j\beta(l-r)}}{l-r} + \frac{e^{-j\beta(l+r)}}{l+r}\right]\times$$

$$\sin\beta(l-r)\,dr. \tag{113}$$

Therefore,

$$Z_a = \frac{\eta}{4\pi}\int_0^l\left[\frac{1 - e^{-2j\beta r}}{r} + e^{-2j\beta l}\frac{1 - e^{2j\beta r}}{r} +\right.$$

$$\left.\frac{1 - e^{-2j\beta(l-r)}}{l-r}\frac{e^{-2j\beta r}}{l+r} - \frac{e^{-2j\beta l}}{l+r}\right]dr. \tag{114}$$

Evaluating, we obtain equation 103.

We might also use equation 54. From equation 108 we find, for $r = l$,

$$lH_\varphi = \frac{jI_0(e^{-j2\beta l \sin \frac{1}{2}\theta} + e^{-j2\beta l \cos \frac{1}{2}\theta} - 1 - e^{-2j\beta l})}{4\pi \sin \theta}. \tag{115}$$

From equation 104,

$$I_0 = \frac{j\,V(l)}{K}\ ;$$

therefore,

$$Z_a = K^2 Y_t = \frac{\eta}{4\pi} \int_0^\pi \frac{1 + e^{-2j\beta l} - e^{-2j\beta l \sin \frac{1}{2}\theta} - e^{-2j\beta l \cos \frac{1}{2}\theta}}{\sin \theta}\, d\theta. \tag{116}$$

Taking account of the symmetry of the integrand with respect to $\theta = \pi/2$ and introducing new variables of integration $x = \sin \frac{1}{2}\theta$ and $y = \cos \frac{1}{2}\theta$, we again obtain equation 103.

Equations 102 and 103 represent the same function.* For finite values of $K$ the function $Z_a$ depends on all three parameters involved in the problem, that is, on $l$, $\lambda$, and the maximum radius of the antenna $a$. From dimensional considerations we conclude that the impedance must involve ratios of these parameters $l/a$, $l/\lambda$, $a/\lambda$; that is, we may use $K$, $\beta l$, and $\beta a$ as three independent parameters. It is not difficult to anticipate that, as $K$ increases indefinitely, we can express $Z_a$ in the following form:

$$Z_a(\beta l, K) = Z_a^{0}(\beta l) + \frac{Z_a^{(1)}(\beta l)}{K} + \frac{Z_a^{(2)}(\beta l)}{K^2} + \cdots. \tag{117}$$

This may be derived from the preceding expressions and from equations 37, 45, and 46. As $\psi$ approaches zero, the ratio $a/\lambda$ also approaches zero; the order of magnitude of the total current $I(l)$ entering the "cap" at the end of the upper antenna arm may thus be calculated from the electrostatic capacitance between the caps at the upper and lower ends. The capacitance of a disk in free space is $8\varepsilon a$. Each cap presents only one face to free space and its capacitance is $4\varepsilon a$. The two caps are in series, and the capacitance between them is $2\varepsilon a$. Hence, the corresponding admittance is $2j\omega\varepsilon a = 4\pi ja/\lambda\eta$. Since $K = 120 \log(2l/a)$, we have

$$a = 2l\, e^{-K/120}, \qquad 2j\omega\varepsilon a = j\,\frac{4\pi}{\eta}\,\frac{2l}{\lambda}\, e^{-K/120}. \tag{118}$$

---

* Hence, in effect, we have summed the series 102 of products of Bessel functions. Following this clue Mr. S. O. Rice, a colleague of the author, undertook to sum the series by direct transformation, and thus was able to sum other series of this type. Subsequently his results were used in the theory of end-fed antennas. The method of summation is described by Rice in his paper, Sums of series of the form $\sum_0^\infty a_n J_{n+\alpha}(z) J_{n+\beta}(z)$, *Phil. Mag.* (7), **35**, October 1944, pp. 686–693.

Hence, *the total current $I(l)$ flowing into the caps at the ends of the cones vanishes exponentially as $K$ increases; that is, it tends to zero more rapidly than any power of $1/K$.*

This means that, to obtain the coefficients of the various powers of $K$ in equation 117, we may assume

$$I(l) = 0. \tag{119}$$

From equations 37, 45, and 46, we then have

$$Y_t = - \frac{\bar{I}(l)}{V(l)} = - \frac{1}{V(l)} \sum_n \frac{a_n}{n(n+1)} \sin \psi \frac{d}{d\psi} M_n(\cos \psi). \tag{120}$$

In the vicinity of $\psi = 0$, we have

$$P_n(\cos \psi) = 1 + O(\psi^2),$$

$$P_n(-\cos \psi) = \frac{2}{\pi} \sin n\pi \left[ \log \sin \frac{\psi}{2} + \psi(n) - \psi(0) \right][1 + O(\psi^2)] +$$

$$[1 + O(\psi^2)] \cos n\pi, \tag{121}$$

$$M_n(\cos \psi) = \frac{1 - \cos n\pi}{2} [1 + O(\psi^2)] -$$

$$\frac{\sin n\pi}{\pi} \left[ \log \sin \frac{\psi}{2} + \psi(n) - \psi(0) \right][1 + O(\psi^2)],$$

where $\psi(n)$ is the logarithmic derivative of the factorial of $n$. Therefore,

$$\frac{d M_n(\cos \psi)}{d\psi} = - \frac{\sin n\pi}{\pi \psi} + O(\psi), \tag{122}$$

and, omitting the terms of order $\psi$,

$$Y_t = \frac{1}{V(l)} \sum_n \frac{a_n \sin n\pi}{n(n+1)\pi}. \tag{123}$$

The index of summation $n$ is a root of $M_n(\cos \psi) = 0$; ignoring the terms of order $\psi^2$ and introducing $K$ in the logarithmic term, we have an approximate equation for the values of $n$:

$$\frac{1 - \cos n\pi}{2} + \sin n\pi \left[ \frac{K}{\eta} + \frac{\psi(0) - \psi(n)}{\pi} \right] = 0, \tag{124}$$

$$2 \cot \frac{n\pi}{2} = - \left[ \frac{K}{\eta} + \frac{\psi(0) - \psi(n)}{\pi} \right]^{-1}.$$

As $K$ increases, $n$ approaches an odd integer; hence, we write

$$n = m + \delta_m, \qquad m = 1, 3, 5, \cdots. \tag{125}$$

Substituting in equation 124, we find

$$\delta_m = \frac{2}{\pi} \tan^{-1}\left[\frac{2K}{\eta} + \frac{2\psi(0) - 2\psi(n)}{\pi}\right]^{-1}. \tag{126}$$

Hence, $\delta_m$ may be expanded in a series of reciprocals of $K$. The first term is

$$\delta_m{}^{(0)} = \frac{\eta}{\pi K}, \tag{127}$$

and

$$n = m + \frac{\eta}{\pi K} + O\left(\frac{1}{K^2}\right). \tag{128}$$

Substituting in equation 123, we find

$$Y_t = -\frac{\eta}{\pi K \, V(l)} \sum_{m=1,3,\ldots} \frac{a_m}{m(m+1)}. \tag{129}$$

As $K$ approaches infinity,

$$\lim M_n(\cos \theta) = P_m(\cos \theta), \qquad m = 1, 3, 5, \cdots. \tag{130}$$

Since $E_r$ must be continuous at $r = l$, we obtain, from equations 31 and 39,

$$\sum_{m=1,3,\ldots} a_m P_m(\cos \theta) = \sum_{k=1,3,\ldots} b_k P_k(\cos \theta). \tag{131}$$

Therefore,

$$a_m = b_m, \tag{132}$$

and

$$Y_t = -\frac{\eta}{\pi K \, V(l)} \sum_{k=1,3,\ldots} \frac{b_k}{k(k+1)}. \tag{133}$$

This is in agreement with equation 55, since in the present case $P_k(\cos \psi) = 1$.

Hence, to evaluate the limit of $Z_a = K^2 Y_t$, we need only the limits of $K b_k$. These limits may be found in various ways. For instance, we can expand some component of the field (equations 108) for large $r$, and compare it with the corresponding expansion obtained from equations 39, 40, 41. For instance, when $r$ is large,

$$\rho = r \sin \theta, \qquad r_1 = r + l \cos \theta, \qquad r_2 = r - l \cos \theta, \tag{134}$$

and, since $I_0 = j V(l)/K$,

$$r \sin \theta \, H_\varphi = - \frac{V(l)}{2\pi K} \left[ \cos(\beta l \cos \theta) - \cos \beta l \right] e^{-j\beta r}. \tag{135}$$

From equations 1–14, we have

$$j\omega \varepsilon r^2 E_r = \frac{1}{\sin \theta} \frac{\partial}{\partial \theta} (r \sin \theta \, H_\varphi); \tag{136}$$

therefore,

$$2\pi j \omega \varepsilon r^2 E_r = - \frac{V(l)}{K} \beta l \sin(\beta l \cos \theta) \, e^{-j\beta r}. \tag{137}$$

From the known expansion,

$$\sin(\beta l \cos \theta) = \sum_{k=1,3,\dots} (-)^{\frac{1}{2}(k-1)} (2k + 1) \sqrt{\frac{\pi}{2\beta l}} \, J_{k+\frac{1}{2}}(\beta l) \, P_k(\cos \theta)$$

$$= \frac{1}{\beta l} \sum_{k=1,3,\dots} (-)^{\frac{1}{2}(k-1)} (2k + 1) \, Jn_k(\beta l) \, P_k(\cos \theta), \tag{138}$$

we have

$$2\pi j \omega \varepsilon r^2 E_r =$$

$$- \frac{V(l)}{K} e^{-j\beta r} \sum_{k=1,3,\dots} (-)^{\frac{1}{2}(k-1)} (2k + 1) \, Jn_k(\beta l) \, P_k(\cos \theta). \tag{139}$$

On the other hand, for large $r$ the functions given by equation 43 become

$$R_k(\beta r) = j^{k+1} e^{-j\beta r} = (-)^{\frac{1}{2}(k+1)} e^{-j\beta r}. \tag{140}$$

Hence, from equation 39, we have

$$2\pi j \omega \varepsilon r^2 E_r = - \sum_{k=1,3,\dots} (-)^{\frac{1}{2}(k+1)} b_k \frac{e^{-j\beta r}}{Jn_k(\beta l) - j \, Nn_k(\beta l)} P_k(\cos \theta). \tag{141}$$

Comparing equations 139 and 141, we find

$$Kb_k = - V(l)(2k + 1) \, Jn_k(\beta l)[Jn_k(\beta l) - j \, Nn_k(\beta l)]. \tag{142}$$

Substituting in equation 133, we obtain equation 102.

## 2.11 Wide-angle conical dipoles

If $\psi$ is neither very small nor near $\pi/2$, we have no alternative but to solve equations 65 and 74 for the $a_n$'s and the $b_k$'s, or the equivalent equations 75 for the $b_k$'s. There are two methods that may be used in solving an infinite system of linear algebraic equations. If the series for the field components are convergent, the high order coefficients must be small enough to be relatively unimportant; hence, we can neglect them and solve the remaining finite system of equations. The other method is to start with approximate values of the coefficients and obtain the higher order approximations by some iterative process.

To illustrate the first method, let us retain only the first internal and external complementary waves. From equations 65 and 74, we have

$$a_{n_1} = u_{n_11}b_1, \qquad b_1 = -\frac{3\eta\, V(l)}{KZ_1^+}\, P_1(\cos\psi) + \frac{Z_{n_1}^-}{Z_1^+}\, v_{1n_1}a_{n_1}, \quad (143)$$

where the $u$ and $v$ coefficients are given by equations 72 and 74. Solving for $b_1$, we have

$$b_1 = -\frac{3\eta\, V(l)\cos\psi}{K(Z_1^+ - v_{1n_1}u_{n_11}Z_{n_1}^-)}. \qquad (144)$$

Here we have

$$v_{1n_1}u_{n_11} = \frac{6(2n_1+1)\sin\psi\cos^2\psi\, \dfrac{dM_{n_1}(\cos\psi)}{d\psi}}{n_1(n_1+1)[2-n_1(n_1+1)]^2\, \dfrac{\partial M_n(\cos\psi)}{\partial n}\bigg|_{n=n_1}}. \qquad (145)$$

We can simplify this expression by noting that $n$ and $\psi$ are not independent but connected by the boundary condition,

$$M_n(\cos\psi) = 0. \qquad (146)$$

Taking the total differential, we obtain

$$\frac{\partial M_n}{\partial\psi}\, d\psi + \frac{\partial M_n}{\partial n}\, dn = 0; \qquad (147)$$

therefore,

$$\frac{\partial M_n/\partial\psi}{\partial M_n/\partial n} = -\frac{dn}{d\psi}. \qquad (148)$$

Thus,

$$v_{1n_1}u_{n_11} = -\frac{6(2n_1+1)\sin\psi\cos^2\psi}{n_1(n_1+1)(n_1+2)^2(n_1-1)^2}\frac{dn_1}{d\psi}. \qquad (149)$$

If $\psi$ is not very small, we find, from equations 80 and 81,

$$n_1 = \frac{2\pi}{\pi-2\psi} - \frac{1}{2} - \frac{\pi-2\psi}{16\pi} - \cdots. \qquad (150)$$

Hence,

$$\frac{dn_1}{d\psi} = \frac{4\pi}{(\pi - 2\psi)^2} + \frac{1}{8\pi} + \cdots. \tag{151}$$

As $\psi$ approaches $\pi/2$,

$$v_{1\,n_1} u_{n_1 1} \to -\frac{3\pi}{8} \left(1 - \frac{2\psi}{\pi}\right)^5 \to 0. \tag{152}$$

In this case, we obtain the same value for $b_1$ as from equation 76 for the spherical antenna. Furthermore, it is evident that $\psi$ does not have to be very near $\pi/2$ for the $vu$ product to be small compared with unity; consequently, equation 77 should hold for wide-angle conical dipoles.

As $\psi$ approaches zero, we have

$$n_1 = 1 + \frac{1}{\log(2/\psi)}, \qquad \frac{dn_1}{d\psi} = \frac{1}{\psi[\log(2/\psi)]^2}, \tag{153}$$

$$v_{1\,n_1} u_{n_1 1} = -1.$$

Substituting in equation 144,

$$b_1 = -\frac{3\eta\,V(l)}{K(Z_1^+ + Z_1^-)} = -\frac{3V(l)}{K} Jn_1(\beta l)[Jn_1(\beta l) - jNn_1(\beta l)]. \tag{154}$$

This is in agreement with equation 142.

Next we could take the TEM wave and one complementary wave in the antenna region together with two external waves. Inasmuch as the susceptance components of $Y_t$ are represented by slowly converging series either when $\psi$ is small or when $\psi$ is near $\pi/2$, it is to be expected that the higher order waves are important; but to take a larger number of these waves would result in excessive algebraic complexity of the final formula. However, it is not difficult to solve linear algebraic equations *numerically*, even if we take as many as ten higher order waves. With this number of terms the results should be accurate for most purposes; even fewer terms may be adequate. In Section 9 we have seen that for wide angle cones the higher order internal waves are not very important. Hence, we should be able to obtain good approximations for such cones by neglecting the internal waves but including all the external waves. On the other hand, for small angle cones we need more internal waves. A graphic picture of their effect on the terminal admittance is shown by C. T. Tai.*

The alternative is to solve our system of equations by successive approximations in such a way that at each stage of approximation, we

* On the theory of biconical antennas, *Jour. Appl. Phys.*, **19**, December 1948, pp. 1155–1160.

may take into account *all* the higher order waves.  For this purpose we shall write equations 75 as follows:

$$Z_k{}^+ b_k = - \frac{2k+1}{K} \eta \, V(l) \, P_k(\cos \psi) - \sum_{\alpha=1,3,\ldots} Z_{k\alpha}{}^- b_\alpha, \qquad (155)$$

$$Z_{k\alpha}{}^- = \sum_n \frac{k(k+1)(2k+1)(2n+1)\sin\psi \, P_k(\cos\psi)\, P_\alpha(\cos\psi)}{n(n+1)(k+n+1)(\alpha+n+1)(k-n)(\alpha-n)} \frac{dn}{d\psi} Z_n{}^-. \qquad (156)$$

Transferring the principal diagonal coefficient to the left side, we obtain

$$(Z_k{}^+ + Z_{kk}{}^-)b_k = - \frac{2k+1}{K} \eta \, V(l) \, P_k(\cos\psi) - \sum_\alpha{}' Z_{k\alpha} b_\alpha, \qquad (157)$$

where the prime signifies the omission of the term corresponding to $\alpha = k$.  We now write

$$b_k = b_k{}^{(0)} + b_k{}^{(1)} + b_k{}^{(2)} + \cdots, \qquad (158)$$

where

$$b_k{}^0 = - \frac{(2k+1)\eta \, V(l) \, P_k(\cos\psi)}{K(Z_k{}^+ + Z_{kk}{}^-)}, \qquad (159)$$

$$b_k{}^{(m+1)} = - \frac{\sum_\alpha{}' Z_{k\alpha}{}^- b_\alpha{}^{(m)}}{Z_k{}^+ + Z_{kk}{}^-}. \qquad (160)$$

This iterative process is based on the assumption that the dominant coefficients are in the principal diagonal, so that the first approximation (equation 159) may be obtained by neglecting all other terms.  In effect, instead of neglecting all the internal higher order waves (given by the $a_n$'s) in calculating a particular external wave, at first we take into consideration their direct effect on this wave and neglect only the indirect effect through the remaining external waves.  The largest contributions to $Z_{kk}{}^-$ come from those terms in the series 156 in which $n$ is nearly equal to $k$.

Substituting from equations 159 and 160 in equation 55, we find

$$Z_a = K^2 Y_t = Z_a{}^{(0)} + Z_a{}^{(1)} + Z_a{}^{(2)} + \cdots, \qquad (161)$$

where

$$Z_a{}^{(0)} = \frac{\eta^2}{\pi} \sum_{k=1,3,\ldots} \frac{(2k+1)[P_k(\cos\psi)]^2}{k(k+1)(Z_k{}^+ + Z_{kk}{}^-)} ; \qquad (162)$$

$$Z_a{}^{(m)} = - \frac{\eta}{\pi \, V(l)} \sum_{k=1,3,\ldots} \frac{K b_k{}^{(m)}}{k(k+1)} P_k(\cos\psi). \qquad (163)$$

The first approximation reduces to the expressions we have already obtained when $\psi$ is small and when $\psi$ is near $\pi/2$; hence, we may anticipate that it will be a correspondingly good approximation for all angles.

For numerical computation we require the values of the Legendre polynomials, and of the functions $n(\psi)$, and $dn/d\psi$. If $\psi$ is not too near zero,

$$n_m(\psi) = -\frac{1}{2} + \left[\left(\frac{2m\pi}{\pi - 2\psi}\right)^2 - \frac{1}{4}\right]^{\frac{1}{2}}, \qquad m = 1, 2, 3, \cdots,$$

$$= \frac{2m\pi}{\pi - 2\psi} - \frac{1}{2} - \frac{\pi - 2\psi}{16m\pi} - \frac{(\pi - 2\psi)^3}{1024m^3\pi^3} - \cdots, \tag{164}$$

and

$$\frac{dn_m(\psi)}{d\psi} = \frac{4m\pi}{(\pi - 2\psi)^2} + \frac{1}{8m\pi} + \cdots. \tag{165}$$

As $\psi$ becomes small, we have the following approximations to the Legendre functions:

$$P_n(\cos\theta) = J_0(p\theta), \qquad p = \sqrt{n(n+1)},$$

$$P_n(-\cos\theta) = J_0(p\theta)\cos n\pi + N_0(p\theta)\sin n\pi, \tag{166}$$

$$M_n(\cos\theta) = \tfrac{1}{2}(1 - \cos n\pi)\,J_0(p\theta) - \tfrac{1}{2}\sin n\pi\, N_0(p\theta).$$

Hence, the zeros of $M_n(\cos\theta)$ may be obtained from

$$\cot\frac{n\pi}{2} = \frac{J_0(p\psi)}{N_0(p\psi)}, \qquad n = \frac{2}{\pi}\cot^{-1}\frac{J_0(p\psi)}{N_0(p\psi)}. \tag{167}$$

If we tabulate solutions of this equation for $n$ as a function of $p\psi$, we have only to divide $p\psi$ by $p$ to obtain a table for $n$ as a function of $\psi$.

We have already seen that, as $\psi$ approaches zero, $n$ approaches an odd integer $2m - 1$, $m = 1, 2, 3, \cdots$. From equation 164 we would find $2m - 0.5$. Hence, we anticipate that equation 164 fails only for really small values of $\psi$. The solid curves in Fig. 2.8 represent $n(\psi)$ as given by equation 164; the dotted curves are taken from equation 167. In the immediate vicinity of $\psi = 0$, the dotted curves approach odd integers so sharply (on the present scale) that they appear to coincide with the vertical coordinate axis. We can obtain a good idea of the accuracy of equation 164 if we note that, when $n$ is an odd integer, $M_n(\cos\theta)$ coincides with $P_n(\cos\theta)$; and, when $n$ approaches an even integer, $M_n(\cos\theta)$ becomes more nearly proportional to $Q_n(\cos\theta)$. In either case it is easy to calculate the zeros of $M_n(\cos\theta)$ as accurately as we wish. The following table presents the exact and approximate (from equation 164) values of $\psi$ when $m = 1$:

| $n$ = | 2, | 3, | 4, | 5; |
|---|---|---|---|---|
| (Exact) $\psi$ = | 0.355, | 0.6847, | 0.8776, | 1.0022; |
| (Approx) $\psi$ = | 0.338, | 0.6822, | 0.8769, | 1.0019. |

For $m = 2$, we have

$$
\begin{array}{cccc}
n & = & 4, & 5, & 6; \\
(\text{Exact})\ \psi & = & 0.198, & 0.4366, & 0.6078; \\
(\text{Approx})\ \psi & = & 0.183, & 0.4331, & 0.6070.
\end{array}
$$

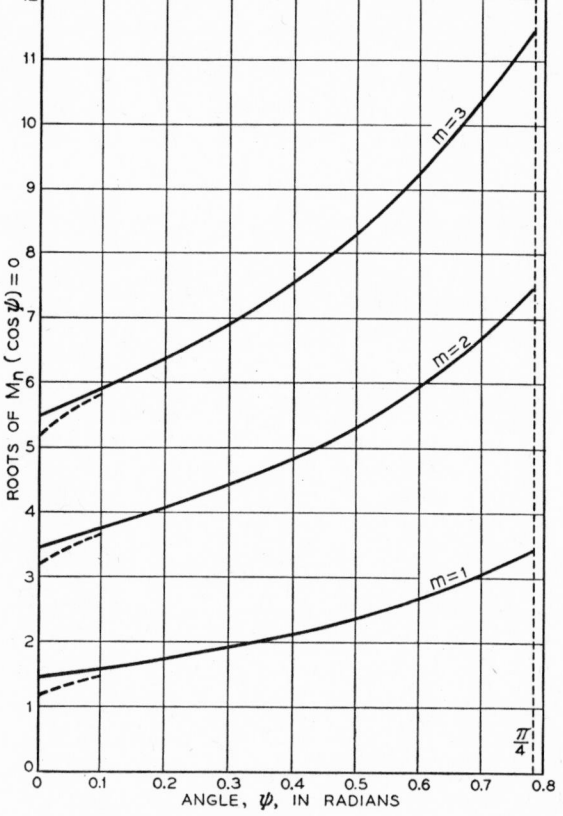

Fig. 2.8  Roots of the characteristic equation $M_n (\cos \psi) = 0$. The solid line represents equation 164; the dotted line represents the results obtained from equation 167.

## 2.12  Antennas in dissipative media

Although we have assumed that the medium surrounding the antenna is nondissipative, the expressions we have obtained may be generalized immediately. We need only replace $j\beta$ by $\sigma = \sqrt{j\omega\mu(g + j\omega\varepsilon)}$ (and $j\omega\varepsilon$ by $g + j\omega\varepsilon$, where necessary). For example, the principal current and transverse voltage in a dissipative medium are obtained from equations 34 and 35,

$$I_0(r) = K^{-1} V(l)[\sinh \sigma(l - r) + KY_t \cosh \sigma(l - r)],$$

$$V(r) = V(l)[\cosh \sigma(l - r) + KY_t \sinh \sigma(l - r)], \tag{168}$$

$$K = \frac{\eta}{\pi} \log \cot \frac{\psi}{2} = \frac{1}{\pi} \sqrt{\frac{j\omega\mu}{g + j\omega\varepsilon}} \log \cot \frac{\psi}{2}.$$

Equation 103 for thin biconical antennas may be written in the form

$$Z_a = K^2 Y_t = \frac{\eta}{4\pi} [2(\text{Cin } 2\beta l + j \text{ Si } 2\beta l) + j\, 2 \log 2 \sin 2\beta l +$$

$$e^{-2j\beta l} (\text{Cin } 2\beta l - j \text{ Si } 2\beta l) + e^{2j\beta l} (\text{Cin } 2\beta l + j \text{ Si } 2\beta l) -$$

$$e^{2j\beta l} (\text{Cin } 4\beta l + j \text{ Si } 4\beta l)]. \tag{169}$$

Replacing $j\beta$ by $\sigma$, we have

$$Z_a = \frac{\eta}{4\pi} [2 \text{ Ein } 2\sigma l + 2 \log 2 \sinh 2\sigma l + e^{-2\sigma l} \text{ Ein}(-2\sigma l) +$$

$$e^{2\sigma l} \text{ Ein } 2\sigma l - e^{2\sigma l} \text{ Ein } 4\sigma l], \tag{170}$$

where

$$\text{Ein } w = \int_0^w \frac{1 - e^{-t}}{t}\, dt = C + \log w + \int_w^\infty \frac{e^{-t}}{t}\, dt. \tag{171}$$

As $\text{re}(\sigma l)$ increases,

$$Z_a \to \frac{\eta}{2\pi} (C + \log 2\sigma l). \tag{172}$$

## 2.13  Extension of known solutions

In the preceding example the known solution was obviously general except in superficial details; even the transformation from equation 169 to equation 170 was made only for convenience. We might equally well have left $Z_a$ in the original form 103; then, in numerical calculations we would simply use the formula $\beta = -j\sigma$. In the following example the changes that should be made in the known solution are slightly more extensive.

Consider a biconical antenna in a medium the constants of which change abruptly at the spherical surface $r = l_1$ (Fig. 2.9). Suppose that the antenna is thin and that we already know the field in the absence of the discontinuity; that is, the $b_k$'s as given by equation 142. We can take this field as the *primary field impressed on the surface of discontinuity* $r = l_1$. From the continuity of $E_\theta$, $H_\varphi$ at this boundary we calculate the field reflected toward the antenna. Since the medium is continuous across the antenna output boundary $S_0$ and since for thin biconical antennas $P_k(\cos \theta)$ equals $M_k(\cos \theta)$, there will be no rereflection at this boundary.   The primary field is given by equations 40 and 41 with $R_k(\beta r)$ defined by equation 43.   For the reflected field $R_k(\beta r) = Jn_k(\beta r)$ and for the transmitted field $R_k = Hn_k(\beta' r)$.   Hence, for the

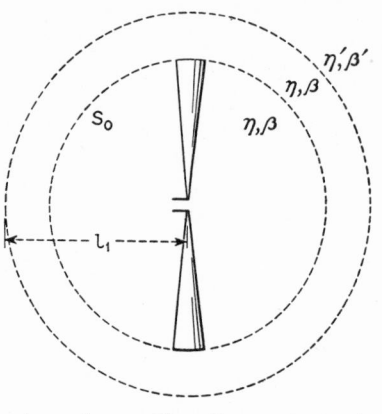

FIG. 2.9   A biconical antenna in a medium the constants of which change abruptly across the sphere $r = l_1$.

$k$th order components we have  (omitting the Legendre functions)

$$2\pi k(k+1)rH_{\varphi,n} = b_k \frac{Hn_k(\beta r)}{Hn_k(\beta l)} + c_k \frac{Jn_k(\beta r)}{Jn_k(\beta l)}, \qquad r \leq l_1,$$

$$= d_k \frac{Hn_k(\beta' r)}{Hn_k(\beta' l_1)}, \qquad r \geq l_1,$$

$$2\pi k(k+1)rE_{\theta,n} = j\eta b_k \frac{Hn_k'(\beta r)}{Hn_k(\beta l)} + j\eta c_k \frac{Jn_k'(\beta r)}{Jn_k(\beta l)}, \qquad r \leq l_1,$$

$$= j\eta' d_k \frac{Hn_k'(\beta' r)}{Hn_k(\beta' l_1)}, \qquad r \geq l_1.$$

$$(173)$$

From the continuity conditions at $r = l_1$,

$$b_k \frac{Hn_k(\beta l_1)}{Hn_k(\beta l)} + c_k \frac{Jn_k(\beta l_1)}{Jn_k(\beta l)} = d_k,$$

$$b_k \frac{Hn_k'(\beta l_1)}{Hn_k(\beta l)} + c_k \frac{Jn_k'(\beta l_1)}{Jn_k(\beta l)} = \frac{\eta'}{\eta} d_k \frac{Hn_k'(\beta' l_1)}{Hn_k(\beta' l_1)}.$$

$$(174)$$

Solving for $c_k/b_k$,

$$\frac{c_k}{b_k} = -\frac{\dfrac{\eta'}{\eta}\dfrac{Hn_k'(\beta' l_1)}{Hn_k(\beta' l_1)}\dfrac{Hn_k(\beta l_1)}{Hn_k(\beta l)} - \dfrac{Hn_k'(\beta l_1)}{Hn_k(\beta l)}}{\dfrac{\eta'}{\eta}\dfrac{Hn_k'(\beta' l_1)}{Hn_k(\beta' l_1)}\dfrac{Jn_k(\beta l_1)}{Jn_k(\beta l)} - \dfrac{Jn_k'(\beta l_1)}{Jn_k(\beta l)}}. \qquad (175)$$

Now at $r = l$,

$$2\pi k(k+1)lH_{\varphi,n} = b_k + c_k = b_k\left(1 + \frac{c_k}{b_k}\right) ; \qquad (176)$$

that is, the old $b_k$'s should be multiplied by $1 + (c_k/b_k)$. This is the factor we have to insert in equation 102.

If, in particular, $l_1 = l$, then,

$$1 + \frac{c_k}{b_k} = -j\left[Jn_k(\beta l) \, Hn_k(\beta l)\right]^{-1}\left[\frac{\eta'}{\eta} \frac{Hn_k'(\beta' l)}{Hn_k(\beta' l)} - \frac{Jn_k'(\beta l)}{Jn_k(\beta l)}\right]^{-1}.$$
$$(177)$$

In this case the first bracketed factor cancels the normalized Bessel functions in equation 102, and the second bracketed factor appears in their stead.

One reason for retaining the radial impedances in equation 162 and the associated equations is that it makes the expressions concise. An even more important reason is that in this form the expressions are very general. Our antenna may be imbedded in a medium consisting of concentric spherical strata, and the same formula will still apply as long as we substitute proper wave impedances. The determination of these wave impedances is a simple one-dimensional problem in reflection.*

## 2.14  Input regions

The general form of the radial wave function in the antenna region is given by equation 36. At $r = 0$, the $Nn_n$ functions become infinite for all $n > 0$; and, if the voltages are to remain finite as $r$ approaches zero, the $p_n$'s must be equal to zero. If the radius $r_i$ of the input boundary is different from zero, these coefficients do not necessarily vanish, and the voltage impressed on the antenna does not define uniquely the field around the antenna — we need the complete specification of $E_\theta$ over the input boundary. Expanding $E_\theta(r_i)$ in a series of the type 33 appropriate to the antenna region we have

$$r_i E_\theta = \frac{\eta \, V(r_i)}{2\pi K \sin\theta} + \sum_n E_n \frac{d}{d\theta} M_n(\cos\theta),$$

$$E_n = \frac{\displaystyle\int_\psi^{\pi-\psi} r_i \, E_\theta(r_i) \sin\theta \frac{d}{d\theta} M_n(\cos\theta) \, d\theta}{\displaystyle\int_\psi^{\pi-\psi} \sin\theta \left[\frac{d}{d\theta} M_n(\cos\theta)\right]^2 d\theta}. \qquad (178)$$

* *Electromagnetic Waves*, pp. 226–227.

Comparing with equation 33, we have

$$\frac{j\eta a_n \, S_n{}'(\beta r_i)}{2\pi n(n+1) \, S_n(\beta l)} = E_n. \tag{179}$$

This represents another infinite system of linear equations which must be added to the systems involving $a_n$'s and $b_n$'s directly.

The handling of these equations can be simplified if we take advantage of the fact that our equations are linear. *If we solve our antenna problem for each term in equation 178, we have only to add our solutions to obtain the solution for an arbitrary input field.* The solution of each component problem involves only a doubly infinite system of coefficients, $a_n$'s and $b_n$'s, the case already treated in the preceding sections, for all the $E_n$'s except one will be equal to zero in each case. We shall presently see that this method simplifies the solution to an even greater extent than might be anticipated.

Let us consider the first term and assume that all $E_n$'s vanish. From equations 179 and 36 we have

$$Jn_n{}'(\beta r_i) + p_n \, Nn_n{}'(\beta r_i) = 0, \qquad p_n = -\frac{Jn_n{}'(\beta r_i)}{Nn_n{}'(\beta r_i)}. \tag{180}$$

Hence,

$$S_n(\beta r) = Jn_n(\beta r) - \frac{Jn_n{}'(\beta r_i)}{Nn_n{}'(\beta r_i)} \, N_n(\beta r), \tag{181}$$

and our problem is not different from that in which the radius of the input region is zero; we simply have another function $S_n(\beta r)$ in place of $Jn_n(\beta r)$. All formal algebraic expressions remain the same, and the only difference is in the numerical values we have to substitute to obtain the answers under specific conditions. Furthermore, we shall usually find that $\beta r_i$ is small compared with unity; then,

$$\frac{Jn_n{}'(\beta r_i)}{Nn_n{}'(\beta r_i)} = \frac{(n+1)\pi}{2^{2n+1}n(n+\frac{1}{2})!(n-\frac{1}{2})!} \, (\beta r_i)^{2n+1}. \tag{182}$$

This quantity is small, particularly for large $n$. The expressions for $Z_a$ involve $S_n(\beta l)$; since the amplitudes of $Nn_n(\beta l)$ are comparable to those of $Jn_n(\beta l)$, the second term in equation 181 is negligible.

Next let us consider any higher order mode in equation 178. If the cones are infinitely long, the radial wave function is given by $p_n = -j$ and the corresponding field by

$$r^2 E_r = -\frac{A_n}{j\omega\varepsilon} \, Hn_n(\beta r) \, M_n(\cos\theta), \qquad Hn_n(\beta r) = Jn_n(\beta r) - j \, Nn_n(\beta r),$$

$$rH_\varphi = \frac{A_n}{n(n+1)} Hn_n(\beta r) \frac{d}{d\theta} M_n(\cos\theta),$$

$$rE_\theta = \frac{j\eta A_n}{n(n+1)} Hn_n'(\beta r) \frac{d}{d\theta} M_n(\cos\theta). \tag{183}$$

At the input boundary,

$$\frac{j\eta A_n}{n(n+1)} Hn_n'(\beta r_i) = E_n, \qquad A_n = \frac{n(n+1)E_n}{j\eta\, Hn_n'(\beta r_i)} ; \tag{184}$$

hence,

$$rH_\varphi = \frac{E_n}{j\eta} \frac{Hn_n(\beta r)}{Hn_n'(\beta r_i)} \frac{d}{d\theta} M_n(\cos\theta),$$

$$rE_\theta = E_n \frac{Hn_n'(\beta r)}{Hn_n'(\beta r_i)} \frac{d}{d\theta} M_n(\cos\theta). \tag{185}$$

For cones of wide angle, $n$ is large and the field at $r = l$ will be only a very small fraction of its value at $r = r_1$; hence it makes little difference whether the cones are continued beyond $r = l$ or not. The same is true for thin cones in the case of any but the lowest mode; in addition there is little difference between the field configurations in the antenna region and in free space, so that the effect of the cones on these modes is small and their termination will cause little reflection. Consequently equations 185 represent the required solution to a high degree of approximation. The increase in the input current due to the departure of the field distribution at the input boundary from that corresponding to the TEM waves is

$$\Delta I_i = \frac{2\pi}{j\eta} \sum_n E_n \frac{Hn_n(\beta r_i)}{Hn_n'(\beta r_i)} \sin\psi \frac{d}{d\psi} M_n(\cos\psi). \tag{186}$$

The ratio $\Delta I_i/V(r_i)$ represents an admittance in parallel with the antenna; it is mainly a capacitive admittance, and it is associated primarily with the input region,* since the length of the antenna is not involved. The admittance is small because the $E_n$'s are normally small and the ratio of the radial wave functions in equation 186 is of the order of $\beta r_i$. If the antenna is fed by a pair of parallel wires, for instance, the distribution of the impressed field is similar to that of the TEM wave in the antenna region and the $E_n$'s represent only the small difference between the distributions corresponding to TEM waves along parallel wires and along divergent cones.

* This is not the total admittance of the input region (which can be made arbitrarily large), but that part of it which represents " fringing " or electric energy stored *outside* the input region due to a possibly irregular field inside the input region.

The above results are adequate for practical applications, but it is instructive to evaluate the effect of the discontinuity at $r = l$ on the field given by equation 185. In accordance with the previously outlined method, we assume that $E_n$ is zero for all values of $n$ except $n = m$, let us say. For these values the radial wave function is given by equation 181. For the TEM wave $V(r_i) = 0$, and, instead of equations 34 and 35, we have

$$I_0(r) = I_0(r_i) \cos \beta(r - r_i), \qquad V(r) = -jK\, I_0(r_i) \sin \beta(r - r_i). \tag{187}$$

Hence, the field in the antenna region may be written as follows:

$$rH_\varphi = (rH_\varphi)_p + \frac{I_0(r)}{2\pi \sin \theta} + \frac{1}{2\pi} \sum_n \frac{a_n}{n(n+1)} \frac{S_n(\beta r)}{S_n(\beta l)} \frac{d}{d\theta} M_n(\cos \theta),$$

$$rE_\theta = (rE_\theta)_p + \frac{V(r)}{2\pi K \sin \theta} + \tag{188}$$

$$j\frac{\eta}{2\pi} \sum_n \frac{a_n}{n(n+1)} \frac{S_n{}'(\beta r)}{S_n(\beta l)} \frac{d}{d\theta} M_n(\cos \theta),$$

where $(rH_\varphi)_p$ and $(rE_\theta)_p$ are the "primary fields" given by equations 185 with $n = m$. If we choose the $S_m(\beta r)$ in the form 181, then the corresponding term in equation 188 contributes nothing to $r_i E_\theta(r_i)$, and at $r = r_i$ the function $rE_\theta$ reduces to $E_m$. The free space field will be of the form given by equations 40, 41, and 43. The equations for the $a_n$'s and $b_k$'s are then obtained as in Section 2.7; there will be only slight alterations in some of the terms.

## 2.15    Thin antennas of arbitrary shape

In theory the general pattern of analysis in the preceding sections is applicable to nonconical boundaries. In practice we are limited by our ability to determine the proper wave functions consistent with the more general boundaries. If the diameter of the antenna is small compared with its length, these wave functions may be calculated from those associated with conical boundaries by a perturbation method. In fact, the general formula for the input impedance, to the same order of accuracy as that obtained in Section 2.10 for thin biconical antennas, can be obtained by evaluating the perturbed wave functions for the TEM waves alone. This follows at once from equations 34 and 35. Since $Y_t$ is of order $1/K^2$, the second terms in the brackets are of order $1/K$. If we perturb the conical boundary into some other shape, the first correction term to be added to $Y_t$ will be of order $1/K^3$, and its effect on the current, voltage, and input impedance will be of order $1/K^2$.

Hence, to obtain the general formula in which only the terms of order $1/K$ are retained, we need only calculate the perturbed wave functions for the TEM waves. Our problem is thus to solve the system of two linear differential equations of the first order (equations 1–86) with variable coefficients given by equations 1–120. The required solutions can be found by the wave perturbation method,* and the results are summarized in Section 1.15.

In deriving equation 1–136 for the input impedance from the general formula 1–133, we have neglected the terms $Z_a M/K_a{}^2$ and $Z_a N_b/K_a{}^2$ since these are of the order $1/K_a{}^2$. If these terms are retained, the values of the antiresonant impedances are increased and the antiresonant lengths become shorter. In problems of this kind it is difficult to know in advance whether the accuracy is increased or decreased when only some terms of higher order are included. In practical applications one would be justified in retaining the higher order terms if a comparison with careful measurements were to show a better agreement.

## 2.16  Asymmetric spherical antennas

In the preceding sections we have treated in detail antennas formed by two coaxial equal cones of the same length. There are many problems with a lesser degree of symmetry which are amenable to the same

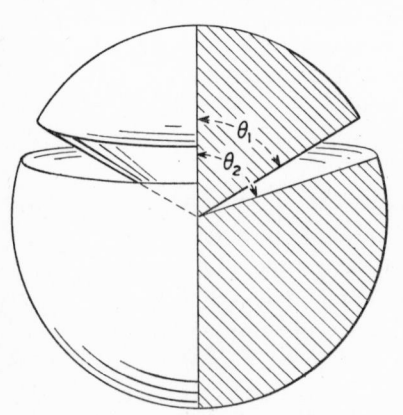

method of treatment. Some of these problems are complicated by lack of symmetry, while others are not. Some are not particularly interesting from the practical point of view, at least at present, while others give useful information. In this and the following sections we shall illustrate by examples the minor changes that have to be made in the formal analysis. In the more complicated situations the major problem consists in finding the best method of obtaining as simple an answer as possible.

FIG. 2.10  An asymmetric spherical antenna.

One of the simplest asymmetric problems is presented by a spherical radiator fed by a pair of coaxial cones, $\theta = \theta_1$ and $\theta = \theta_2$, where $\theta_2 - \theta_1$ is small (Fig. 2.10). As in the symmetric case, the higher order waves between the coaxial cones are

* *Applied Mathematics*, Chapter 11.

highly attenuated and store a negligible amount of energy in the vicinity of the gap. Hence, at the surface of the sphere of radius $l$, we have

$$E_\theta(l, \theta) = 0, \qquad\qquad\qquad \text{if} \quad 0 \le \theta < \theta_1;$$

$$= \frac{\eta \, V(l)}{2\pi Kl \sin \theta}, \qquad \text{if} \quad \theta_1 < \theta < \theta_2; \qquad (189)$$

$$= 0, \qquad\qquad\qquad\quad \text{if} \quad \theta_2 < \theta \le \pi;$$

where

$$K = \frac{\eta}{2\pi} \log\left( \cot \frac{\theta_1}{2} \tan \frac{\theta_2}{2} \right),$$

and $V(l)$ is the transverse voltage between the two sections of the spherical antenna. The expressions for the field outside the sphere differ from equations 39, 40, 41, and 43 only in that the index of summation $k$ now assumes all positive integral values. If

$$E_\theta(l, \theta) = \sum_{k=1,2,3,\ldots} A_k P_k{}^1(\cos \theta), \quad P_k{}^1(\cos \theta) = \frac{d \, P_k(\cos \theta)}{d\theta}, \qquad (190)$$

then, in view of the orthogonal properties of the associated Legendre functions,

$$A_k = \frac{2k+1}{2k(k+1)} \int_0^\pi E_\theta(l, \theta) P_k{}^1(\cos \theta) \sin \theta \, d\theta. \qquad (191)$$

In particular, when $E_\theta(l, \theta)$ is given by equation 189,

$$A_k = \frac{\eta(2k+1) \, V(l)[P_k(\cos \theta_2) - P_k(\cos \theta_1)]}{4\pi k(k+1)Kl}. \qquad (192)$$

The propagation factors for various modes from $r = l$ to $r = r$ are the ratios $Hn_k{}'(\beta r)/Hn_k{}'(\beta l)$; therefore,

$$E_\theta(r, \theta) = \sum_k A_k \frac{Hn_k{}'(\beta r)}{Hn_k{}'(\beta l)} P_k{}^1(\cos \theta). \qquad (193)$$

The radial wave admittances at $r = l$ for the various modes are the reciprocals of the wave impedances (equation 60),

$$Y_k{}^+ = \frac{Hn_k(\beta l)}{j\eta \, Hn_k{}'(\beta l)} = \frac{Jn_k(\beta l) - j \, Nn_k(\beta l)}{j\eta \, [Jn_k{}'(\beta l) - j \, Nn_k{}'(\beta l)]}, \qquad (194)$$

and the propagation factors for the various components of $H_\varphi$ are the ratios $Hn_k(\beta r)/Hn_k(\beta l)$; hence,

$$H_\varphi(r, \theta) = \sum_k A_k Y_k{}^+ \frac{Hn_k(\beta r)}{Hn_k(\beta l)} P_k{}^1(\cos \theta). \qquad (195)$$

From equation 54 we now find the inverse radiation impedance,

$$Z_a = K^2 Y_t = \frac{\eta^2}{4\pi} \sum_{k=1,2,3,\ldots} \frac{2k+1}{k(k+1)} Y_k^+ [P_k(\cos\theta_2) - P_k(\cos\theta_1)]^2. \quad (196)$$

The admittance $Y_t$ of the sphere and the space outside it, as seen across the gap, is thus a parallel combination of an infinite number of admittances of networks of the type shown in Fig. 6.2a. The multipliers of $Y_k^+$ are merely transformer ratios either raising or lowering the general admittance level of each network.

Green's function for the spherical antenna is the response to a unit voltage across an infinitesimal gap. When the response is the current in the sphere, this function is called the transfer admittance. From the above equations we find the following expression for the transfer admittance between $\theta_1 = \theta_2 = \psi$ and $\theta = \theta$:

$$Y(\theta;\psi) = 2\pi \sin\theta \sin\psi \sum_k \frac{2k+1}{2k(k+1)} Y_k^+ P_k^1(\cos\theta) P_k^1(\cos\psi). \quad (197)$$

The wave admittances $Y_k^+$ may be expanded in partial fractions representing natural oscillations of the sphere with the gap conductively closed. Because of radiation the natural oscillation constants are complex, and for their determination it is more convenient to replace $j\omega$ by $p$ and write the wave admittance in the following form:

$$Y_k^+ = -\frac{Kn_k(w)}{\eta Kn_k'(w)}, \qquad w = pl\sqrt{\mu\varepsilon},$$

$$Kn_k(w) = e^{-w} \sum_{m=0}^{k} \frac{(k+m)!}{m!\,(k-m)!\,(2w)^m}. \qquad (198)$$

For natural oscillations,

$$Y_k^+ = \infty, \qquad Kn_k'(w) = 0. \qquad (199)$$

Let the $n$th root of this equation be $w = w_{k,n}$. The residue of $Y_k^+$ at the corresponding pole is

$$B_{k,n} = \lim(w - w_{k,n}) \frac{-Kn_k(w)}{\eta\,Kn_k'(w)} = -\frac{Kn_k(w_{k,n})}{\eta} \lim \frac{w - w_{k,n}}{Kn_k'(w)}$$

$$= -\frac{Kn_k(w_{k,n})}{\eta\,Kn_k''(w_{k,n})}. \qquad (200)$$

But the normalized Bessel function $Kn_k(w)$ satisfies the differential equation

$$\frac{d^2 Kn}{dw^2} = \left[1 + \frac{k(k+1)}{w^2}\right] Kn; \qquad (201)$$

hence, the residue is

$$B_{k,n} = -\eta^{-1}\left[1 + \frac{k(k+1)}{w_{k,n}^2}\right]^{-1}. \qquad (202)$$

From equation 198 we see that, since the exponential factor may be canceled, the radial admittance is a rational fraction. The degree of the numerator equals that of the denominator; this we find either directly or by observing that, as $w$ approaches infinity, $Kn$ approaches $\exp(-w)$ and $Y_k^+$ the ratio $1/\eta$. Hence, the expansion in partial fractions is

$$Y_k^+ = \frac{1}{\eta} + \sum_n \frac{B_{k,n}}{w - w_{k,n}}$$

$$= \frac{1}{\eta}\left\{1 - \sum_n \frac{w_{k,n}^2}{[w_{k,n}^2 + k(k+1)](w - w_{k,n})}\right\}. \qquad (203)$$

Thus, on the real frequency axis,

$$Y_k^+ = \frac{1}{\eta}\left\{1 - \sum_n \frac{w_{k,n}^2}{[w_{k,n}^2 + k(k+1)](j\omega - p_{k,n})\sqrt{\mu\varepsilon}\,l}\right\}, \qquad (204)$$

where the natural oscillation constants are given by

$$p_{k,n} = \frac{w_{k,n}}{l\sqrt{\mu\varepsilon}}. \qquad (205)$$

Substituting in equation 196, we find an expression for $Y_t$ in terms of the natural oscillation constants. Similarly, substituting in equation 197, we obtain another expression for the transfer admittance.

For any finite gap extending from $\theta = \theta_1$ to $\theta = \theta_2$ we can express the current $I(\theta)$ in terms of the meridian electric intensity in the gap,

$$I(\theta) = l\int_{\theta_1}^{\theta_2} Y(\theta; \psi)\, E_\theta(l, \psi)\, d\psi. \qquad (206)$$

If $E_\theta(l, \theta)$ is given by equation 189, $I(\theta) = 2\pi l \sin\theta\, H_\varphi(l, \theta)$ may be obtained more directly from equation 195. Substituting from equation 204 and noting that outside the gap

$$\sum_k A_k P_k^1(\cos\theta) = 0, \qquad (207)$$

we have

$$I(\theta) = -\sum_{k,n} \frac{2\pi l A_k w_{k,n}^2 P_k^1(\cos\theta)\sin\theta}{\eta[w_{k,n}^2 + k(k+1)](j\omega - p_{k,n})\sqrt{\mu\varepsilon}\,l}, \qquad (208)$$

where $A_k$ is given by equation 192.

## 2.17 Asymmetric conical dipoles

We now assume that the arms of a conical dipole are of equal length (along the generators of the cones) but that the cone angles are different. The conical dipole is similar to the spherical antenna (Fig. 2.10) except that the angles $\theta_1$, $\theta_2$ are arbitrary. The differences between the symmetric and asymmetric cases are minor, although the equations are somewhat more complicated, principally in the antenna region. In free space, the field is given by equations 39, 40, and 41 with $k$ assuming all positive integral values. In the antenna region the values of the index of summation $n$ are the roots of equation 17. The corresponding meridian wave functions become

$$\Theta(\theta) = P_n(\cos\theta) - \frac{P_n(\cos\theta_1)}{P_n(-\cos\theta_1)} P_n(-\cos\theta), \qquad (209)$$

instead of

$$\Theta(\theta) = M_n(\cos\theta) = \tfrac{1}{2}[P_n(\cos\theta) - P_n(-\cos\theta)]. \qquad (210)$$

In the symmetric case it was natural to introduce the factor $\tfrac{1}{2}$ in the expression for $\Theta(\theta)$, but in the general case nothing could be gained by introducing it. The $a_n$'s absorb whatever factor we choose to include. For convenience, we shall rewrite the expressions for $H_\varphi$ and $E_\theta$ in the antenna region,

$$rH_\varphi = \frac{I_0(r)}{2\pi \sin\theta} + \frac{1}{2\pi} \sum_n \frac{a_n}{n(n+1)} \frac{S_n(\beta r)}{S_n(\beta l)} \Theta_n{}'(\theta),$$

$$rE_\theta = \frac{\eta\, V(r)}{2\pi K \sin\theta} + j\, \frac{\eta}{2\pi} \sum_n \frac{a_n}{n(n+1)} \frac{S_n{}'(\beta r)}{S_n(\beta l)} \Theta_n{}'(\theta). \qquad (211)$$

If the radius of the input region is zero,

$$S_n(\beta r) = Jn_n(\beta r). \qquad (212)$$

The characteristic impedance is

$$K = \frac{\eta}{2\pi} \log\!\left(\cot\frac{\theta_1}{2} \tan\frac{\theta_2}{2}\right). \qquad (213)$$

The normalized terminal admittance is represented by a formula analogous to equation 54,

$$KY_t = \frac{\eta}{V(l)} \int_{\theta_1}^{\theta_2} l\, H_\varphi(l, \theta)\, d\theta. \qquad (214)$$

Substituting from

$$rH_\varphi = \frac{1}{2\pi} \sum_{k=1}^{\infty} \frac{b_k}{k(k+1)} \frac{R_k(\beta r)}{R_k(\beta l)} \frac{d}{d\theta} P_k(\cos\theta),$$

$$rE_\theta = j \frac{\eta}{2\pi} \sum_{k=1}^{\infty} \frac{b_k}{k(k+1)} \frac{R_k'(\beta r)}{R_k(\beta l)} \frac{d}{d\theta} P_k(\cos\theta),$$
(215)

we find

$$KY_t = \frac{\eta}{2\pi V(l)} \sum_k \frac{b_k}{k(k+1)} [P_k(\cos\theta_2) - P_k(\cos\theta_1)]. \quad (216)$$

As in Section 2.8 we can express the $a_n$'s in terms of the $b_k$'s, and vice versa. Thus,

$$a_n = \sum_k u_{nk} b_k,$$

$$b_k = \frac{(2k+1)\eta V(l)}{2KZ_k^+} [P_k(\cos\theta_2 - P_k(\cos\theta_1)] + \sum_n v_{kn} a_n,$$
(217)

where

$$u_{nk} = \frac{n(n+1)\displaystyle\int_{\theta_1}^{\theta_2} \sin\theta \, \frac{d\Theta_n}{d\theta} \, \frac{d\,P_k(\cos\theta)}{d\theta} \, d\theta}{k(k+1)\displaystyle\int_{\theta_1}^{\theta_2} [\Theta_n'(\theta)]^2 \sin\theta \, d\theta}$$

$$= \frac{(2n+1) \sin\theta \, P_k(\cos\theta) \dfrac{\partial\Theta_n}{\partial\theta}\Big|_{\theta_1}^{\theta_2}}{(k-n)(n+k+1) \sin\theta \dfrac{\partial\Theta_n}{\partial\theta} \dfrac{\partial\Theta_n}{\partial n}\Big|_{\theta_1}^{\theta_2}}, \quad (218)$$

$$v_{kn} = \frac{k(k+1)(2k+1)}{2n(n+1)(n-k)(k+n+1)} \frac{Z_n^-}{Z_k^+} \sin\theta \, P_k(\cos\theta) \frac{\partial\Theta_n}{\partial\theta}\Big|_{\theta_1}^{\theta_2}. \quad (219)$$

Eliminating the $a_n$'s from equations 217, we have

$$b_k = \frac{(2k+1)\eta V(l)}{2KZ_k^+} [P_k(\cos\theta_2) - P_k(\cos\theta_1)] + \sum_{n,k} v_{kn} u_{n\alpha} b_\alpha. \quad (220)$$

As in Section 2.10 we shall write these equations as follows:

$$Z_k^+ b_k = \frac{(2k+1)\eta V(l)}{2K} [P_k(\cos\theta_2) - P_k(\cos\theta_1)] - \sum_\alpha Z_{k\alpha}^- b_\alpha, \quad (221)$$

$$Z_{k\alpha}^- = -Z_k^+ \sum_n v_{kn} u_{n\alpha}. \quad (222)$$

Transferring the principal diagonal coefficient to the left side, we obtain

$(Z_k{}^+ + Z_{kk}{}^-)b_k$

$$= \frac{2k+1}{2K}\,\eta\,V(l)[P_k(\cos\theta_2) - P_k(\cos\theta_1)] - \sum_\alpha{}' Z_{k\alpha}{}^- b_\alpha, \quad (223)$$

where the prime after $\sum$ signifies the omission of the term corresponding to $\alpha = k$. This equation is of the same form as equation 157, and we may write $b_k$ in the form 158 with

$$b_k{}^0 = \frac{(2k+1)\eta[P_k(\cos\theta_2) - P_k(\cos\theta_1)]}{2K(Z_k{}^+ + Z_{kk}{}^-)}\,V(l). \quad (224)$$

Substituting from equations 218 and 219, we find

$Z_{kk}{}^- = -Z_k{}^+ \sum_n v_{kn}u_{nk}$

$$= \sum_n \frac{k(k+1)(2n+1)(2k+1)Z_n{}^-\left[\sin\theta\,P_k(\cos\theta)\,\dfrac{\partial\Theta_n}{\partial\theta}\Big|_{\theta_1}^{\theta_2}\right]^2}{2n(n+1)(n-k)^2(n+k+1)^2\sin\theta\,\dfrac{\partial\Theta_n}{\partial\theta}\dfrac{\partial\Theta_n}{\partial n}\Big|_{\theta_1}^{\theta_2}}.$$

$$(225)$$

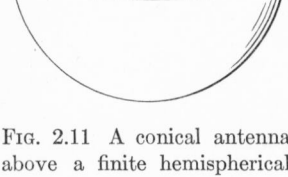

In evaluating the various terms of the series we note that a constant multiplier associated with $\Theta$ does not affect the results and we may write

$$\Theta_n(\theta) = P_n(-\cos\theta_1)\,P_n(\cos\theta) - P_n(\cos\theta_1)\,P_n(-\cos\theta) \quad (226)$$

instead of equation 209. When $\theta = \theta_1$, $\Theta$ vanishes for all $n$; hence,

$$\frac{\partial\Theta_n}{\partial n}\bigg|_{\theta=\theta_1} = 0. \quad (227)$$

We also have*

FIG. 2.11 A conical antenna above a finite hemispherical ground.

$$\frac{\partial\Theta_n}{\partial\theta}\bigg|_{\theta=\theta_1} = -\frac{2\sin n\pi}{\pi\sin\theta_1}. \quad (228)$$

Since $\theta_2$ and $n$ are connected by the equation

$$\Theta_n(\theta_2) = 0, \quad (229)$$

we have

$$\frac{\partial\Theta_n(\theta_2)}{\partial\theta_2}\,d\theta_2 + \frac{\partial\Theta_n(\theta_2)}{\partial n}\,dn = 0, \qquad \frac{\partial\Theta_n(\theta_2)}{\partial n} = -\frac{\partial\Theta_n(\theta_2)}{\partial\theta_2}\,\frac{d\theta_2}{dn}. \quad (230)$$

The largest contributions to $Z_{kk}{}^-$ come from values of $n$ nearest to $k$.

* *Applied Mathematics*, p. 433.

If $\theta_2 = \pi/2$, we have the case of an antenna above a finite hemispherical ground (Fig. 2.11).

## 2.18   End-fed antennas

It is possible to connect one terminal of a generator to a wire and leave the other terminal floating (Fig. 2.12a).   The antenna will thus be operated against the capacitance of the generator.   An idealized struc-

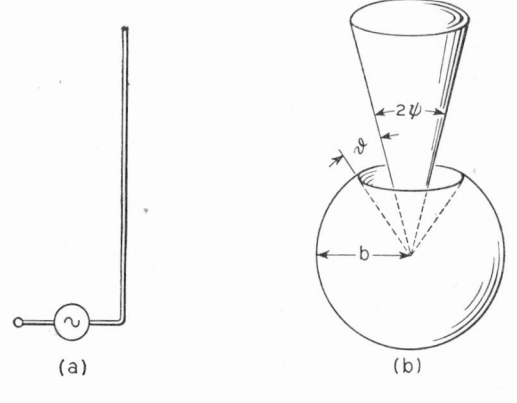

(a)                                          (b)

FIG.  2.12    End-fed antennas.

ture representing all the essential features of an end-fed antenna is shown in Fig. 2.12b, where the voltage is impressed between a cone and a small sphere of radius $b$.   Thin cones may be deformed into cylindrical wires and wires of other shapes and the results obtained for cones may

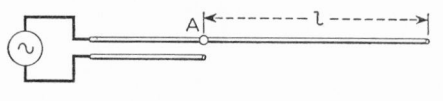

FIG.  2.13    An end-fed antenna.

thus be extended by the perturbation method explained in Section 2.15. A practical method of feeding an antenna from one of its ends is shown in Fig. 2.13.

The impedance of the antenna shown in Fig. 2.12b as seen at the gap equals the impedance of the antenna proper in series with the capacitive admittance of the sphere.   There is also a parallel capacitance shunting the cone and the sphere.   Our model contains all the essential features of an actual antenna, and the various effects are clearly separated, so that we can make proper allowances in applying theoretical results to various practical situations.

The impedance of an infinitely long cone of small angle $2\psi$ is found to be

$$K = 60 \log \frac{2}{\psi} - 30. \tag{231}$$

The first term equals one half of the impedance of two such cones going in opposite directions. The capacitance of the small sphere of radius $b$ in series with this cone is

$$C_{se} = \frac{4\pi\varepsilon b}{1 - \frac{1}{2}\log(2/\psi)}. \tag{232}$$

The numerator is the capacitance of the sphere in free space; the denominator expresses the effect of the cone. Equation 232 is of practical interest only insofar as it illustrates our ideas about the imped-ance of the end-fed antenna; the actual value of the capacitance is of little interest since it varies with the structure of practical generators and practical input regions. Similarly, if $\vartheta$ and $\psi$ are both small, and yet $\vartheta$ is large compared with $\psi$, then the capacitance in shunt between the cone and the sphere is

$$C_{sh} = \frac{\pi\varepsilon a\left(1 + \frac{\pi^2}{6}\right)}{[\log(2/\psi)]^2}. \tag{233}$$

This is small compared with the capacitance of the sphere. It will be large if $\vartheta$ is small compared with $\psi$.

The input impedance of a thin cone of length $l$ is

$$Z_i = K \frac{Z_a \sin \beta l - j(K + 60) \cos \beta l}{(K + 60) \sin \beta l - jZ_a \cos \beta l}, \tag{234}$$

where

$$Z_a = K^2 Y_t = 30 \operatorname{Ein} 2\beta l - 15(1 - e^{-2j\beta l}),$$
$$R_a = 30 \operatorname{Cin} 2\beta l - 15(1 - \cos 2\beta l), \tag{235}$$
$$X_a = 30 \operatorname{Si} 2\beta l - 15 \sin 2\beta l.$$

As might have been expected, $R_a$ represents the radiation resistance with reference to the current antinode, when the current is sinusoidally distributed and vanishes at the end of the antenna opposite to that connected to the generator.*

* Note that $R_a$ and $X_a$ for an end-fed wire are the functions $R_{11}$ and $X_{11}$, re-spectively, tabulated in Appendix II.

For an end-fed antenna of any shape,

$$Z_i = K_a \frac{R_a \sin \beta l + j[(X_a - N) \sin \beta l - (K_a + 60 - M) \cos \beta l]}{[(K_a + 60 + M) \sin \beta l + (X_a + N) \cos \beta l] - jR_a \cos \beta l} .$$

(236)

Here $K_a$ is the average value of $K$; the $M$ and $N$ functions are the corresponding functions for the balanced two-arm antenna divided by two (see Section 1.15).

These results may be obtained by any one of the methods already explained in connection with thin biconical antennas. Likewise the solution for cones of large angles is analogous to that of large angle dipoles. The proper functions for the antenna region are $P_n(-\cos \theta)$, and the values of $n$ are the roots of

$$P_n(-\cos \psi) = 0. \qquad (237)$$

For very small $\psi$,

$$n = m + \frac{1}{2 \log (2/\psi)}, \qquad m = 0, 1, 2, \cdots. \qquad (238)$$

Otherwise we use equation 78 and obtain

$$n = \frac{m + \frac{3}{4}}{1 - (\psi/\pi)} - \frac{1}{2} - \frac{1 - (\psi/\pi)}{8m + 6} - \cdots. \qquad (239)$$

For $m = 0$ and $\psi = 0$ we find from this formula $n = \frac{1}{12}$, while the exact value from equation 238 is zero. Thus, it is only for very small values of $\psi$ that equation 239 fails.

In the case of a single cone, TEM waves do not exist; however, if $\psi$ is small, the waves corresponding to the smallest root,

$$n = \frac{1}{2 \log (2/\psi)}, \qquad (240)$$

closely resemble TEM waves in that the current associated with them is sinusoidally distributed except in the immediate vicinity of the apex. Thus, one of the radial wave functions is

$$Kn_n(j\beta r) = e^{-j\beta r} - n(n + 1)e^{j\beta r} [\text{Ci } 2\beta r + j(\tfrac{1}{2}\pi - \text{Si } 2\beta r)], \qquad (241)$$

and the other is its conjugate. For larger cone angles the resemblance disappears.

Figures 2.14 and 2.15 show the input impedance of a cylindrical monopole for $K_a = 320$ ohms. The characteristic impedance of the dipole made by two such monopoles is 700 ohms. The maximum resistance of the monopole is 1380 ohms; computed on the same basis, the maximum resistance of the dipole is 1820 ohms. Hence, the maximum resistance of the monopole is substantially greater than one half of the maximum resistance of the dipole. As the characteristic imped-

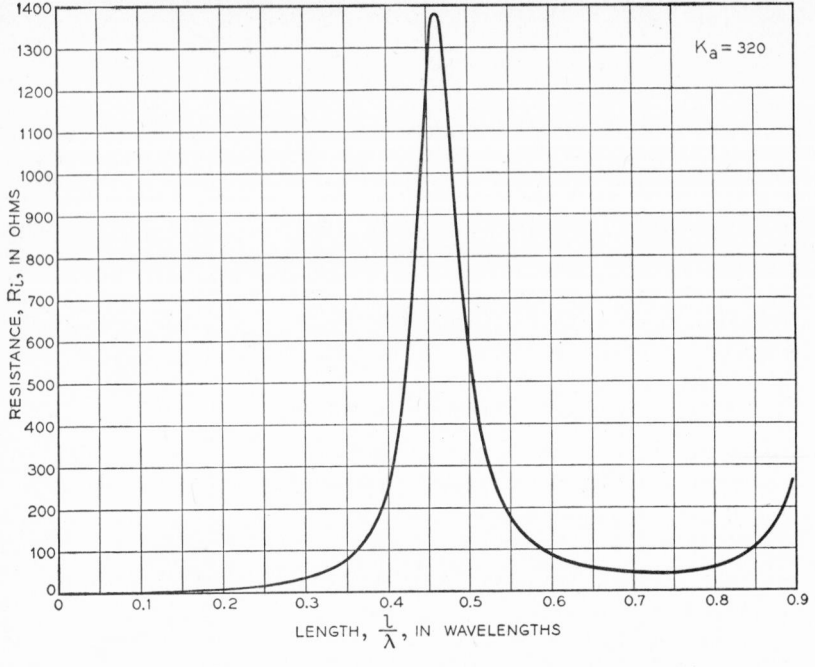

FIG. 2.14　The input resistance of a cylindrical end-fed antenna in free space.

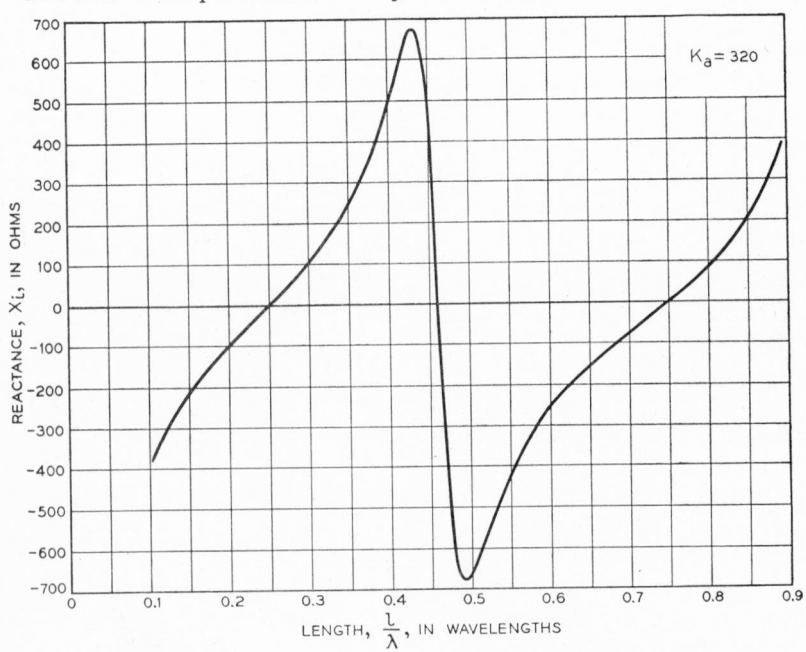

FIG. 2.15　The input reactance of a cylindrical end-fed antenna in free space.

ance increases, the stored energies per unit length in the monopole and dipole tend to become equal; but the radiated power is different. The difference is caused by the mutual radiation of the two arms. At antiresonance the monopole is just a half-wave antenna, and its radiation resistance with reference to the current antinode is 73 ohms, so that the antiresonant resistance is $K_a(K_a - 146)/73$; the corresponding radiation resistance of the full dipole is 199 ohms, and that of one half of it 100 ohms. Thus, the ultimate ratio of the maximum resistance of the monopole to half that of the dipole is 100 to 73. In the preceding example the ratio is 100 to 66.

### 2.19    Current element above a discoid ground

As another illustration of mode analysis, let us consider a current element of moment $Is$ just above a perfectly conducting disk of radius $l$ (Fig. 2.16). Here we might write general expressions for the fields in the three separate regions into which the entire space is subdivided by the disk and a hypothetical sphere $S$ of radius $l$ centered at the center of the disk. In this formulation we would have three sets of coefficients in the expressions for the fields. The problem is simplified if we note that the field of our current element must be the sum of the fields associated with pairs of current elements, each of moment $\frac{1}{2}Is$, and arranged as shown in Figs. 2.17$a$ and 2.17$b$. In the sum the elements below the

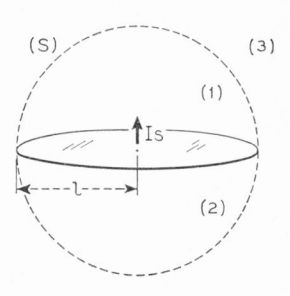

FIG. 2.16   A current element above a discoid ground.

plane cancel and leave that region source free. In the arrangement shown in Fig. 2.17$b$, there are no currents in the disk; hence the disk can be removed without disturbing the field, and we are left with a single current element of moment $Is$. In the arrangement shown in Fig. 2.17$a$,

$$E_r(\theta) = E_r(\pi - \theta). \tag{242}$$

This condition enables us to express the field in regions 1 and 2 in terms of a single set of coefficients.

Since $E_r$ must be finite on the axis, $\theta = 0$, (except at the element) the proper angular wave function is

$$\Theta(\theta) = P_n(\cos \theta). \tag{243}$$

Since $E_r$ should vanish at the surface of the disk where $\theta = \pi/2$, the proper values of $n$ are roots of

$$P_n(0) = 0. \tag{244}$$

These roots are

$$n = 1, 3, 5, \cdots. \tag{245}$$

The corresponding radial wave functions are

$$S_n(\beta r) = Jn_n(\beta r) + p_n Nn_n(\beta r). \tag{246}$$

The expressions for the field are analogous to those given by equations 31, 32, and 33 except that the TEM wave is absent. As $r \to 0$, $Nn_n$ approaches infinity as $1/r^n$; hence, the corresponding term in $E_r$

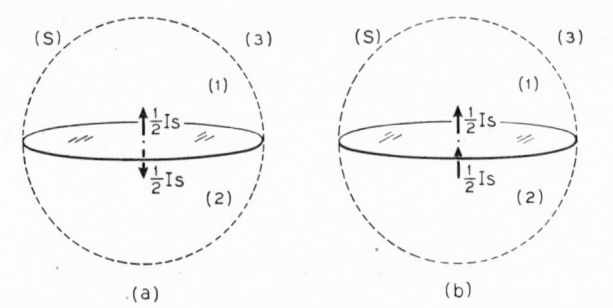

FIG. 2.17   Two arrangements of current elements in the presence of a discoid ground.

approaches infinity as $1/r^{n+2}$. On the other hand, the radial electric intensity of the given current element approaches infinity only as $1/r^3$; hence, for all $n > 1$, the coefficient $p_n$ should be made zero, and

$$S_n(\beta r) = Jn_n(\beta r). \tag{247}$$

For $n = 1$ it is convenient to split the radial wave function into two components: (1) the "primary component" representing the field of the current element above a disk extended to infinity so that there is no discontinuity at $r = l$, and (2) the component representing the wave reflected from the discontinuity. The second component must be finite at $r = 0$, and the corresponding wave function is

$$S_1(\beta r) = Jn_1(\beta r). \tag{248}$$

The first component represents the field equal to the free-space field of the current element of moment $Is$. In the present notation this is

$$r^2 E_r{}^p = -\frac{\eta Is}{2\pi} Hn_1(\beta r) P_1(\cos \theta),$$

$$rH_\varphi{}^p = \frac{j\beta Is}{4\pi} Hn_1(\beta r) P_1{}^1(\cos \theta), \tag{249}$$

$$rE_\theta{}^p = j\eta \frac{j\beta Is}{4\pi} Hn_1'(\beta r) P_1{}^1(\cos \theta).$$

In writing the general expression for the field above the disk ($\theta < \pi/2$) after the pattern given by equations 31, 32, and 33, we shall now find it convenient to absorb the factor $1/2\pi n(n + 1)$ in the coefficient $a_n$. Thus,

$$j\omega\varepsilon r^2 E_r = j\omega\varepsilon r^2 E_r{}^p - \sum_{n=1,3,5,\dots} n(n + 1)a_n \frac{Jn_n(\beta r)}{Jn_n(\beta l)} P_n(\cos\theta),$$

$$rH_\varphi = rH_\varphi{}^p + \sum_n a_n \frac{Jn_n(\beta r)}{Jn_n(\beta l)} P_n{}^1(\cos\theta), \qquad (250)$$

$$rE_\theta = rE_\theta{}^p + j\eta \sum_n a_n \frac{Jn_n{}'(\beta r)}{Jn_n(\beta l)} P_n{}^1(\cos\theta).$$

For odd integral values of $n$,

$$P_n[\cos(\pi - \theta)] = P_n(-\cos\theta) = -P_n(\cos\theta), \qquad (251)$$

hence, to satisfy equation 242 the expressions for the field below the disk are the same as equations 250 with the sign reversed.

In region 3 defined by $r > l$ the field must be finite when $\theta = 0$, $\pi$; hence, the proper angular function is

$$\Theta(\theta) = P_k(\cos\theta), \qquad (252)$$

with the added condition that $k$ is an integer. From equation 242 we find

$$P_k[\cos(\pi - \theta)] = P_k(-\cos\theta) = P_k(\cos\theta); \qquad (253)$$

that is, the wave function must be an even function of $\cos\theta$. Hence, $k$ must be an even integer,

$$k = 2, 4, 6, \cdots. \qquad (254)$$

Thus, in region 3 (Fig. 2.17$a$) we have

$$j\omega\varepsilon r^2 E_r = - \sum_{k=2,4,6,\dots} k(k + 1)b_k \frac{Hn_k(\beta r)}{Hn_k(\beta l)} P_k(\cos\theta),$$

$$rH_\varphi = \sum_k b_k \frac{Hn_k(\beta r)}{Hn_k(\beta l)} P_k{}^1(\cos\theta), \qquad (255)$$

$$rE_\theta = j\eta \sum_k b_k \frac{Hn_k{}'(\beta r)}{Hn_k(\beta l)} P_k{}^1(\cos\theta).$$

At $r = l$ the field must be continuous. In accordance with Maxwell's equations the continuity of $E_r$ implies the continuity of $H_\varphi$, and vice versa; hence, we can match either the pair $E_r$, $E_\theta$ or $H_\varphi$, $E_\theta$. We shall take the latter pair. The coefficients $b_k$ may be expressed either in terms of $H_\varphi(l)$ or in terms of $E_\theta(l)$ by using the orthogonal properties of Legendre functions and the symmetry of the field,*

$$b_k = \frac{2k+1}{k(k+1)} \int_0^{\pi/2} l\, H_\varphi(l)\, P_k{}^1(\cos\theta)\, \sin\theta\, d\theta,$$

$$Z_k{}^+ b_k = \frac{2k+1}{k(k+1)} \int_0^{\pi/2} l\, E_\theta(l)\, P_k{}^1(\cos\theta)\, \sin\theta\, d\theta, \qquad (256)$$

$$Z_k{}^+ = j\eta\, \frac{Hn_k{}'(\beta l)}{Hn_k(\beta l)}\,.$$

From equation 250 we have

$$l\, H_\varphi(l) = \frac{j\beta Is}{4\pi}\, Hn_1(\beta l)\, P_1{}^1(\cos\theta) + \sum_{n=1,3,\ldots} a_n\, P_n{}^1(\cos\theta), \qquad \theta < \tfrac{1}{2}\pi,$$

$$l\, E_\theta(l) = \frac{j\beta Is}{4\pi}\, Hn_1(\beta l) Z_1{}^+ P_1{}^1(\cos\theta) - \sum_n Z_n{}^- a_n\, P_n{}^1(\cos\theta), \qquad (257)$$

$$Z_n{}^- = -j\eta\, \frac{Jn_n{}'(\beta l)}{Jn_n(\beta l)}\,.$$

Substituting in equations 256, we obtain

$$b_k = A u_{k1} + \sum_{n=1,3,\ldots} u_{kn} a_n, \qquad A = \frac{j\beta Is}{4\pi}\, Hn_1(\beta l), \qquad (258)$$

$$Z_k{}^+ b_k = A Z_1{}^+ u_{k1} - \sum_n Z_n{}^- u_{kn} a_n, \qquad k = 2, 4, 6, \cdots, \qquad (259)$$

where

$$u_{kn} = \frac{2k+1}{k(k+1)} \int_0^{\pi/2} P_k{}^1(\cos\theta)\, P_n{}^1(\cos\theta)\, \sin\theta\, d\theta$$

$$= (2k+1) \int_0^{\pi/2} P_k(\cos\theta)\, P_n(\cos\theta)\, \sin\theta\, d\theta$$

$$= \frac{2k+1}{(k-n)(k+n+1)}\, \sin\theta \times$$

$$\left[ P_k(\cos\theta)\, P_n{}^1(\cos\theta) - P_n(\cos\theta)\, P_k{}^1(\cos\theta) \right]_0^{\pi/2}.$$

$$= \frac{2k+1}{(k-n)(k+n+1)}\, P_k(0) P_n{}^1(0)$$

$$= \frac{2(-)^{\frac{1}{2}(k+n+1)}(2k+1)}{\pi(k-n)(k+n+1)}\, \frac{(\tfrac{1}{2}k-\tfrac{1}{2})!\,(\tfrac{1}{2}n)!}{(\tfrac{1}{2}n-\tfrac{1}{2})!\,(\tfrac{1}{2}k)!}\,. \qquad (260)$$

* Incidentally $H_\varphi$ vanishes for $r > l$ in the plane of the disk. Hence, this part of the plane may be considered as an effective magnetic conductor which, together with the disk, separates the upper half of space from the lower. See S. A. Schelkunoff, Generalized boundary conditions in electromagnetic theory, *Proc. Nat. Elec. Conf.*, **2**, 1946, pp. 317–322.

Similarly, we can express the $a_n$'s in terms of either $l\,H_\varphi(l)$ or $l\,E_\theta(l)$; thus,

$$a_1 = -A + \frac{3}{2}\int_0^{\pi/2} l\,H_\varphi(l)\,P_1^1(\cos\theta)\,\sin\theta\,d\theta,$$

$$a_n = \frac{2n+1}{n(n+1)}\int_0^{\pi/2} l\,H_\varphi(l)\,P_n^1(\cos\theta)\,\sin\theta\,d\theta, \qquad n > 1; \tag{261}$$

or

$$Z_1{}^- a_1 = Z_1{}^+ A - \frac{3}{2}\int_0^{\pi/2} l\,E_\theta(l)\,P_1^1(\cos\theta)\,\sin\theta\,d\theta,$$

$$Z_n{}^- a_n = -\frac{2n+1}{n(n+1)}\int_0^{\pi/2} l\,E_\theta(l)\,P_n^1(\cos\theta)\,\sin\theta\,d\theta. \tag{262}$$

From equations 255,

$$l\,H_\varphi(l) = \sum_k b_k\,P_k^1(\cos\theta), \qquad l\,E_\theta(l) = \sum_k Z_k{}^+ b_k\,P_k^1(\cos\theta). \tag{263}$$

Substituting in equations 261 and 262, we find

$$a_1 = -A + \sum_k v_{1k}b_k, \qquad a_n = \sum_k v_{nk}b_k, \qquad n > 1, \tag{264}$$

$$Z_1{}^- a_1 = Z_1{}^+ A - \sum_k Z_k{}^+ v_{1k}b_k, \qquad Z_n{}^- a_n = -\sum_k Z_k{}^+ v_{nk}b_k, \tag{265}$$

where

$$v_{nk} = \frac{k(k+1)(2n+1)}{n(n+1)(2k+1)}\,u_{kn}$$

$$= \frac{2(-)^{\frac{1}{2}(k+n+1)}(2n+1)}{\pi(k-n)(k+n+1)}\,\frac{k(k+1)}{n(n+1)}\,\frac{(\frac{1}{2}k-\frac{1}{2})!\,(\frac{1}{2}n)!}{(\frac{1}{2}n-\frac{1}{2})!\,(\frac{1}{2}k)!}. \tag{266}$$

Equations 258, 259, 264, and 266 are not independent. Equations 258 and 264 are obtained by expanding the same function $l\,H_\varphi(l)$ into two different series of Legendre functions; they simply express one set of coefficients in terms of the other. If we substitute from equation 264 in equation 258, we should have an identity. Hence, from

$$b_k = Au_{k1} - u_{k1}A + \sum_{n,\alpha} u_{kn}v_{n\alpha}b_\alpha, \tag{267}$$

we conclude that

$$\sum_n u_{kn}v_{n\alpha} = 0, \qquad \alpha \neq k,$$

$$= 1, \qquad \alpha = k. \tag{268}$$

Similarly, by substituting from equation 258 in equation 264, we find

$$\sum_k v_{nk}u_{k\alpha} = 0, \qquad n \neq \alpha,$$

$$= 1, \qquad n = \alpha. \tag{269}$$

Likewise equations 259 are equivalent to equations 265. To find the coefficients $a_n$ and $b_k$, we may select any pair of nonequivalent sets of equations from 258, 259, 264, and 265. For example, we may choose equations 258 and 259; then, if we multiply equation 258 by $Z_k{}^+$ and subtract equation 259, we obtain

$$\sum_{n=1,3,\ldots} (Z_k{}^+ + Z_n{}^-)u_{kn}a_n = -(Z_k{}^+ - Z_1{}^+)u_{k1}A. \qquad (270)$$

We may also make the type of substitution we used in the case of biconical antennas. The actual method of handling such systems of equations should be selected after a study of the orders of magnitude of the coefficients. We may also rely on physical intuition to guide us in adopting a particular method of successive approximations. There is no general rule which we could follow successfully on all occasions.

If the function $Jn_n(\beta l)$ vanishes for some particular value of $n$, the corresponding terms in equations 250 become indeterminate. This may or may not cause a difficulty in solving the equations. The difficulty can be removed by writing

$$a_n = \bar{a}_n\, Jn_n(\beta l), \qquad Z_n{}^-a_n = -j\eta\, Jn_n{}'(\beta l)\, \bar{a}_n, \qquad (271)$$

where $\bar{a}_n$ is a new coefficient.

If the disk is large, we expect that the coefficients of reflection $a_n$ will be small when the order of the wave is small. Thus, we may neglect these coefficients in equations 258 and 259 and determine the coefficients of transmission $b_k$. For small $k$ and large $l$ the radial impedance $Z_k{}^+$ is nearly equal to $\eta$; hence, each set of equations gives approximately the same result. It is to be expected, however, that a better approximation might be obtained by using both equations. Let us multiply equation 258 by $Z_k{}^+$ and add equation 259; using the substitution 271, we have

$$b_k = \frac{Z_k{}^+ + Z_1{}^+}{2Z_k{}^+}\, Au_{k1} + \sum_n \frac{Z_k{}^+ Jn_n(\beta l) + j\eta\, Jn_n{}'(\beta l)}{2Z_k{}^+}\, u_{kn}\bar{a}_n. \qquad (272)$$

Neglecting the $a$'s, we have

$$b_k{}^{(0)} = \frac{Z_k{}^+ + Z_1{}^+}{2Z_k{}^+}\, Au_{k1}. \qquad (273)$$

Next we turn to equations 264 and 265 and introduce equation 271,

$$\bar{a}_1\, Jn_1(\beta l) = -A + \sum_k v_{1k}b_k, \qquad \bar{a}_n\, Jn_n(\beta l) = \sum_k v_{nk}b_k, \qquad (274)$$

$$-j\eta\bar{a}_1\, Jn_1{}'(\beta l) = Z_1{}^+A - \sum_k Z_k{}^+v_{1k}b_k,$$

$$-j\eta\bar{a}_n\, Jn_n{}'(\beta l) = -\sum_k Z_k{}^+v_{nk}b_k. \qquad (275)$$

Multiplying the $n$th equation of each set, respectively, by $j\eta\, Nn_n{}'(\beta l)$ and $Nn_n(\beta l)$ and adding, we find

$$j\eta\bar{a}_1 = [Z_1{}^+\, Nn_1(\beta l) - j\eta\, Nn_1{}'(\beta l)]A +$$
$$\sum_k [j\eta\, Nn_1{}'(\beta l) - Z_k{}^+\, Nn_1(\beta l)]v_{1k}b_k, \quad (276)$$

$$j\eta\bar{a}_n = \sum_k [j\eta\, Nn_n{}'(\beta l) - Z_k{}^+\, Nn_n(\beta l)]v_{nk}b_k. \quad (277)$$

Substituting from equation 273, we have

$$j\eta\bar{a}_1 = [Z_1{}^+\, Nn_1(\beta l) - j\eta\, Nn_1{}'(\beta l)]A +$$
$$A\sum_k [j\eta\, Nn_1{}'(\beta l) - Z_k{}^+\, Nn_1(\beta l)]\frac{Z_k{}^+ + Z_1{}^+}{2Z_k{}^+} v_{1k}u_{k1}, \quad (278)$$

$$j\eta\bar{a}_n = A\sum_k [j\eta\, Nn_n{}'(\beta l) - Z_k{}^+\, Nn_n(\beta l)]\frac{Z_k{}^+ + Z_1{}^+}{2Z_k{}^+} v_{nk}u_{k1}. \quad (279)$$

Using equation 269, we have an identity

$$A = A\sum_k v_{1k}u_{k1}. \quad (280)$$

Introducing this in the first term of equation 278 and combining the result with the second term, we obtain

$$\bar{a}_1 = A\sum_k \tfrac{1}{2}(Z_1{}^+ - Z_k{}^+)\left[\frac{Nn_1(\beta l)}{j\eta} + \frac{Nn_1{}'(\beta l)}{Z_k{}^+}\right]v_{1k}u_{k1}. \quad (281)$$

Similarly, for $n \neq 1$,

$$0 = \sum_k v_{nk}u_{k1}. \quad (282)$$

We can multiply this by $j\eta\, Nn_n{}'(\beta l)$ and subtract from equation 279; we can also multiply the same equation by $Nn_n(\beta l)$ and add to equation 279; in this manner we find

$$\bar{a}_n = A\sum_k \tfrac{1}{2}(Z_1{}^+ - Z_k{}^+)\left[\frac{Nn_n(\beta l)}{j\eta} + \frac{Nn_n{}'(\beta l)}{Z_k{}^+}\right]v_{nk}u_{k1}. \quad (283)$$

Thus we have obtained approximate expressions for waves of various orders reflected from the edge of the disk and for waves transmitted beyond the edge. From the latter we can obtain the effect of the disk on the radiation pattern of the current element; from the former the effect of the edge on the element itself. At the element $r = 0$, and there is no contribution from waves of any order but the first. For small values of $\beta r$, $Jn_1(\beta r) = \tfrac{1}{3}\beta^2 r^2$, and from equation 250 we find that along the element

$$E_r = E_r{}^{(p)} + \tfrac{2}{3}j\omega\mu\bar{a}_1. \quad (284)$$

Let us recall that when the element of moment $Is$ is placed above the disk, the field is the sum of the fields corresponding to the arrangements shown in Fig. 2.17. We have seen that, for the arrangement $b$, the field equals the free-space field of the current element of moment $Is$. For the arrangement $a$, we have represented the total field in region 1 as the sum of the "primary field," obtained on the assumption that the radius of the disk is infinite, and the reflected field. The former equals the free-space field of a current element of moment $Is$. Hence, the total field of the element of moment $Is$ above the disk (Fig. 2.16) equals the sum of the free-space field of an element of moment $2Is$ and the reflected field obtained above. This means that the second term in equation 284 represents the effect of the finite radius of the disk as compared to the infinite radius. The corresponding increment in the impedance of the element is

$$\Delta Z_i = -\frac{E_r s}{I} = -\frac{2j\omega\mu\bar{a}_1 s}{I}\,, \qquad (285)$$

where $\bar{a}_1$ is given by equation 281 and $A$ by equation 258.

### 2.20  Treatment of reflection phenomena by successive approximations

It is important to remember that a sequence of "successive approximations" to an unknown quantity may converge either rapidly or slowly; it may even diverge. The success of the method depends on the proper choice of recurrence relations, and this requires a study of the problem and the equations involved. We shall stress the point by a simple example in which we know the exact answer, and compare it with various sequences of successive approximations. Consider a transmission line of length $l$ and characteristic impedance $K$; let $Z$ be the impedance across the end of the line. The current and voltage in the line may be expressed as follows:

$$
\begin{aligned}
I(x) &= Ae^{-j\beta(x-l)} + ae^{-j\beta(l-x)}, \\
V(x) &= KAe^{-j\beta(x-l)} - Kae^{-j\beta(l-x)}.
\end{aligned}
\qquad (286)
$$

We assume that the amplitude $A$ of the wave moving toward $Z$ is given Let $I(l) = b$; then the boundary conditions are

$$A + a = b, \qquad KA - Ka = Zb. \qquad (287)$$

We may solve the first equation for $b$ and the second for $a$,

$$b = A + a, \qquad a = A - \frac{Z}{K}\, b. \qquad (288)$$

Suppose that $Z$ is nearly equal to $K$; then the reflection coefficient should be small. Hence, we may start by neglecting it in calculating $b$, thus obtaining $b = A$; then we may substitute this value in the second equation to obtain $a$. Hence, in the first approximation we have

$$b = A, \qquad a = A\left(1 - \frac{Z}{K}\right). \tag{289}$$

We now use the new value of $a$ in the first equation 288 and substitute the result in the second equation. Thus, in the second approximation,

$$b = A + A\left(1 - \frac{Z}{K}\right), \qquad a = A\left(1 - \frac{Z}{K}\right)\left(1 - \frac{Z}{K}\right). \tag{290}$$

Repeating the process, we obtain the third and fourth approximations:

$$b = A + A\left(1 - \frac{Z}{K}\right)\left(1 - \frac{Z}{K}\right),$$

$$a = A\left(1 - \frac{Z}{K}\right)\left(1 - \frac{Z}{K} + \frac{Z^2}{K^2}\right).$$

$$b = A + A\left(1 - \frac{Z}{K}\right)\left(1 - \frac{Z}{K} + \frac{Z^2}{K^2}\right), \tag{291}$$

$$a = A\left(1 - \frac{Z}{K}\right)\left(1 - \frac{Z}{K} + \frac{Z^2}{K^2} - \frac{Z^3}{K^3}\right).$$

The $n$th approximation can be obtained by induction.

Now the exact values are

$$a = A\,\frac{1 - (Z/K)}{1 + (Z/K)}, \qquad b = A + a. \tag{292}$$

As we inspect our sequence of successive approximations, we find that it converges if the absolute value of $Z$ *is smaller* than $K$; otherwise it diverges. We have apparently predicated our iterative process on the assumption that $Z$ is nearly equal to $K$; and yet, when the sequence converges, it converges very slowly for such values. The sequence converges rapidly, not when $Z$ is nearly equal to $K$ and when $a$ is small as we assumed, but when $Z$ is small compared to $K$ and when $a$ *is not small*. While the error in $b$ given by the first approximation 289 is small, only the absolute error in $a$ is small; the relative error in $a$ is nearly 100 per cent (when $Z \simeq K$). The second approximation to $a$ is even worse, although the third is better.

If we start our sequence of approximations by neglecting $a$ *in the second* equation of the set 287 and obtain $a$ from the first, the sequence will converge only when $Z > K$. It will converge rapidly when $Z \gg K$ and slowly when $Z \simeq K$.

On the other hand, we may solve both equations 288 for $a$ and take the average,

$$a = \frac{K - Z}{2K}\, b, \tag{293}$$

as the defining equation for $a$, while retaining

$$b = A + a \tag{294}$$

as the equation for $b$. Then our sequence of approximations becomes,

$$b = A, \qquad\qquad a = A\,\frac{K - Z}{2K}\ ;$$

$$b = A\left(1 + \frac{K - Z}{2K}\right), \qquad a = A\left[\frac{K - Z}{2K} + \left(\frac{K - Z}{2K}\right)^2\right];$$

$$b = A\left[1 + \frac{K - Z}{2K} + \left(\frac{K - Z}{2K}\right)^2 + \cdots\right],$$

$$a = A\left[\frac{K - Z}{2K} + \left(\frac{K - Z}{2K}\right)^2 + \left(\frac{K - Z}{2K}\right)^3 + \cdots\right].$$

$$\tag{295}$$

These series converge rapidly when $Z \simeq K$. We could also obtain expansions in powers of $(K - Z)/2Z$. Neither of these expansions converges as rapidly as one of the previous ones when $Z \ll K$ or $Z \gg K$. Each expansion has its own region of rapid convergence so that they are supplementary to each other.

The primary wave may be chosen in different ways. We can choose a progressive wave or a wave totally reflected at the discontinuity. The totally reflected wave may be of a kind in which $H$ reduces to zero at the discontinuity or of a kind in which $E$ vanishes there.

## 2.21  Miscellaneous problems

There are many problems which can be treated by spherical mode analysis. In this section we shall discuss some of them briefly. The case of a conical monopole above a hemispherical ground of the same radius as the length of the monopole (Fig. 2.11) is just a special case of a dipole with arms of the same length but different spread (Fig. 2.10). If the radius of the ground is different from the length of the monopole (Fig. 2.18a), we have a special case of the general asymmetric dipole (Fig. 2.18b). In this case we have three regions to consider, with different boundary conditions. In region 1 the angular wave function is of the form

$$\Theta(\theta) = A_1 P_n(\cos \theta) + B_1 P_n(-\cos \theta), \qquad (296)$$

and the proper values of $n$ are determined by the boundary conditions $\Theta(\theta_1) = \Theta(\theta_2) = 0$. In region 2

$$\Theta(\theta) = A_2 P_n(\cos \theta), \qquad (297)$$

and the proper values of $n$ are the zeros of $P_n(\cos \theta_2)$. In region 3, $\Theta$ is also of the form 297 but with $n$ required to assume only integral values.

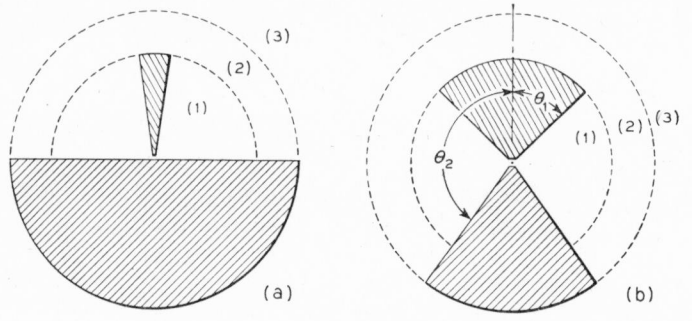

FIG. 2.18    (a) A monopole above a hemispherical ground and (b) a general asymmetric dipole.

In region 1 we shall have a TEM wave and TM waves, with the requirement that their intensities be finite at $r = 0$; thus, the radial wave functions are $a_n Jn_n(\beta r)$. In region 2, both solutions of Bessel's equation

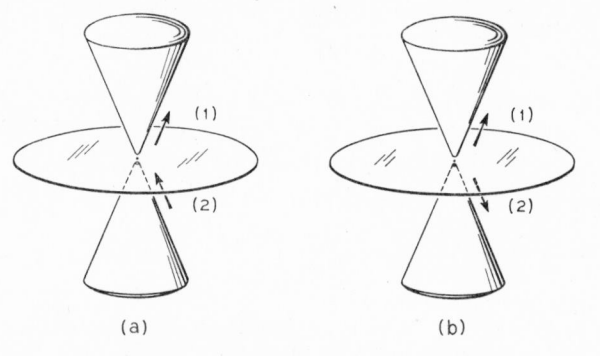

FIG. 2.19    Conical antennas on two sides of a discoid shield.

are finite, and the radial wave function is $b_n Jn_n(\beta r) + c_n Nn_n(\beta r)$. In region 3, $c_n = -jb_n$. Hence, we have four sets of coefficients in the general series representing the field around the dipole. They can be calculated from the four boundary conditions expressing the continuity of $E_\theta$ and $H_\varphi$.

A monopole above a discoid ground can be treated more conveniently by considering first two symmetric arrangements (Fig. 2.19). In the arrangement $a$ there are no currents in the disk, the disk may be

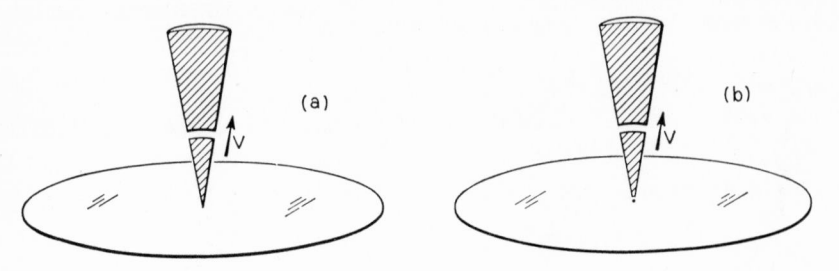

FIG. 2.20   Conical antennas with a voltage source above a conducting disk.

removed, and we have a symmetric dipole in free space. In the arrangement $b$ the general form of the field in region 1 is exactly the same as in the arrangement $a$; but in region 2 the algebraic signs of the

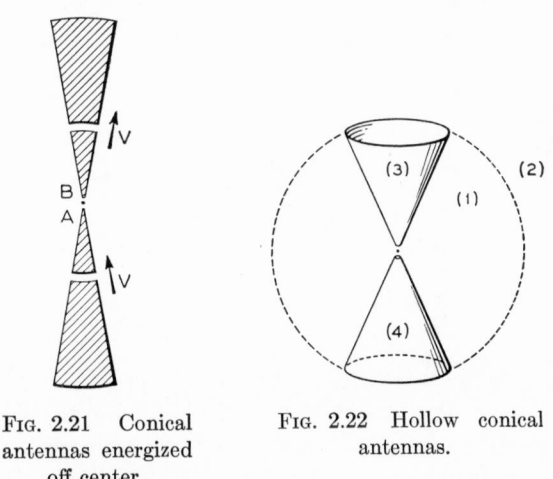

FIG. 2.21   Conical          FIG. 2.22   Hollow   conical
antennas energized                 antennas.
off center.

coefficients should be reversed. In the free-space region surrounding the system $b$ the field is given by series of the types 39, 40, and 41, but with $k$ assuming *even values*.

In Fig. 2.20$a$ we have a monopole connected to ground and fed at some point above the apex; in Fig. 2.20$b$ we have the same monopole disconnected from ground. For an infinite ground both of these arrangements are equivalent to a symmetric dipole fed symmetrically at two points (Fig. 2.21). In the case $a$ the apices $A$ and $B$ should be short-circuited and $V(0)$ vanishes; in the case $b$ the boundary condition is $I(0) = 0$.

If the cones are hollow (Fig. 2.22), we have two interior regions, 3 and 4, to consider; but, on account of symmetry, only one set of additional coefficients. Since $E_r$ is an odd function of $\cos \theta$, the field in region 3 will be of the form

$$j\omega\varepsilon r^2 E_r = \sum_n c_n Jn_n(\beta r) P_n(\cos \theta), \tag{298}$$

and, in region 4,

$$j\omega\varepsilon r^2 E_r = -\sum_n c_n Jn_n(\beta r) P_n(-\cos \theta). \tag{299}$$

Proper values of $n$ are roots of

$$P_n(\cos \psi) = 0. \tag{300}$$

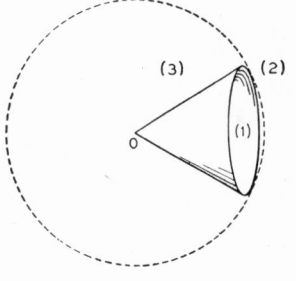

In the case of a single hollow cone (Fig. 2.23) we have two possibilities. The impressed voltage may be near the apex $O$ in region 3; then we have an end-fed antenna. If the source is in region 1, we have a circular horn. For the dominant wave in the horn the angular wave function is

FIG. 2.23   A circular horn.

$$T(\theta, \varphi) = P_n{}^1(\cos \theta) \cos \varphi, \tag{301}$$

where $n$ is the first root of

$$\frac{d}{d\psi} P_n{}^1(\cos \psi) = 0. \tag{302}$$

In this equation $2\psi$ is the interior angle of the horn. At $r = l$ the horn is terminated, and a fraction of the dominant wave is reflected. In addition, other interior modes are generated, with angular wave functions of the form 301 where $n$ is a root of equation 302. In region 3 the angular wave function is

$$T(\theta, \varphi) = P_m{}^1(-\cos \theta) \cos \varphi, \tag{303}$$

where $m$ is a root of

$$\frac{d}{d\psi} P_m{}^1(-\cos \psi) = 0. \tag{304}$$

Besides TE modes there will be TM modes for which $n$ and $m$ are the zeros of $P_n{}^1(\cos \psi)$ and $P_m{}^1(-\cos \psi)$.

Figure 2.22 also shows two horns arranged back to back; hence, we have a way of calculating the " cross-talk " between two horns.

A nearly rectangular horn is bounded by the half-planes, $\varphi = 0$ and $\varphi = \varphi_0$, by the plane $\theta = \pi/2$, and by the cone $\theta = \theta_0$ (Fig. 2.24).

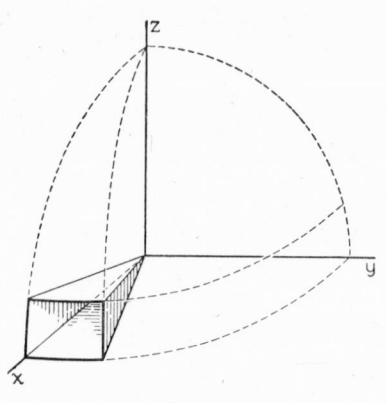

Fig. 2.24   A nearly rectangular horn.

If the radius of the sphere in Fig. 2.12$b$ is large, we have an antenna above a spherical ground.   Figure 2.25 shows an antenna radiating into a horn.   In Fig. 2.26 we have a spherical resonator radiating through

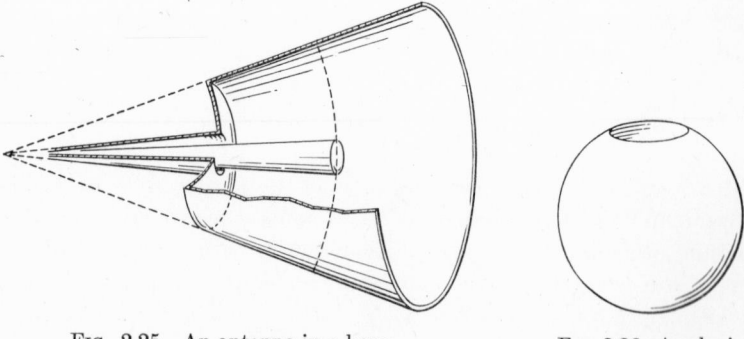

Fig. 2.25   An antenna in a horn.          Fig. 2.26   A spherical resonator with a hole.

a hole.   In this case we may represent $E_\theta$ and $E_\varphi$ in the hole by a series of suitable Legendre functions.   For example, a circularly symmetric field with $E_\varphi = 0$ in a hole of angular diameter $2\psi$ may be expressed in the form

$$E_\theta(l, \theta) = \sum_n a_n P_n{}^1(\cos \theta), \tag{305}$$

where $n$ is a zero of $P_n(\cos \psi)$. This function may then be expanded in series of Legendre functions appropriate to the interior and the exterior of the resonator, that is, in a series of the form

$$E_\theta(l, \theta) = \sum_m b_m P_m{}^1(\cos \theta), \qquad m = 1, 2, 3, \cdots, \qquad (306)$$

where $b_m$ is a linear function of the $a_n$'s. From this we obtain the transmitted magnetic intensity just outside the sphere,

$$H_\varphi{}^t(l, \theta) = \sum_m \frac{b_m}{Z_m{}^+} P_m{}^1(\cos \theta), \qquad (307)$$

and the reflected magnetic intensity just inside,

$$H_\varphi{}^r(l, \theta) = -\sum_m \frac{b_m}{Z_m{}^-} P_m{}^1(\cos \theta). \quad (308)$$

In addition we shall have the primary field generated by the given source when the resonator is completely closed; for example, we may have

$$E_\theta{}^p(l, \theta) = 0,$$
$$H_\varphi{}^p(l, \theta) = A \, P_1{}^1(\cos \theta), \qquad (309)$$

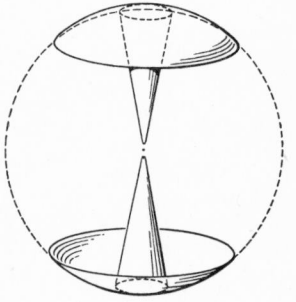

Fig. 2.27  A capacitively loaded antenna.

where $A$ is given in terms of the strength of the source. In passing through the hole the magnetic field should remain continuous; hence,

$$\sum_m \left( \frac{1}{Z_m{}^+} + \frac{1}{Z_m{}^-} \right) b_m P_m{}^1(\cos \theta) - A \, P_1{}^1(\cos \theta) = 0, \qquad 0 < \psi.$$
$$(310)$$

Multiplying this equation by $P_n{}^1(\cos \theta) \sin \theta$, where $n$ is a typical zero of $P_n(\cos \psi)$, and integrating, we obtain linear equations for the $b_m$'s and therefore for the $a_n$'s.

Capacitively loaded dipoles (Fig. 2.27) may be treated in the same way.

### 2.22  V antennas, fans, porcupines

In the case of less symmetric radiating systems, such as a V antenna (Fig. 2.28a), a "fan antenna," (Fig. 2.28b), or an antenna with a counterpoise (Fig. 2.28c), which is a special case of a "porcupine arrangement" of conductors, the boundary value problem becomes much more complicated unless the conductors are thin. To illustrate what is involved, consider the V antenna with two arms of length $l$.

The "antenna region" is bounded by the sphere of radius $l$ centered at the common apex of the antenna arms. For this region we must obtain a set of angular wave functions which vanish at the surface of each arm. These angular wave functions must be finite everywhere except in the interiors of the conductors, which are excluded from the

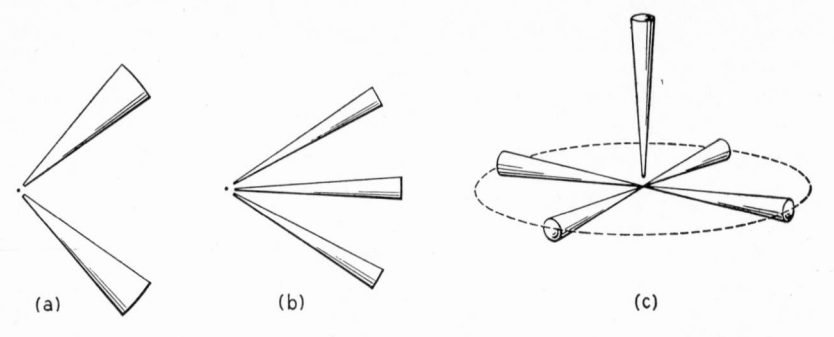

(a)  (b)  (c)

FIG. 2.28 (a) A V antenna, (b) a "fan" antenna, and (c) a "porcupine" antenna.

antenna region. If the cone angles are small compared with the angle $\vartheta$ between the axes of the cones, the current is distributed nearly uniformly around each cone, and the angular wave function is

$$\Theta = P_n(-\cos \theta') - P_n(-\cos \theta''), \qquad (311)$$

where $\theta'$ and $\theta''$ are, respectively, the angles made by a typical direction with the axes of the cones. The negative sign reflects the fact that, while in one cone the current flows away from the apex, in the other it flows toward the apex. Proper values of $n$ are roots of

$$P_n(-\cos \psi) - P_n(-\cos \vartheta) = 0. \qquad (312)$$

If the cone angles are not small, the current is not uniformly distributed around each cone, and the wave function is of a more general form,

$$\Theta = \sum_{m=0,1,2,\ldots} (A_m \cos m\varphi' + B_m \sin m\varphi') P_n{}^m(-\cos \theta') -$$
$$\sum_{m=0,1,2,\ldots} (A_m \cos m\varphi'' + B_m \sin m\varphi'') P_n{}^m(-\cos \theta''), \qquad (313)$$

where $\varphi'$ and $\varphi''$ are the azimuth angles associated with the cones. If $\varphi'$ and $\varphi''$ are measured from the plane passing through the axes of the cones, then $B_m = 0$; the remaining coefficients as well as the proper values of $n$ have to be determined from the condition that $\Theta$ is zero on the surface of each cone. A typical direction on the surface of one cone is $(\psi, \varphi')$; the axis of the cone is given by $(\vartheta, 0)$; hence, the cosine of the angle $\theta''$ between these directions is

$$\cos \theta'' = \cos \vartheta \cos \psi + \sin \vartheta \sin \psi \cos \varphi'. \qquad (314)$$

This enables us to express $P_n(-\cos \theta'')$ in terms of $\varphi'$. Next we have to express $P_n{}^m(-\cos \theta'') \cos m\varphi''$ in terms of $\varphi'$. On substitution in equation 313, we shall then have a function of $\varphi'$ alone which should vanish for all values of $\varphi'$. Hence, if this function is expanded in a Fourier series, all coefficients must vanish. In this way we can obtain a system of linear equations for the $A_n$'s. It will be a homogeneous system; hence, it will have nontrivial solutions only when the determinant of all the coefficients vanishes. This condition gives the equation for the proper values of $n$.

Thus, even the calculation of proper wave functions constitutes a complicated problem. When this is solved, we still have to match the fields at the boundary between the antenna region and the free space region. In the case of cones of small angles, however, we need not obtain proper wave functions nor do we have to match the fields. We can use the first method described in Section 2.10 for thin biconical antennas; then we can generalize the result as in Section 2.15 and obtain a formula for the impedance of V antennas made with cylindrical wires (or wires of any shape). The general formula 1–136 is the same, irrespective of the angle $\vartheta$ between the arms of the antenna; the $M$ and $N$ functions are also independent of $\vartheta$; and the formula for $Z_a$ is

$$Z_a = K^2 Y_t = R_a + jX_a, \qquad k = \sin \tfrac{1}{2}\vartheta,$$

$$R_a = 60 \operatorname{Cin} 2k\beta l +$$
$$30[2 \operatorname{Cin} 2\beta l - \operatorname{Cin} 2(1 - k)\beta l - \operatorname{Cin} 2(1 + k)\beta l] \cos 2\beta l +$$
$$30[-2 \operatorname{Si} 2\beta l + \operatorname{Si} 2(1 - k)\beta l + \operatorname{Si} 2(1 + k)\beta l] \sin 2\beta l, \qquad (315)$$
$$X_a = 60 \operatorname{Si} 2k\beta l + 30[\operatorname{Si} 2(1 - k)\beta l - \operatorname{Si} 2(1 + k)\beta l] \cos 2\beta l +$$
$$30[\operatorname{Cin} 2(1 - k)\beta l - \operatorname{Cin} 2(1 + k)\beta l + 2 \log(1 + k)] \sin 2\beta l.$$

Similar expressions in closed form can be obtained for the "fan" and "porcupine" arrangements of radiating wires.

## 2.23 Variational methods

An important contribution to the theory of biconical antennas was recently made by Tai.* Following Schwinger's variational method for waveguide problems, he derived the following expression for the terminal admittance in terms of the aperture field (the aperture is the

* C. T. Tai, Application of a variational principle to biconical antennas, *Jour. Appl. Phys.*, **20**, November 1949, pp. 1076–1084.

part of the boundary sphere where $\psi < \theta < \pi - \psi$):

$$Y_t = \sum_n \frac{2\pi Y_n^- \left[\int_\psi^{\pi-\psi} E_a(\theta) \frac{d}{d\theta} M_n(\cos\theta) \sin\theta \, d\theta\right]^2}{n(n+1) N_n^i \left[\int_\psi^{\pi-\psi} E_a(\theta) \, d\theta\right]^2} +$$

$$\sum_k \frac{2\pi Y_k^+ \left[\int_\psi^{\pi-\psi} E_a(\theta) \frac{d}{d\theta} P_k(\cos\theta) \sin\theta \, d\theta\right]^2}{k(k+1) N_k^e \left[\int_\psi^{\pi-\psi} E_a(\theta) \, d\theta\right]^2}, \qquad (316)$$

where $N_n^i$ and $N_k^e$ are the normalizing factors,

$$N_n^i = \int_\psi^{\pi-\psi} [M_n(\cos\theta)]^2 \sin\theta \, d\theta, \qquad N_k^e = \int_0^\pi [P_k(\cos\theta)]^2 \sin\theta \, d\theta. \qquad (317)$$

The first summation in equation 316 is extended over the zeros of $M_n(\cos\psi)$ and the second summation over the odd integers. The terminal admittance is thus expressed as the sum of the wave admittances $Y_n^-$, $Y_k^+$ of the various normal modes (as seen from the boundary sphere in both directions) with appropriate weighting factors.

In the aperture we have

$$E_a(\theta) = -\frac{A_0}{\sin\theta} + \sum_n A_n \frac{d}{d\theta} M_n(\cos\theta), \qquad (318)$$

where the $A$'s are so far unknown coefficients. The first coefficient $A_0$, however, may be made equal to unity since $Y_t$ is independent of the scale of the aperture field. Substituting in equation 316, we have

$$Y_t = Y_{t0} + 2\sum_n \alpha_n A_n + \sum_n \beta_n A_n^2 + \sum_{n,m} \gamma_{nm} A_n A_m, \qquad (319)$$

where

$$Y_{t0} = \frac{\eta^2}{\pi K^2} \sum_k \frac{2k+1}{k(k+1)} [P_k(\cos\psi)]^2 \, Y_k^+,$$

$$I_{nk} = \int_\psi^{\pi-\psi} M_n(\cos\theta) \, P_k(\cos\theta) \sin\theta \, d\theta,$$

$$\alpha_n = \frac{\eta^2}{\pi K^2} \sum_k \frac{I_{nk}}{N_k^e} P_k(\cos\psi) \, Y_k^+,$$

$$\beta_n = \frac{\eta^2}{2\pi K^2} n(n+1) \, N_n^i \, Y_n^-,$$

$$\gamma_{nm} = \gamma_{mn} = \frac{\eta^2}{2\pi K^2} \sum_k k(k+1)(N_k{}^e)^{-1} I_{nk} I_{mk} Y_k{}^+.$$

The terminating admittance $Y_t$ is stationary with respect to the variation of $E_a(\theta)$. Hence, the unknown coefficients $A_n$ may be determined from the condition $\partial Y_t / \partial A_n = 0$. Thus,

$$\alpha_n + \beta_n A_n + \sum_m \gamma_{nm} A_m = 0, \qquad n = n_1, n_2, \cdots. \qquad (320)$$

Multiplying by $A_n$ and summing, we have

$$\sum_n \alpha_n A_n + \sum_n \beta_n A_n{}^2 + \sum_{n,m} \gamma_{nm} A_n A_m = 0. \qquad (321)$$

Subtracting from equation 319, we obtain

$$Y_t = Y_{t0} + \sum_n \alpha_n A_n. \qquad (322)$$

The first term on the right is $Y_t$ given by equation 77 where all higher-order internal waves were neglected. As we have anticipated

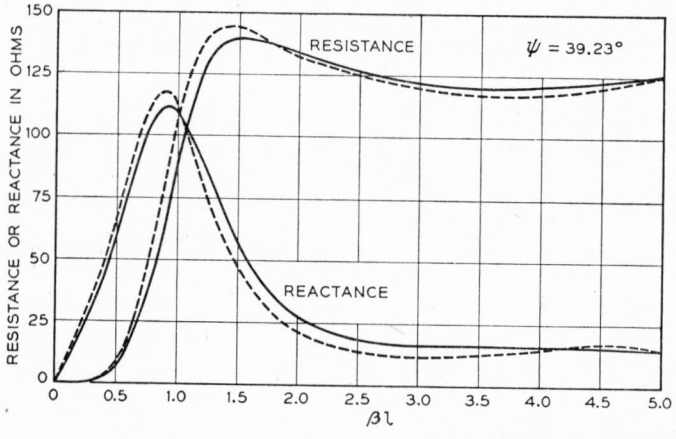

*Tai, Courtesy Jour. Appl. Phys.*

FIG. 2.29　Inverse radiation impedance of a biconical antenna, $\psi = 39.23°$; the dotted curve is a plot of equation 77; the solid curve includes a correction term obtained by Tai.

in Section 2.9, the correction term represented by the sum in equation 322 turns out to be small unless the cone angle is small. The solid curve in Fig. 2.29 includes the first correction while the dotted curve is a plot of $Y_{t0}$. The characteristic impedance of the antenna whose cone angle is $\psi = 39.23°$ is about 124 ohms; hence, this antenna is well matched to free space when $\beta l > 2$.

Equation 316 may be obtained from equations 56, 57, 62, and 63.

First we use the last two equations and determine both sets of coefficients $a_n$, $b_k$ in terms of the aperture field $E_a(\theta)$. Then we substitute these coefficients in the first two equations which represent the magnetic intensity in the aperture in different forms. Equating these two forms, we obtain an integral equation for $E_a(\theta)$. Following this outline, we obtain

$$a_n = - \frac{2\pi}{N_n{}^i} Y_n{}^- \int_\psi^{\pi-\psi} l E_a(\theta) \frac{d}{d\theta} M_n(\cos \theta) \sin \theta \, d\theta,$$

$$b_k = \frac{2\pi}{N_k{}^e} Y_k{}^+ \int_\psi^{\pi-\psi} l E_a(\theta) \frac{d}{d\theta} P_k(\cos \theta) \sin \theta \, d\theta,$$

$$V(l) = \int_\psi^{\pi-\psi} l E_a(\theta) \, d\theta, \tag{323}$$

$$\frac{Y_t}{2\pi \sin \theta} \int_\psi^{\pi-\psi} E_a(\theta) \, d\theta - \sum_n \frac{Y_n{}^- \dfrac{d}{d\theta} M_n(\cos \theta)}{n(n+1)N_n{}^i} \times$$

$$\int_\psi^{\pi-\psi} E_a(\theta) \frac{d}{d\theta} M_n(\cos \theta) \sin \theta \, d\theta,$$

$$= \sum_k \frac{Y_k{}^+ \dfrac{d}{d\theta} P_k(\cos \theta)}{k(k+1)N_k{}^e} \int_\psi^{\pi-\psi} E_a(\theta) \frac{d}{d\theta} P_k(\cos \theta) \sin \theta \, d\theta.$$

Multiplying the last equation by $E_a(\theta) \sin \theta$ and integrating with respect to $\theta$ between $\theta = \psi$ and $\theta = \pi - \psi$, we obtain equation 316.

## 2.24 Spherical waves on infinitely thin wires

The formation of spherical waves on infinitely thin wires can be studied with the aid of a simple solution of Maxwell's equations discovered by Manneback.* He gives the following expressions for waves originating at one end of an infinitely thin wire extending to infinity (Fig. 2.30),

$$H_\varphi = \frac{I\left(t - \dfrac{r}{c}\right)}{4\pi r} \frac{1 + \cos \theta}{\sin \theta}, \qquad E_\theta = \eta H_\varphi, \tag{324}$$

where $I(t)$ is the current flowing from the end. He shows by direct substitution that these equations satisfy Maxwell's equations when $r$ is large and when terms of order $1/r^2$ are neglected. This solution is regular everywhere except on the radius $\theta = 0$. Since the magneto-

* C. Manneback, Radiation from transmission lines, *AIEE Jour.*, **42**, February 1923, pp. 95–105.

motive force $2\pi\rho H_\varphi = 2\pi r \sin \theta H_\varphi$ approaches $I\left(t - \dfrac{r}{c}\right)$ as $\theta$ approaches zero, the current along this radius is indeed $I\left(t - \dfrac{r}{c}\right)$.

Manneback was interested primarily in the problem of radiation from transmission lines in which the apparently approximate character of equations 324 is of no importance. However, these equations are really exact. They appeared to him to be approximate only because in their verification the radial component of $E$ was neglected.

The existence of this component we deduce from the fact that the current $I(t)$ flowing out of the origin $O$ implies a point charge

$$q(t) = -\int_{-\infty}^{t} I(t)\, dt, \tag{325}$$

and, hence, the radial field

$$E_r = \frac{q\left(t - \dfrac{r}{c}\right)}{4\pi\varepsilon r^2}, \qquad \frac{\partial E_r}{\partial t} = -\frac{I\left(t - \dfrac{r}{c}\right)}{4\pi\varepsilon r^2}. \tag{326}$$

When this equation is combined with equation 324, we find that Maxwell's equations are satisfied exactly. It appears, however, that the boundary condition along the wire, where $E_r$ must vanish, is not satisfied. Actually it is satisfied. Later in this section we shall obtain the exact expressions for a cone of finite angle $\psi$ and prove that the limit of $E_r$ as the cone angle approaches zero is given by equation 326 as long as $\theta \neq 0$; but the limit of $E_r(\psi)$ is zero since $E_r(\psi)$ is identically zero. All that happens is that the function $E_r(r, \theta; \psi)$ for the finite cone approaches the limit (equation 326) nonuniformly.

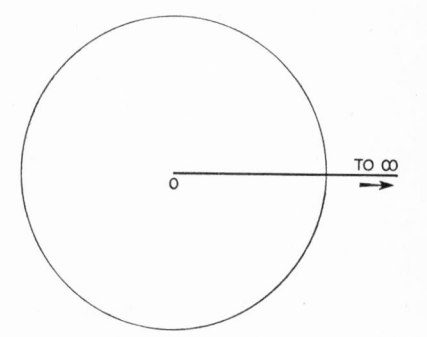

FIG. 2.30  The wavefront of a wave starting at the end of a semi-infinite thin wire.

The above equations represent the spherical wave generated by an arbitrary current source at $O$. If $I(t)$ is a step function, the wave may be illustrated graphically by an expanding spherical wavefront as in Fig. 2.30. A general time function may be considered as a succession of step functions and thus represented by a succession of wavefronts.

Suppose that the wire is terminated at $A$ (Fig. 2.31). First let us consider the case in which the energy reaching $A$ is absorbed. To obtain the corresponding solution we superimpose on the field given by equations 324 and 326 the following field:

$$\frac{\partial E_r{'}}{\partial t} = \frac{I\left(t - \dfrac{l}{c} - \dfrac{r'}{c}\right)}{4\pi\varepsilon(r')^2},$$

$$H_\varphi{'} = -\frac{I\left(t - \dfrac{l}{c} - \dfrac{r'}{c}\right)}{4\pi r'}\ \frac{1 + \cos\theta'}{\sin\theta'}, \qquad E_\theta{'} = \eta H_\varphi{'}, \tag{327}$$

where $l$ is the length of the wire and $r'$, $\theta'$ are spherical coordinates with respect to $A$. The magnetic intensity $H_\varphi{'}$ vanishes on the radius

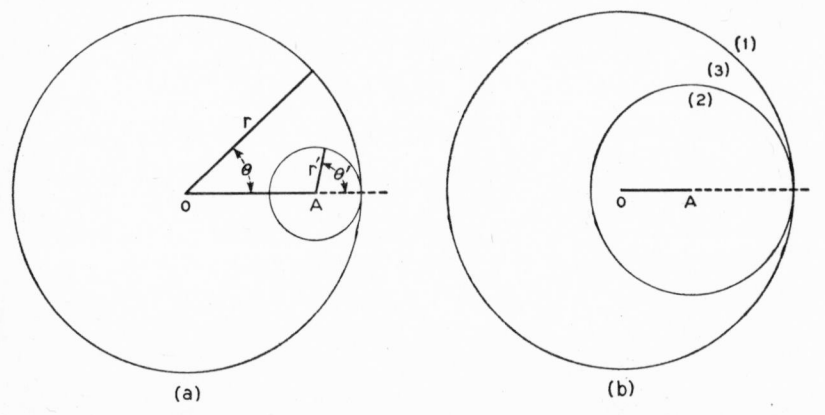

FIG. 2.31   The wavefronts of waves originating at the ends of a finite thin wire.

$\theta' = \pi$ (Fig. 2.31$a$); hence, the original current starting at $O$ continues to flow. On the radius $\theta' = 0$ the total magnetic intensity $H_\varphi + H_\varphi{'}$ vanishes.* Hence, the continuation of $OA$ is no longer a singular line of the field. Equations 327 represent a spherical wave originating at $A$. As this wave expands, it slides off the wire at $O$ without causing a new wave since no current is associated with it along $\theta' = \pi$. When the current is given by a step function, the wavefronts of the waves originating at $O$ and $A$ divide the space into three regions (Fig. 2.31$b$): region 1 which is field-free, region 2 where the field has reached its steady state, and the intermediate region 3. This intermediate region contains the energy lost by radiation.

* Note that $r\sin\theta = r'\sin\theta' = \rho$, where $\rho$ is the distance from the wire.

Suppose now that there is no absorption of power at $A$ and that the wire is merely discontinued at this point. In this case the current must vanish at $A$ at all times. This condition is satisfied if we assume that $A$ is the source of current toward $O$ equal to the current arriving from $O$. This source generates the following wave:

$$\frac{\partial E_r{}''}{\partial t} = -\frac{I\left(t - \frac{l}{c} - \frac{r'}{c}\right)}{4\pi\varepsilon(r')^2},$$

$$H_\varphi{}'' = -\frac{I\left(t - \frac{l}{c} - \frac{r'}{c}\right)}{4\pi r'}\frac{1 - \cos\theta'}{\sin\theta'}, \qquad E_\theta{}'' = \eta H_\varphi{}''. \tag{328}$$

The total field is the sum of equations 324, 326, 327, and 328. The point charge at $A$ disappears, and $E_r{}' + E_r{}'' = 0$.

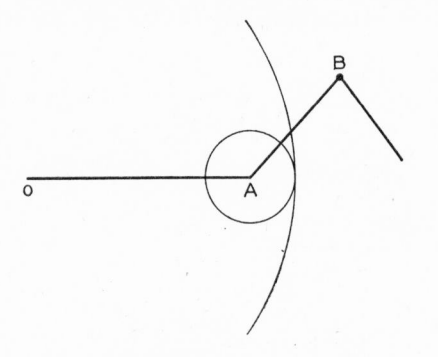

FIG. 2.32 Waves on a bent wire.

A bend in the wire (Fig. 2.32) becomes a source of current in the new direction as well as the source of opposite current in the former direction. The field will be the sum of equations 324, 326, 327, and

$$\frac{\partial E_r{}''}{\partial t} = -\frac{I\left(t - \frac{l}{c} - \frac{r'}{c}\right)}{4\pi\varepsilon(r')^2},$$

$$H_\varphi{}'' = \frac{I\left(t - \frac{l}{c} - \frac{r'}{c}\right)}{4\pi r'}\frac{1 + \cos\theta''}{\sin\theta''}, \qquad E_\theta{}'' = \eta H_\varphi{}'', \tag{329}$$

where $\theta''$ is the angle made by a typical radius from $A$ with the new direction $AB$ of the wire. The electric intensity due to the current segment $OA$ is impressed on $AB$; but the induced current is vanishingly small since the wire is infinitely thin. The field of the induced current is also vanishingly small everywhere except on $AB$ where it is just sufficient to balance out the impressed electric intensity. For wires of finite radius the induced current and its field are small but not vanishingly small.

The point charge at the origin $O$ occurs only because we have assumed that a charge of some kind is being driven away from it. When the charge is merely transferred from one wire to another as at

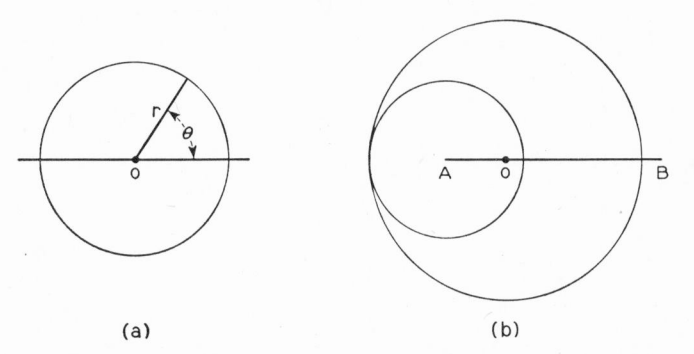

(a)                    (b)

Fig. 2.33   The wavefronts when the source of waves is between the ends of a wire.

point $O$ in Fig. 2.33, there will be no accumulation of charge at the source. In addition to the field (equations 324 and 326) associated with the positive, let us say, charge flowing out of $O$ to the right, we have the following field of negative charge flowing out of $O$ to the left:

$$\frac{\partial E_r'}{\partial t} = \frac{I\left(t - \dfrac{r}{c}\right)}{4\pi\varepsilon r^2},$$

$$H_\varphi' = \frac{I\left(t - \dfrac{r}{c}\right)}{4\pi r}\ \frac{1 - \cos\theta}{\sin\theta}, \qquad E_\theta' = \eta H_\varphi'.$$

(330)

The total radial field is seen to vanish. Both spherical waves in this case have the same wavefront. When one of the component waves reaches an open end (Fig. 2.33$b$), a new wave is generated. New waves are produced at the other open end as the waves from $O$ and $A$ reach it.

Consider now a pair of parallel wires (Fig. 2.34a).   Let us assume that equal and opposite charges are driven from the ends of these wires. The corresponding field is given by the sum of equations 324, 326, and 327, provided that in the latter set we let $l = 0$.   The coordinates $(r, \theta)$ and $(r', \theta')$ are relative to the wires.   The wavefronts subdivide the space into three regions: Region 1 is external to both fronts and is field free, region 2 is common to both fields with the steady state already established, and the intermediate region 3 contains energy lost by radiation in starting the current.   When $\theta$ and $\theta'$ are small, the meridian components of $E$ are perpendicular to the wires, $\cos \theta$ and $\cos \theta'$ are sub-

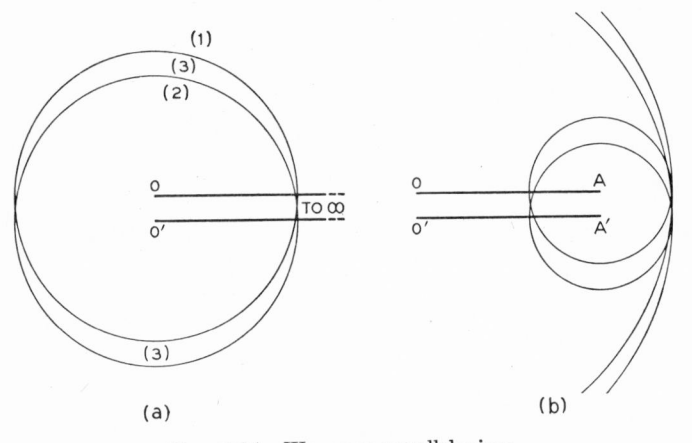

FIG. 2.34   Waves on parallel wires.

stantially equal to unity, and the denominators $4\pi r \sin \theta$ and $4\pi r \sin \theta'$ are equal to $4\pi\rho$ and $4\pi\rho'$, where $\rho$ and $\rho'$ are the distances from the wires.   Hence, for small $\theta$ and $\theta'$ the field in region 2 represents substantially a plane wave guided by the wires.   The region of the plane wave increases with the distance from the ends of the wires since it depends on the smallness of $\theta$ and $\theta'$ and does not depend directly on the distances from the wires.   If the wires are open at $A$, $A'$ as in Fig. 2.34b, we shall lose additional energy.   The loss will be there even if we short-circuit the wires or insert a resistor to absorb the incoming energy.   In the practical case of transmission of energy from one place to another, we have a complete conductive circuit (Fig. 2.35).   Here spherical waves originate at the generator $G$, at each bend, and at the load $L$.

Thus Manneback's equations give clear pictures of radiation and of formation of plane waves guided by parallel wires.   We should remember, of course, that these equations are exact only when the wires are infinitely thin.   However, the main difference between infinitely thin wires and thin wires is in the energy carried in the vicinity of the wires. In the former case this energy is infinite; in the latter case it is finite but large. In both cases the radiated energy is the same (assuming that the currents are the same).

We shall now connect Manneback's equations with the mode theory of antennas. Instead of the infinitely thin wire, we shall consider a thin cone coaxial with it. The field around this cone can be expressed in terms of spherical waves as explained in Section 2.4. We are interested in the particular field that corresponds to a charge driven from the apex. An equal and opposite charge is kept at the apex. From equation 326 we see that, in the case of an infinitely thin cone, the field of this point charge is the same as in free space. In the case of a thin cone we expect that this field will be relatively unaffected by the cone, except near its surface. From equations 7 we find that the inverse square law is obtained only if $R(r)$ is finite at $r = 0$. When $n = 0$, we have

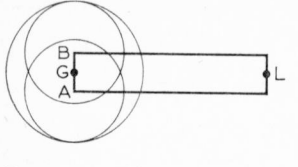

FIG. 2.35   Waves on parallel wires near a point source at $G$.

$$Jn_0(\beta r) = \sin \beta r, \qquad Nn_0(\beta r) = -\cos \beta r,$$
$$R(r) = A \sin \beta r - B \cos \beta r. \tag{331}$$

In this case, the inverse square law is exact. From equation 9 we find that, if $n$ is small, the $R$-function is the same as above except when $r$ is small; but, when $r$ is sufficiently small, so that we can neglect $\beta^2$, then $R(r)$ behaves as $r^{-n}$. Thus, for small values of $n$ we have very nearly the square law. Hence, we shall study those solutions for which $n$ is small. The $\Theta$ function must be finite at $\theta = \pi$ since along this radius we have no singularity in the field. Therefore, $\Theta(\theta) = P_n(-\cos \theta)$. For small $n$, we have

$$P_n(-\cos \theta) = 1 + 2n \log \sin \tfrac{1}{2}\theta. \tag{332}$$

Hence,

$$\frac{d}{d\theta} P_n(-\cos \theta) = n \frac{1 + \cos \theta}{\sin \theta}. \tag{333}$$

For waves traveling from the apex $B_n = -jA_n$. If we approximate $R_n(r)$ by $\exp(-j\beta r)$, then from equations 7 we obtain

$$j\omega \varepsilon r^2 E_r = -A e^{-j\beta r}(1 + 2n \log \sin \tfrac{1}{2}\theta),$$
$$rE_\theta = \eta A e^{-j\beta r} \frac{1 + \cos \theta}{\sin \theta}, \qquad rH_\varphi = A e^{-j\beta r} \frac{1 + \cos \theta}{\sin \theta}. \tag{334}$$

On the surface of the cone $\theta = \psi$, the radial component of $E$ must vanish; hence,

$$n = -\frac{1}{2 \log \sin \frac{1}{2}\psi}. \tag{335}$$

The product $2\pi r \sin \psi \, H_\varphi(r, \psi)$ must equal the current in the cone. This product is $2\pi A(1 + \cos \psi)\exp(-j\beta r)$, or approximately $4\pi A \exp(-j\beta r)$. If $I_0$ is the current at the apex, $4\pi A = I_0$ and $A = I_0/4\pi$. We have thus determined the required field for waves of any frequency.

The exponential factor indicates that the waves travel with the speed of light. Interpreting $j\omega$ as differentiation with respect to time, we have the following equations for any wave on a thin cone:

$$\frac{\partial E_r}{\partial t} = -\frac{I\left(t - \dfrac{r}{c}\right)}{4\pi\varepsilon r^2}\left(1 - \frac{\log \sin \frac{1}{2}\theta}{\log \sin \frac{1}{2}\psi}\right),$$

$$H_\varphi = \frac{I\left(t - \dfrac{r}{c}\right)}{4\pi r}\frac{1 + \cos \theta}{\sin \theta}, \tag{336}$$

$$E_\theta = \eta H_\varphi.$$

As $\psi$ approaches zero, the radial component approaches the expression given in equation 326 for any $\theta$ greater than zero. Since $E_r(r, \psi) = 0$ for every $\psi$, its limit as $\psi$ approaches zero is zero. We can picture the radial field as a uniform field with a deep well around the cone. As the cone becomes thinner, the well becomes narrower without ever disappearing altogether.

## REFERENCES

1. S. A. Schelkunoff, Theory of antennas of arbitrary size and shape, *IRE Proc.*, **29**, September 1941, pp. 493–521.
2. J. A. Stratton and L. J. Chu, Forced oscillations of a conducting sphere, *Jour. Appl. Phys.*, **12**, March 1941, pp. 236–240.
3. S. A. Schelkunoff, Spherical antennas, U. S. Patent 2,235,506, March 18, 1941.
4. S. A. Schelkunoff, Principal and complementary waves in antennas, *IRE Proc.*, **34**, January 1946, pp. 23P–32P.
5. P. D. P. Smith, The conical dipole of wide angle, *Jour. Appl. Phys.*, **19**, January 1948, pp. 11–23.
6. C. T. Tai, On the theory of biconical antennas, *Jour. Appl. Phys.*, **19**, December 1948, pp. 1155–1160.
7. C. T. Tai, Application of a variational principle to biconical antennas, *Jour. Appl. Phys.*, **20**, November 1949, pp. 1076–1084.
8. J. Aharoni, *Antennae — An Introduction to Their Theory*, Clarendon Press, Oxford, 1946.

9. E. Roubine, Les récentes théories de l'antenne, *Rev. Tech.*, Thomson-Houston, Paris, 1947.

10. J. R. Whinnery, The effect of input configuration on antenna impedance, *Jour. Appl. Phys.*, **21**, October 1950, pp. 945–956.

11. C. H. Papas and Ronold King, Input impedance of wide-angle conical antennas fed by a coaxial line, *IRE Proc.*, **37**, November 1949, pp. 1269–1271.

12. J. T. Bolljahn, Antennas near conducting sheets of finite size, *University of California Department of Engineering Report* **162**, December 1949.

13. C. H. Papas and Ronold King, Radiation from wide-angle conical antennas fed by a coaxial line, *IRE Proc.*, **39**, January 1951, pp. 49–51.

# 3

# SPHEROIDAL ANTENNAS

## 3.1 Prolate spheroidal antennas

A prolate spheroidal antenna is shown in Fig. 3.1 where the voltage is applied symmetrically between two halves of the spheroid by means of a biconical transmission line. In this case the field is independent of the $\varphi$ coordinate, the current flows along the meridians of the spheroid, the magnetic lines are circles coaxial with the spheroid, and the electric lines lie in meridian planes. Let $a$ and $b$ be the semimajor and semiminor axes of the spheroid and $l$ the semifocal distance. This spheroid is one of a family of confocal spheroids given by the following parametric equations:*

$$z = luv, \qquad \rho = l(u^2 - 1)^{\frac{1}{2}}(1 - v^2)^{\frac{1}{2}},$$
$$u = \cosh \xi, \qquad v = \cos \vartheta, \tag{1}$$

when $u$ (or $\xi$) is constant. If $v$ is constant, the surface is a hyperboloid. The major axis of a typical spheroid is $lu$, so that our particular spheroid is defined by

$$u_0 = \frac{a}{l} = a(a^2 - b^2)^{-\frac{1}{2}}. \tag{2}$$

For a thin spheroid $u_0$ is slightly greater than unity. If $u_0$ is large, the spheroid approximates a sphere of radius $lu_0$; then the angle $\vartheta$ is the polar angle $\theta$. The parameters $u, v$ or $\xi, \vartheta$ are called spheroidal coordinates.

If the field is circularly symmetric about the major axis, Maxwell's equations in spheroidal coordinates 1–10 consist of two independent sets, one involving only $E_u, E_v, H_\varphi$ and the other only $H_u, H_v, E_\varphi$. The first case, in which the magnetic lines are circles and the currents flow in

* *Applied Mathematics*, p. 151.

111

axial planes, is the one we are interested in. The metric form is

$$ds^2 = l^2(u^2 - v^2)\left(\frac{du^2}{u^2 - 1} + \frac{dv^2}{1 - v^2}\right) + \rho^2 \, d\varphi^2. \tag{3}$$

Hence,

$$e_1 = l\left(\frac{u^2 - v^2}{u^2 - 1}\right)^{1/2}, \qquad e_2 = l\left(\frac{u^2 - v^2}{1 - v^2}\right)^{1/2}, \tag{4}$$

$$e_3 = \rho = l(u^2 - 1)^{1/2}(1 - v^2)^{1/2}.$$

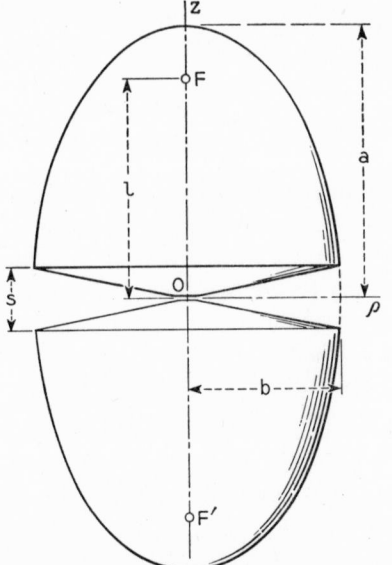

FIG. 3.1 A prolate spheroidal antenna fed by a biconical transmission line.

Maxwell's equations are

$$e_2 E_u = \frac{1}{j\omega\varepsilon\rho} \frac{\partial(\rho H_\varphi)}{\partial v}, \qquad e_1 E_v = -\frac{1}{j\omega\varepsilon\rho} \frac{\partial(\rho H_\varphi)}{\partial u},$$

$$\frac{\partial(e_2 E_v)}{\partial u} - \frac{\partial(e_1 E_u)}{\partial v} = -j\omega\mu e_1 e_2 H_\varphi. \tag{5}$$

The field intensities may thus be expressed in terms of the auxiliary wave function,

$$A = \rho H_\varphi. \tag{6}$$

Thus

$$E_u = -\frac{j\eta}{\beta l^2}\left[(u^2 - 1)(u^2 - v^2)\right]^{-1/2}\frac{\partial A}{\partial v},$$

$$E_v = \frac{j\eta}{\beta l^2} [(1 - v^2)(u^2 - v^2)]^{-\frac{1}{2}} \frac{\partial A}{\partial u}, \tag{7}$$

$$H_\varphi = \frac{1}{l} [(u^2 - 1)(1 - v^2)]^{-\frac{1}{2}}A,$$

where $A$ satisfies the following differential equation,

$$(u^2 - 1) \frac{\partial^2 A}{\partial u^2} + (1 - v^2) \frac{\partial^2 A}{\partial v^2} + \beta^2 l^2 (u^2 - v^2)A = 0. \tag{8}$$

We note that $2\pi A$ is the magnetomotive force round a typical magnetic line. Hence, the current in the antenna is

$$I(v) = 2\pi A(u_0, v). \tag{9}$$

The substitution,

$$A = U(u) V(v), \tag{10}$$

separates the variables in equation 8, and the differential equations for $U$ and $V$ are

$$(u^2 - 1) \frac{d^2 U}{du^2} + (\beta^2 l^2 u^2 - k)U = 0, \tag{11}$$

$$(1 - v^2) \frac{d^2 V}{dv^2} + (k - \beta^2 l^2 v^2)V = 0. \tag{12}$$

Both $U$ and $V$ satisfy the same equation.

If we substitute

$$U(u) = (u^2 - 1)^{\frac{1}{2}} \bar{U}(u), \qquad V(v) = (1 - v^2)^{\frac{1}{2}} \bar{V}(v). \tag{13}$$

then,

$$(u^2 - 1) \frac{d^2 \bar{U}}{du^2} + 2u \frac{d\bar{U}}{du} - \left(k + \frac{1}{u^2 - 1}\right)\bar{U} + \beta^2 l^2 u^2 \bar{U} = 0, \tag{14}$$

$$(1 - v^2) \frac{d^2 \bar{V}}{dv^2} - 2v \frac{d\bar{V}}{dv} + \left(k - \frac{1}{1 - v^2}\right)\bar{V} - \beta^2 l^2 v^2 \bar{V} = 0. \tag{15}$$

Another substitution,

$$U(u) = (u^2 - 1) \hat{U}(u), \qquad \hat{U}(u) = (u^2 - 1)^{\frac{1}{2}} \bar{U}(u),$$
$$V(v) = (1 - v^2) \hat{V}(v), \qquad \hat{V}(v) = (1 - v^2)^{-\frac{1}{2}} \bar{V}(v), \tag{16}$$

gives

$$(u^2 - 1) \frac{d^2 \hat{U}}{du^2} + 4u \frac{d\hat{U}}{du} + (\beta^2 l^2 u^2 - k + 2)\hat{U} = 0, \tag{17}$$

$$(1 - v^2) \frac{d^2 \hat{V}}{dv^2} - 4v \frac{d\hat{V}}{dv} + (k - 2 - \beta^2 l^2 v^2)\hat{V} = 0. \tag{18}$$

The last form of the equation for spheroidal wave functions is used by Stratton* and by Morse*. Some of the earlier writers† have dealt with the form 15 which becomes an associated Legendre equation when $pl = 0$. Page and Adams use equations 12 and 15. Abraham and Ryder employ the form 12. The transformation equations 13 and 16 enable us to pass from one form to another.

At the upper and lower ends ($v = \pm 1$) of the spheroid the current vanishes; hence,

$$V(\pm 1) = 0. \tag{19}$$

This condition also follows from the fact that, outside the spheroid, $E_v$ should vanish on the $z$ axis. For most values of $k$, equation 12 has no solutions satisfying the above condition; thus, equation 19 defines the proper values of $k$. Let $V_k$ be the set of proper functions. At large distances from the spheroid $u$ is large, and equation 11 becomes

$$\frac{d^2 U}{du^2} + \beta^2 l^2 U = 0. \tag{20}$$

At these distances we also have

$$r = \sqrt{z^2 + \rho^2} = lu. \tag{21}$$

At such distances the field must be proportional to $\exp(-j\beta r) = \exp(-j\beta lu)$. Hence, the proper $U$ functions are those solutions of equation 11 that satisfy the following condition:

$$U_k \to e^{-j\beta lu} \quad \text{as} \quad u \to \infty. \tag{22}$$

Thus, we have a general solution satisfying the requirements on the $z$ axis and at infinity,

$$A = \sum_k a_k \, U_k(u) \, V_k(v). \tag{23}$$

From equations 7 we obtain the electric intensity tangential to a typical spheroid confocal with the given spheroid,

$$E_v(u, v) = \frac{j\eta}{\beta l^2} \, [(1 - v^2)(u^2 - v^2)]^{-\frac{1}{2}} \sum_k a_k \, U_k{}'(u) \, V_k(v). \tag{24}$$

---

* J. A. Stratton, Spheroidal functions, *Nat. Acad. Sci. Proc.*, **21**, January 1935, pp. 51–56; Philip M. Morse, Addition formulae for spheroidal functions, *ibid.*, pp. 56–62. L. J. Chu and J. A. Stratton, Elliptic and spheroidal wave functions, *Jour. Math. Phys.*, **20**, August 1941, pp. 259–309.

† R. C. Maclaurin, On the solutions of the equation $(V^2 + \kappa^2)\psi = 0$ in elliptic coordinates and their physical applications, *Camb. Phil. Soc. Trans.*, **17**, 1898, pp. 41–108.

E. T. Hanson, Ellipsoidal functions and their applications to some wave problems, *Roy. Soc. Lond. Phil. Trans.*, Series A, **232**, June 1933, pp. 223–283.

M. J. O. Strutt, *Lamésche- Mathieusche- und verwandte Funktionen in Physik und Technik*, Springer, 1932.

At the perfectly conducting surface of the given spheroid $u = u_0$ the total electric intensity should vanish,

$$E_v(u_0, v) + E_v{}^i(u_0, v) = 0;$$ (25)

therefore,

$$\frac{j\eta}{\beta l^2} [(1 - v^2)(u_0{}^2 - v^2)]^{-\frac{1}{2}} \sum_k a_k U_k{}'(u_0) V_k(v) = -E_v{}^i(u_0, v).$$ (26)

To obtain the coefficients we shall use the orthogonality property of the $V$ functions which we can prove as follows. Let $V_k$ and $V_n$ be two solutions of equation 12 which satisfy equation 19; then,

$$(1 - v^2) \frac{d^2 V_k}{dv^2} + (k - \beta^2 l^2 v^2) V_k = 0,$$

$$(1 - v^2) \frac{d^2 V_n}{dv^2} + (n - \beta^2 l^2 v^2) V_n = 0.$$ (27)

Multiplying the first equation by $V_n$ and the second by $V_k$, and subtracting, we have

$$(1 - v^2) \frac{d}{dv} \left( V_n \frac{dV_k}{dv} - V_k \frac{dV_n}{dv} \right) + (k - n) V_k V_n = 0.$$ (28)

Dividing by $(1 - v^2)$ and integrating from $v = -1$ to $v = 1$, we have

$$(k - n) \int_{-1}^{1} \frac{V_k V_n}{1 - v^2} dv = \left( V_k \frac{dV_n}{dv} - V_n \frac{dV_k}{dv} \right) \Bigg|_{-1}^{1} = 0.$$ (29)

If $k \neq n$,

$$\int_{-1}^{1} (1 - v^2)^{-1} V_k V_n \, dv = 0.$$ (30)

Multiplying equation 26 by $(\beta l^2/j\eta)(u_0{}^2 - v^2)^{\frac{1}{2}}(1 - v^2)^{-\frac{1}{2}} V_n(v)$, integrating, and using equation 30, we find

$$a_n = \frac{\beta l^2}{j\eta N_n U_n{}'(u_0)} \int_{-1}^{1} E_v{}^i(u_0, v) \frac{\sqrt{u_0{}^2 - v^2}}{\sqrt{1 - v^2}} V_n(v) \, dv,$$ (31)

where $N_n$ is the normalizing factor

$$N_n = \int_{-1}^{1} (1 - v^2)^{-1} [V_n(v)]^2 \, dv.$$ (32)

A voltage $V_0$ impressed between $v = v_0$ and $v = v_1$ is the line integral of $E_v{}^i \, ds_v$, where $ds_v$ is an element of length along the ellipse $u = u_0$; hence,

$$V_0 = - \int_{v_0}^{v_1} E_v{}^i \frac{l\sqrt{u_0{}^2 - v^2}}{\sqrt{1 - v^2}} \, dv.$$ (33)

If the difference $v_1 - v_0$ is infinitesimal,

$$V_0 = - \frac{l\sqrt{u_0^2 - v_0^2}}{\sqrt{1 - v_0^2}} \int_{v_0}^{v_1} E_v{}^i \, dv. \qquad (34)$$

In this case,

$$a_n = \frac{\beta l \, V_n(v_0)}{j\eta N_n \, U_n{}'(u_0)} \, V_0. \qquad (35)$$

Substituting this value in equation 23 and then in equation 9, we obtain the antenna current,

$$I(v, v_0) = -jV_0 \frac{2\pi\beta l}{\eta} \sum_k \frac{U_k(u_0) \, V_k(v_0)}{N_k \, U_k{}'(u_0)} \, V_k(v). \qquad (36)$$

If we divide the current by $V_0$, we shall have the transfer admittance between $v = v_0$ and $v = v$,

$$Y(v; v_0) = -j \frac{2\pi\beta l}{\eta} \sum_k \frac{U_k(u_0) \, V_k(v_0)}{N_k \, U_k{}'(u_0)} \, V_k(v). \qquad (37)$$

As $v$ approaches $v_0$, the transfer admittance increases logarithmically as* $-\log|s - s_0|$, where $s$ is the distance along the spheroid. This is natural, since, in the immediate vicinity of the infinitely narrow gap across which we have applied our voltage, the two sections of the spheroid are substantially plane and thus form a 180° wedge. This is true no matter how small the radius of the spheroid as long as $s - s_0$ is correspondingly small.

Suppose now that the voltage is applied by means of a biconical transmission line across a small gap of length $s$ in the equatorial plane of the spheroid. The differential element of length along the meridians is

$$ds_v = \frac{l\sqrt{u_0^2 - v^2}}{\sqrt{1 - v^2}} \, dv. \qquad (38)$$

At the equator $v = 0$; hence, near the equator

$$ds_v = lu_0 \, dv, \qquad (39)$$

and the gap extends between $v = -s/2lu_0$ and $v = s/2lu_0$. If the voltage is distributed uniformly, then the current at $v = s/2lu_0$ may be obtained by integration from equation 36. Dividing this current by $V_0$, we obtain the input admittance

$$Y_i = \frac{I(\frac{1}{2}s)}{V_0} = \sum_{k=1}^{\infty} Y_k,$$

$$Y_k = -\frac{j2\pi\beta l}{\eta} \frac{U_k(u_0) \, V_k(s/2lu_0)}{N_k \, U_k{}'(u_0)(s/lu_0)} \int_{-s/2lu_0}^{s/2lu_0} V_k(v) \, dv. \qquad (40)$$

---

* L. Infeld, The influence of the width of the gap upon the theory of antennas, *Quart. Appl. Math.*, **5**, July 1947, pp. 113–132.

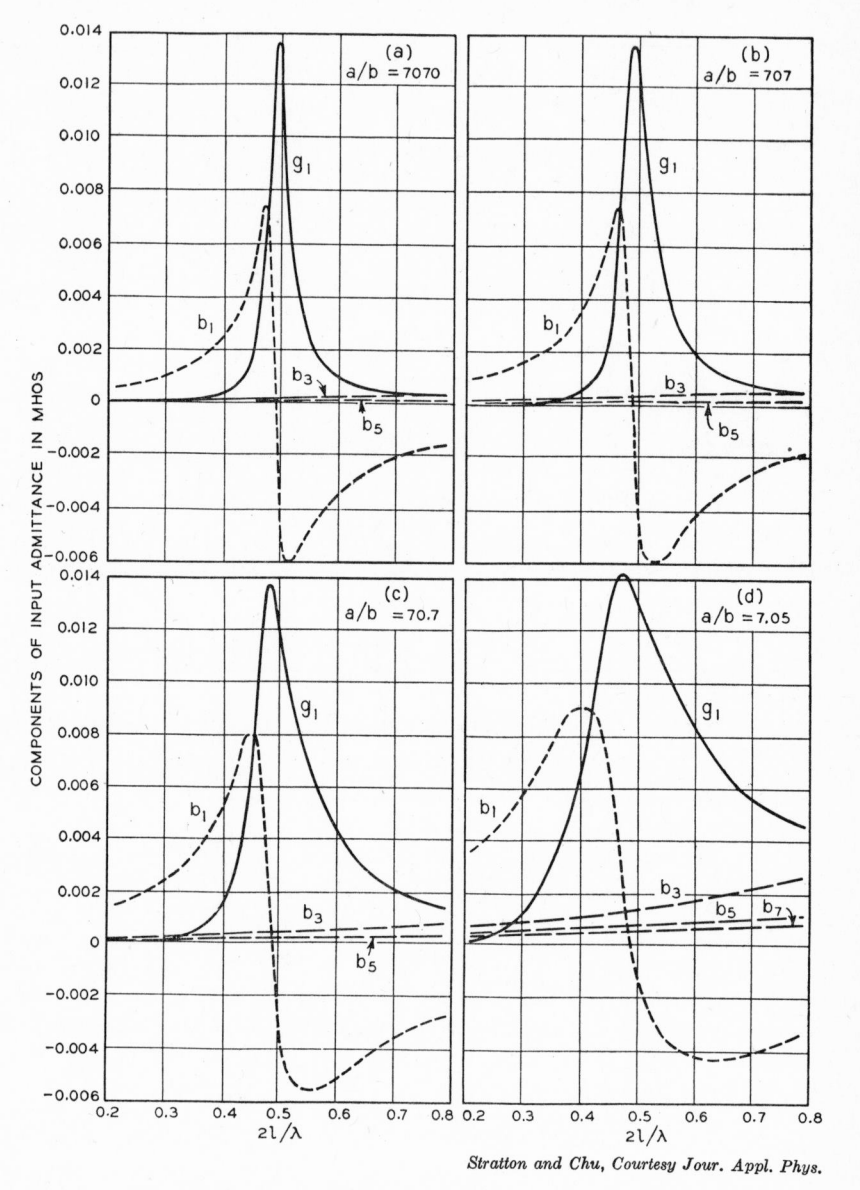

Stratton and Chu, Courtesy Jour. Appl. Phys.

FIG. 3.2   The conductance $g_n$ and susceptance $b_n$ of the $n$th spheroidal mode of propagation as seen at the equator of the spheroidal antenna.

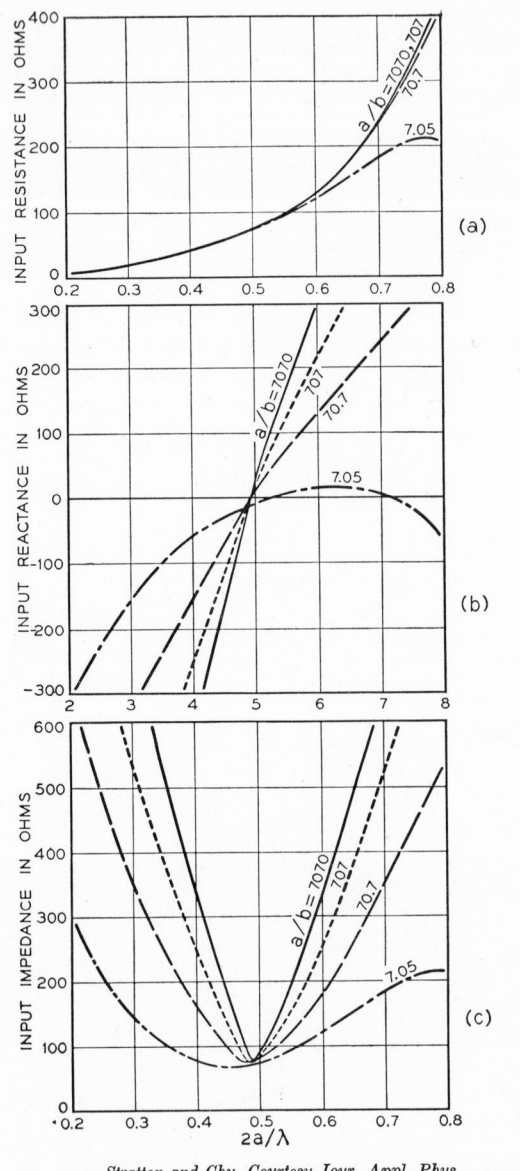

FIG. 3.3   The input impedances of spheroidal antennas of various eccentricities.

The input admittance is thus expressed as the admittance of an infinite number of admittances in parallel. Each admittance component represents the reaction of the corresponding spheroidal wave on the source at the gap. Stratton and Chu give the conductance $g_1$ and susceptance $b_1$ of the first mode for various ratios $2a/2b$ of the major and minor axes of the spheroid (Fig. 3.2). The figure shows also the susceptances of the first few higher modes; the conductances are too small to be shown (except when $2a/\lambda$ is greater than unity). The figure shows clearly that the admittance of the first mode behaves as the admittance of a resonant circuit. The same is true of the higher modes, but their resonances occur at higher frequencies than those shown in the figure. The input impedance obtained by Stratton and Chu is shown in Fig. 3.3. The conductance components obtained from these curves should be exact, but the susceptance components are uncertain.*

It is easy to calculate the admittance of each mode at resonance. Equation 12 has a simple solution when

$$k = \beta^2 l^2, \tag{41}$$

since it becomes

$$\frac{d^2V}{dv^2} + \beta^2 l^2 V = 0. \tag{42}$$

The solution is

$$V = p \cos \beta l v + q \sin \beta l v. \tag{43}$$

Since this function should be even and should vanish at $v = \pm 1$, we must have $q = 0$ and

$$\cos \beta l = 0, \qquad \beta l = (2n - 1) \frac{\pi}{2}, \qquad n = 1, 2, \cdots. \tag{44}$$

The corresponding $V$ function is

$$V_n = \cos \frac{(2n - 1)\pi v}{2}. \tag{45}$$

The equation for $U$ is the same as equation 42, but the proper function should represent a divergent wave; hence,

$$U_n = \exp\left[-j\,\frac{(2n - 1)\pi u}{2}\right]. \tag{46}$$

For a gap of zero length, we find, from equation 40,

$$Y_n = -j\,\frac{(2n - 1)\pi^2\,U_n(u_0)}{\eta\,U_n{}'(u_0)\,N_n}. \tag{47}$$

* *Ibid.*

Substituting from equation 46, we have

$$Y_n = \frac{2\pi}{\eta N_n} \cdot \tag{48}$$

The normalizing factor is obtained from equations 32 and 45; thus,

$$N_n = \int_0^1 \frac{1 + \cos(2n - 1)\pi v}{1 - v^2} \, dv = \tfrac{1}{2} \operatorname{Cin} 2(2n - 1)\pi. \tag{49}$$

Hence,

$$Z_n = \frac{\eta}{4\pi} \operatorname{Cin} 2(2n - 1)\pi = 30 \operatorname{Cin} 2(2n - 1)\pi. \tag{50}$$

For the first mode we have

$$Z_1 = 30 \operatorname{Cin} 2\pi = 73.13. \tag{51}$$

In a spheroid,

$$a^2 = l^2 + b^2; \tag{52}$$

hence, for thin spheroids for which $b \ll a$, $l$ and $a$ are substantially equal. Therefore equation 44 becomes

$$\frac{2l}{\lambda} \simeq \frac{2a}{\lambda} = \frac{2n - 1}{2} \; ; \tag{53}$$

thus, the resonances of the various modes occur when the length of the spheroid is nearly equal to an odd multiple of $\lambda/2$.

As $\beta l$ approaches zero, equation 15 approaches an associated Legendre equation. Hence, for low frequencies the proper values of $k$ are

$$k \simeq n(n + 1), \qquad n = 1, 2, 3, \cdots, \tag{54}$$

and

$$\bar{V}_n(v) = P_n^1(v), \qquad V_n(v) = \sqrt{1 - v^2}\, P_n^1(v). \tag{55}$$

The corresponding $\bar{U}$ functions are

$$\bar{U}_n(u) = Q_n^1(u), \qquad U_n(u) = \sqrt{u^2 - 1}\, Q_n^1(u). \tag{56}$$

The normalizing factor becomes

$$N_n = \int_{-1}^1 [P_n^1(v)]^2 \, dv = \frac{2n(n + 1)}{2n + 1} \cdot \tag{57}$$

Therefore,

$$Y_n = -j\omega\pi\varepsilon l \, \frac{2n + 1}{n(n + 1)} \, \frac{\sqrt{u_0^2 - 1}\, Q_n^1(u_0)}{\dfrac{d}{du_0}\left[\sqrt{u_0^2 - 1}\, Q_n^1(u_0)\right]} \chi_n, \tag{58}$$

where the factor $\chi_n$ depends on the gap and is approximately equal to

$$\chi_n = \frac{2lu_0}{s} P_n\left(\frac{s}{2lu_0}\right) P_n{}^1\left(\frac{s}{2lu_0}\right). \tag{59}$$

For the first admittance component we have

$$Y_1 = \chi_1 \frac{3j\omega\pi\varepsilon l\left(1 - \frac{b^2}{al}\log\frac{a+l}{b}\right)}{4\left(\log\frac{a+l}{b} - \frac{l}{a}\right)}. \tag{60}$$

For thin spheroids this becomes

$$Y_1 \simeq \chi_1 \frac{3j\omega\pi\varepsilon l}{4\left(\log\frac{2l}{b} - 1\right)}. \tag{61}$$

The next admittance component for thin spheroids is

$$Y_3 \simeq \chi_3 \frac{7j\omega\pi\varepsilon l}{144\left(\log\frac{2l}{b} - \frac{11}{6}\right)}. \tag{62}$$

In general, if we neglect the terms of order $b^2/l^2$ but retain those of order $(b^2/l^2)\log(2l/b)$, we have

$$Y_n \simeq \chi_n \frac{j\omega\pi\varepsilon l(2n+1)}{n^2(n+1)^2} \times$$

$$\frac{1 - \frac{1}{2} n(n+1)\frac{b^2}{l^2}\log\frac{2l}{b}}{\log\frac{2l}{b} - 1 - \frac{1}{2} - \frac{1}{3} - \cdots - \frac{1}{n} + \frac{1}{4}(n-1)(n+2)\frac{b^2}{l^2}\log\frac{2l}{b}}. \tag{63}$$

The $\chi_n$ factor is (for small $s/2l$)

$$\chi_n = \left[\frac{2(n/2)!}{\left(\frac{n-1}{2}\right)!\sqrt{\pi}}\right]^2, \qquad \chi_n \to \frac{2n}{\pi} \quad \text{as} \quad n \to \infty. \tag{64}$$

However $\chi_n$ is independent of $u_0$ only if $n$ is not too large.

From the above expressions we find that at low frequencies the terms in the series 40 for the admittance diminish as $(1/n)^2$, provided $n$ is not too large. An estimate of the upper bound for $n$ may be obtained by inspecting equation 63. Suppose that $\log(2l/b) = 5$; then the second term in brackets of the numerator in equation 63 will equal approximately one tenth if $n = 15$. As $n$ becomes greater, the convergence of the series becomes slower; in fact, unless we keep a finite gap, the series diverges. To prove this we shall obtain an approximation for the $U_n$ function as $n$ increases indefinitely. For large $k = n(n + 1)$, equation 11 becomes

$$\frac{d^2 U_n}{du^2} = \frac{n(n + 1)}{u^2 - 1} U_n. \tag{65}$$

Liouville's approximation to the solution of this equation is

$$U_n \simeq A \sqrt[4]{u^2 - 1} \, \exp[\pm \sqrt{n(n + 1)} \cosh^{-1} u]. \tag{66}$$

The proper function in our case should decrease as $n$ increases; hence, we take the lower sign. Therefore,

$$\frac{U_n(u_0)}{U_n{}'(u_0)} \simeq - \frac{\sqrt{u_0{}^2 - 1}}{\sqrt{n(n + 1)}} = - \frac{b}{\sqrt{n(n + 1)}\,l}. \tag{67}$$

Instead of equation 58, we now have

$$Y_n = \frac{j\omega\pi\varepsilon b(2n + 1)}{n(n + 1)\sqrt{n(n + 1)}} \chi_n. \tag{68}$$

In the case of a vanishingly small gap $\chi_n$ is proportional to $n$ (see equation 64); then $Y_n$ will be proportional to $1/n$, and the series will diverge. On the other hand, if we retain the finite gap, $\chi_n$ becomes an oscillating function, and the series converges. If we replace the Legendre functions occurring in $\chi_n$ by their Liouville approximations, it can be shown that

$$\sum_{n=M}^{\infty} Y_n = -2j\omega\varepsilon b \, \text{Ci}\left(\frac{Ms}{a}\right). \tag{69}$$

For details of the derivation the reader is referred to the paper by Infeld already cited. If $b$ is much smaller than $a$ and if $s$ is not much smaller than $b$, then the effect of $s$ on the admittance is negligible; for practical dimensions of the conductors this will usually be the case. Nevertheless, on account of the relatively slow convergence of the series for the susceptance component in equation 40, a rather large number of terms should be taken.

The major problem in connection with spheroidal antennas consists in calculating the spheroidal functions. From the physical point of view they are not very suitable for the treatment of forced oscillations, except in thin spheroids near resonance; but they are forced upon us by the nature of the spheroidal system of coordinates. The main difficulty

is the complex dependence of spheroidal functions on the frequency and
the eccentricity of the spheroid.    This is not surprising since the same
functions are expected to describe waves on very thin spheroids and on
spheres.    Figure 3.4 shows Ryder's sketch of the behavior of the ninth

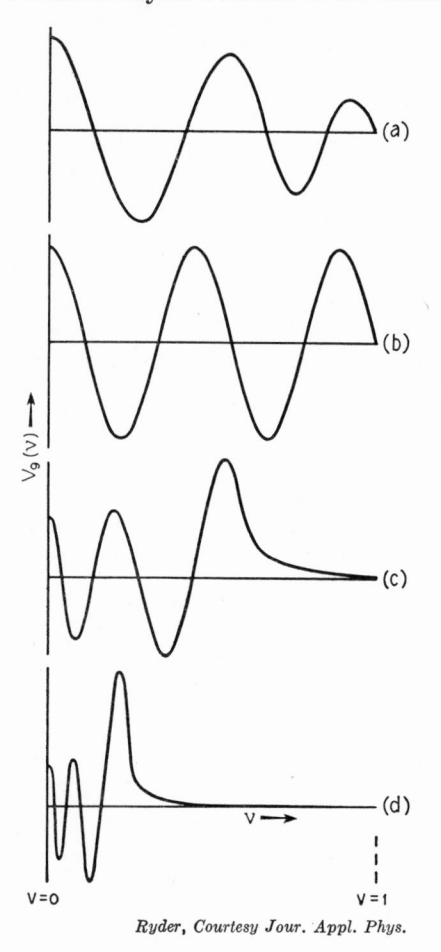

Ryder, *Courtesy Jour. Appl. Phys.*

FIG. 3.4    Qualitative behavior of the ninth harmonic $V_9(v)$:  (a)  when $\beta l = 0$,
(b) when $\beta l = 9\pi/2$; (c) and (d) when $\beta l > 9\pi/2$.

harmonic $V_9(v)$.    The curve $a$ is for $\beta l = 0$:  that is, either at zero frequency for any spheroid or for a sphere at any frequency.    The curve $b$
represents the case $\beta l = 9\pi/2$: that is, the case of spheroids in which the
distance between the foci equals nine half wavelengths.    In this case the
length of the spheroid varies from nine half wavelengths for thin spheroids to near infinity for near spheres.    The curves $c$ and $d$ represent two

cases for which $\beta l > 9\pi/2$. Spheroidal functions have to behave in a complex manner to enable them to represent so many widely different physical cases. Of course, it is possible that further studies may disclose simple approximations. It is also likely that in some cases at least different sets of proper functions will give simpler results. Thus we may replace the boundary condition 19 by

$$V(1) = 0 \quad \text{or} \quad V(-1) = 0. \tag{70}$$

Equation 12 always possesses a solution which vanishes at $v = 1$ and another solution which vanishes at $v = -1$, irrespective of the value of $k$. The proper values of $k$ are then obtained from the boundary condition

$$U_k(u_0) = 0. \tag{71}$$

The roots of this equation will be complex. The difference between the two methods of expansion may be explained by analogy with strings under tension with their ends fixed. One set of proper wave functions is formed by sinusoids; these correspond to the $V$ functions defined by the boundary condition 19. These functions are very convenient for the treatment of free oscillations. In the case of forced oscillations we calculate the interaction between the proper modes and the source. But we can also use progressive waves emerging from the source; these waves are reflected from the ends and react on the source, and the intensity of the total wave is calculated from the conditions at the source. In the case of the string this second solution is preferable because it gives the result in simple closed form instead of an infinite series. In the case of waves on spheroids however, we shall have an infinite number of modes of propagation consistent with equation 71; but some will be more highly attenuated than others, and it is likely that under some conditions the final results will be simpler. On very long, thin spheroids, for example, we may expect waves to travel substantially with the velocity of light and to be gradually attenuated. Hence, equation 71 will probably have a root $\sqrt{k} \simeq \beta l - j\vartheta$ where $\vartheta$ will depend on $\beta l$ and on $\log(u_0 - 1)$, the latter quantity being proportional to the average characteristic impedance in the mode theory of antennas. Studies of this kind would be of immense value in bringing mathematics into line with intuitive physical ideas concerning the behavior of antennas. It is a mistake to assume that, if a particular mathematical method of analysis of a given problem seemingly conflicts with intuitive physical ideas about the nature of its solution, then the intuitive ideas are wrong; and that, if the numerical results support the intuitive ideas in spite of this apparent conflict, then the agreement is only a coincidence. Actually there are infinitely many methods of mathematical analysis of any given problem, of which we choose one or more that we happen to know; and these methods may not always be the best and most straightforward. These methods will often suffer from limitations imposed, not by the physical nature of the problem, but by their mathematical characteristics. The solution of a physical problem, for example, may be well behaved in a given range of a real independent variable; but the representation of this solution by a power series may be impossible on account of a singularity in the complex plane which has nothing to do with the physical conditions. In such a case it may happen that a representation of the solution by a series of Legendre polynomials will converge rapidly; even though, when the power series and Legendre series are terminated, we have polynomials which superficially do not look alike. The difference is in the method of obtaining the final coefficients of the polynomial approximation.

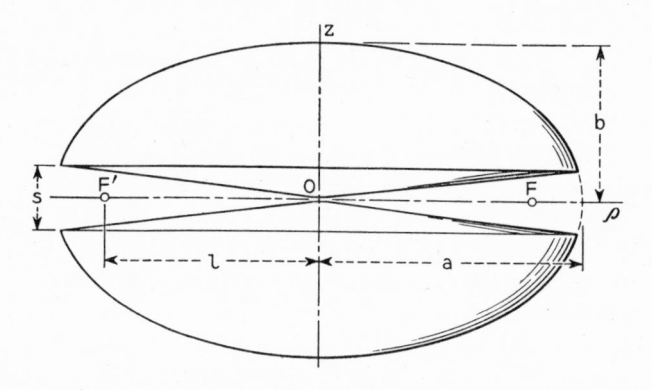

Fig. 3.5 An oblate spheroidal antenna fed by a biconical transmission line.

## 3.2 Oblate spheroidal antennas

Oblate spheroidal coordinates are defined by the following parametric expressions for the cylindrical coordinates:

$$z = luv, \qquad \rho = l\sqrt{(u^2 + 1)(1 - v^2)},$$

$$u = \sinh \xi, \qquad v = \sin \vartheta, \qquad 0 \leq \xi < \infty, \qquad -\frac{\pi}{2} \leq \vartheta \leq \frac{\pi}{2}. \tag{72}$$

A typical oblate spheroid (Fig. 3.5) corresponds to a fixed value of $\xi$ or $u$ in the above equations. If $\xi = 0$ or $u = 0$, we have a disk of radius $l$; if $u$ is large, we have an approximate sphere. Just as in the case of prolate spheroids, we can express the field in terms of an auxiliary wave function $A$ defined by equation 6; thus,

$$E_u = -\frac{j\eta}{\beta l^2}\left[(u^2+1)(u^2+v^2)\right]^{-\frac{1}{2}}\frac{\partial A}{\partial v},$$

$$E_v = \frac{j\eta}{\beta l^2}\left[(1-v^2)(u^2+v^2)\right]^{-\frac{1}{2}}\frac{\partial A}{\partial u}, \tag{73}$$

$$H_\varphi = \frac{1}{l}\left[(u^2+1)(1-v^2)\right]^{-\frac{1}{2}}A, \qquad 2\pi\rho H_\varphi = 2\pi A,$$

where $A$ satisfies

$$(u^2+1)\frac{\partial^2 A}{\partial u^2} + (1-v^2)\frac{\partial^2 A}{\partial v^2} = -\beta^2 l^2(u^2+v^2)A. \tag{74}$$

By substituting

$$A = U(u)\,V(v), \tag{75}$$

we obtain

$$(u^2+1)\frac{d^2 U}{du^2} + (-k+\beta^2 l^2 u^2)U = 0, \tag{76}$$

$$(1-v^2)\frac{d^2 V}{dv^2} + (k+\beta^2 l^2 v^2)V = 0. \tag{77}$$

If we write

$$u = j\bar{u}, \tag{78}$$

we find that the equations for $U$ and $V$ become identical.

The substitutions,

$$U(u) = (u^2+1)^{\frac{1}{2}}\,\bar{U}(u), \qquad V(v) = (1-v^2)^{\frac{1}{2}}\,\bar{V}(v), \tag{79}$$

lead to

$$(u^2+1)\frac{d^2\bar{U}}{du^2} + 2u\frac{d\bar{U}}{du} + \left(\frac{1}{u^2+1}-k\right)\bar{U} + \beta^2 l^2 u^2\bar{U} = 0, \tag{80}$$

$$(1-v^2)\frac{d^2\bar{V}}{dv^2} - 2v\frac{d\bar{V}}{dv} + \left(k-\frac{1}{1-v^2}\right)\bar{V} + \beta^2 l^2 v^2\bar{V} = 0. \tag{81}$$

On the other hand, the substitutions,

$$U(u) = (u^2+1)\,\hat{U}(u), \qquad \hat{U}(u) = (U^2+1)^{-\frac{1}{2}}\,\bar{U}(u), \tag{82}$$

$$V(v) = (1-v^2)\,\hat{V}(v), \qquad \hat{V}(v) = (1-v^2)^{-\frac{1}{2}}\,\bar{V}(v), \tag{83}$$

give

$$(u^2+1)\frac{d^2\hat{U}}{du^2} + 4u\frac{d\hat{U}}{du} + (\beta^2 l^2 u^2 - k + 2)\hat{U} = 0, \tag{84}$$

$$(1-v^2)\frac{d^2\hat{V}}{dv^2} - 4v\frac{d\hat{V}}{dv} + (k-2+\beta^2 l^2 v^2)\hat{V} = 0. \tag{85}$$

When $\beta l = 0$, $\bar{V}$ is an associated Legendre function of $v$ and $\bar{U}$ of $ju$. The $V$ functions are those solutions that remain finite at $v = \pm 1$; for large values of $u$, the proper $U$ functions should vary as $\exp(-j\beta l u)$. In this manner we form a solution

$$A = \sum_k a_k U_k(u) V_k(v),$$

$$E_v = \frac{j\eta}{\beta l^2} [(1 - v^2)(u^2 + v^2)]^{-\frac{1}{2}} \sum_k a_k U_k'(u) V_k(v),$$

(86)

where the proper values of $k$ are obtained from the condition $V_k(\pm 1)$ $= 0$. Then we determine the coefficients as we did in the case of prolate spheroids. Finally we obtain the input impedance in exactly the same form 40; only the functions are different.

Oblate spheroidal coordinates may be used to evaluate the effect of a discoid ground on the performance of a thin monopole. We should find the field of the monopole in free space and expand the component tangential to the disk in spheroidal coordinates; this will give the field reflected by the disk. The solution of this problem requires " addition formulas " derived by Morse, and also formulas for the calculation of spheroidal functions obtained by Stratton and Chu. Circular plate reflectors parallel to the antennas can also be treated in this manner.

## REFERENCES

1. L. Page and N. I. Adams, The electrical oscillations of a prolate spheroid, I, *Phys. Rev.*, **53**, May 15, 1938, pp. 819–831.
2. L. J. Chu and J. A. Stratton, Forced oscillations of a prolate spheroid, *Jour. Appl. Phys.*, **12**, March 1941, pp. 241–248.
3. R. M. Ryder, The electrical oscillations of a perfectly conducting prolate spheroid, *Jour. Appl. Phys.*, **13**, May 1942, pp. 327–343.
4. L. Page, The electrical oscillations of a prolate spheroid, II and III, *Phys. Rev.*, **65**, February 1 and 15, 1944, pp. 98–117.
5. E. Roubine, Les récentes théories de l'antenne, *Rev. Tech*, Thomson-Houston, Paris, 1947.
6. A. Leitner and R. D. Spence, Effect of a circular ground-plane on antenna radiation, *Jour. Appl. Phys.* **21**, October 1950, pp. 1001–1006.
7. W. S. Lucke, Electric dipoles in the presence of elliptic and circular cylinders, *Jour. Appl. Phys.*, **22**, January 1951, pp. 14–19.
8. L. Brillouin, Antennae for ultra-high frequencies—wide-band antennae, *Elect. Comm.*, **21**, 1944, pp. 257–281; and **22**, 1945, pp. 11–39.

# 4

# INTEGRAL EQUATIONS

## 4.1 Nonhomogeneous Maxwell's equations

In the preceding chapters the sources of electromagnetic fields were represented by boundary conditions. This enabled us to work with solutions of homogeneous Maxwell's equations (that is, equations admitting the trivial solution $E = H = 0$) for source-free regions. We can, however, alter our point of view and express the field intensities in terms of the conditions existing inside the true and the virtual sources of the field. A true source is a region that contributes energy to the field, and a virtual source is a region that acts on energy borrowed from the true source. In regions including sources Maxwell's equations are nonhomogeneous,

$$\text{curl } E = -j\omega\mu H - M, \qquad \text{curl } H = j\omega\varepsilon E + J, \qquad (1)$$

where $J$ and $M$ are the densities of electric and magnetic currents other than those given by the first terms on the right-hand side of the equations. In this form of Maxwell's equations the electronic currents in vacuum tubes (true sources) and the conduction currents in antennas (virtual sources) are all included in $J$. If there are any dielectric media, the polarization currents are included in $J$. If there are any magnetizable media, the magnetization currents are included in $M$. Loop currents and double current sheets may be represented either by $J$ or more conveniently by $M$.

The field intensities may be expressed in terms of $J$ and $M$ as follows*

$$E = -j\omega\mu A - \text{grad } V - \text{curl } F,$$
$$H = \text{curl } A - \text{grad } U - j\omega\varepsilon F, \qquad (2)$$

* *Electromagnetic Waves*, pp. 126–132.

where

$$A = \iiint \frac{Je^{-j\beta r}}{4\pi r}\, dv, \qquad F = \iiint \frac{Me^{-j\beta r}}{4\pi r}\, dv,$$

$$V = \iiint \frac{q_v e^{-j\beta r}}{4\pi \varepsilon r}\, dv, \qquad U = \iiint \frac{m_v e^{-j\beta r}}{4\pi \mu r}\, dv,$$

(3)

where $q_v$, $m_v$ are the volume densities of electric and magnetic charge, and $r$ is the distance between a typical element of current and charge and a typical point of the field. The charge densities are not independent of the current densities since the current passing out of a given volume must equal the rate of decrease of the charge in the volume. Hence, the scalar potentials $V$, $U$ must depend on the vector potentials $A$, $F$. In fact,

$$\operatorname{div} A = -j\omega\varepsilon V, \qquad \operatorname{div} F = -j\omega\mu U. \tag{4}$$

If the currents are confined to surfaces, we should replace the volume integrals (equations 3) by surface integrals with the corresponding changes in the moments $J\, dv$, $M\, dv$ of the current elements and in the elements $q_v\, dv$, $m_v\, dv$ of electric and magnetic charge. Thus, the moment of a typical electric current element will be $J\, dv = C\, dS$, where $C$ is the linear density of current. If currents are confined to lines, then $J\, dv = I\, ds$, where $I$ is the current.

Equations 1 are useful for media that are almost everywhere non-dissipative. While they are perfectly general, they are useless in the case of antennas in sea water, since in that case the conduction currents exist everywhere, and the integrals 3 must be taken throughout the entire medium. In dissipative media we should subtract the conduction current density $gE$ from $J$, where $g$ is the conductivity of the medium. Then in the antenna we shall have only that part of the conduction current density which is in excess of $gE$.

## 4.2  Special solutions

If all electric currents are parallel to the $z$ axis and if there are no magnetic currents, the magnetic vector potential $A$ is parallel to the $z$ axis, and the electric potential $F$ vanishes. From equations 4 we have

$$\frac{\partial A_z}{\partial z} = -j\omega\varepsilon V. \tag{5}$$

From equations 2 we have

$$E_z = -j\omega\mu A_z - \frac{\partial V}{\partial z} = \frac{1}{j\omega\varepsilon}\left(\frac{\partial^2 A_z}{\partial z^2} + \beta^2 A_z\right). \tag{6}$$

In particular, for a current element $J\,dv$, we have

$$dE_z = \frac{1}{4\pi j\omega\varepsilon}\left(\frac{\partial^2\psi}{\partial z^2} + \beta^2\psi\right)J\,dv, \tag{7}$$

where

$$\psi = \frac{e^{-j\beta r}}{r}. \tag{8}$$

Hence, for any distribution of currents parallel to the $z$ axis,

$$E_z = \frac{1}{4\pi j\omega\varepsilon}\iiint\left(\frac{\partial^2\psi}{\partial z^2} + \beta^2\psi\right)J\,dv. \tag{9}$$

In the case of a current filament extending from $z = z_1$ to $z = z_2$, the moment $J\,dv$ equals $I(\xi)\,d\xi$. Since

$$r = [(z - \xi)^2 + \rho^2]^{\frac{1}{2}} \tag{10}$$

where $\rho$ is the distance from the axis of the filament, $\partial\psi/\partial z = -\partial\psi/\partial\xi$ and $\partial^2\psi/\partial z^2 = \partial^2\psi/\partial\xi^2$. Integrating the first term in the integral 9 by parts, we find

$$E_z = \frac{1}{4\pi j\omega\varepsilon}\int_{z_1}^{z_2}\left(\frac{\partial^2 I}{\partial\xi^2} + \beta^2 I\right)\psi(\xi - z, \rho)\,d\xi -$$

$$\frac{1}{4\pi j\omega\varepsilon}\left[I(\xi)\frac{\partial\psi}{\partial z} + I'(\xi)\psi\right]_{z_1}^{z_2}. \tag{11}$$

In the course of this integration we must assume that $I(\xi)$ and its derivative are continuous in the interval $(z_1, z_2)$.

If the current is distributed uniformly round a cylinder of radius $a$, $J\,dv = I(\xi)\,d\xi\,d\phi/2\pi$, and

$$A_z = \frac{1}{4\pi}\int_{z_1}^{z_2} G(\xi - z, \rho)\,I(\xi)\,d\xi, \tag{12}$$

$$E_z = \frac{1}{4\pi j\omega\varepsilon}\int_{z_1}^{z_2}\left(\frac{\partial^2 G}{\partial z^2} + \beta^2 G\right)I(\xi)\,d\xi, \tag{13}$$

where

$$G(\xi - z, \rho) = \frac{1}{2\pi}\int_0^{2\pi}\frac{e^{-j\beta r}}{r}\,d\varphi,$$
$$r = [(\xi - z)^2 + \rho^2 - 2\rho a\cos\varphi + a^2]^{\frac{1}{2}}. \tag{14}$$

There is also an equation similar to equation 11 except that $G$ replaces $\psi$.

### 4.3 Equations for surface currents

Suppose that we have one or more surfaces capable of supporting electric currents. Let $u, v$ be the coordinates of a typical point on a typical surface.  Let $C_u(u, v)$ and $C_v(u, v)$ be the components of the linear current density.  From equations 2 and 3 we can obtain $E_u(u, v)$ and $E_v(u, v)$ at the surface.  If the components of the impressed electric intensity are $E_u{}^i(u, v)$ and $E_v{}^i(u, v)$ and if the surface impedance is $Z(u, v)$, then,

$$E_u + E_u{}^i = ZC_u, \qquad E_v + E_v{}^i = ZC_v. \tag{15}$$

In particular, if the surfaces are perfect conductors, $Z = 0$, and

$$E_u = -E_u{}^i, \qquad E_v = -E_v{}^i. \tag{16}$$

These are integral or integrodifferential equations for $C_u$ and $C_v$.

Consider, for example, a perfectly conducting hollow cylinder coaxial with the $z$ axis, and assume that the impressed field $E_z{}^i(z)$ is distributed uniformly round the cylinder.  From equation 13 we have the integral equation of the first kind,

$$\int_{z_1}^{z_2} \left( \frac{\partial^2 G}{\partial z^2} + \beta^2 G \right) I(\xi) \, d\xi = -4\pi j\omega\varepsilon \, E_z{}^i(z), \tag{17}$$

and from equations 6 and 12 the integrodifferential equation,

$$\frac{d^2}{dz^2} \int_{z_1}^{z_2} G(\xi - z, a) \, I(\xi) \, d\xi + \beta^2 \int_{z_1}^{z_2} G(\xi - z, a) \, I(\xi) \, d\xi$$
$$= -4\pi j\omega\varepsilon \, E_z{}^i(z). \tag{18}$$

Equations of the type 17 were used by Pocklington[*] to show that on thin wires (straight or bent) electric waves travel approximately with the velocity of light, and that the current distributions are approximately sinusoidal.  These results have been extremely important in the development of radio engineering.  He also obtained the damping constants for free oscillations in circular loops.  Hallén's theory of antennas is based on the integrodifferential equation 18, which can readily be reduced to an integral equation of the first kind with some arbitrary constants of integration.

### 4.4  External and internal oscillations on closed surfaces of revolution

Consider a perfectly conducting surface of revolution (Fig. 4.1).  Circularly symmetric excitation can be obtained in several ways.  One or more toroidal solenoids, coaxial with such an antenna, can be used to generate an impressed field which will drive electric currents along the meridians of the antenna.  Since the field cannot penetrate a perfectly conducting surface, we must have either internal or external oscillations,

---

[*] H. C. Pocklington, Electrical oscillations in wires, *Camb. Phil. Soc. Proc.*, **9**, October 25, 1897, pp. 324–332.

depending on whether the driving solenoids are inside or outside the antenna. We can also cut a circular ribbon out of the antenna, between two circles of parallel, and imagine that, in the gap previously occupied by the ribbon, there exist electric forces which transfer electric charge back and forth between two sections of the antenna, without any opposition other than that of the charges and currents in the antenna. That is, we assume that the internal impedance of the gap is zero. If the internal impedance of the gap is finite, it can later be added in series with the input impedance of the antenna. In this method of driving, the external and internal regions are connected through the gap, the total current in the antenna equals the sum of the external and internal currents, the external and internal regions are electrically in parallel, and the input admittance equals the sum of the external and internal input admittances. Thus, if we assume that the impressed field exists only in the gap and derive equations of the types represented by equations 17 and 18, we shall obtain equations for *combined* external and internal oscillations.

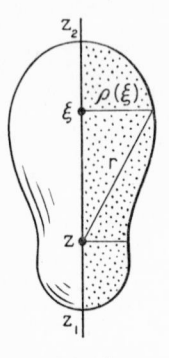

FIG. 4.1 An antenna of revolution.

In the case of spheroids, external and internal oscillations are easily distinguished by the type of characteristic functions. For the external oscillations these functions must obey certain conditions at infinity, and for the internal oscillations the characteristic functions must be regular on the axis. It was shown by Synge* that a similar separation between external and internal oscillations can be made in integral equations. In addition his method leads to simpler general equations. Thus, for a circularly symmetric antenna in a circularly symmetric field Synge's equation is

$$\int_{z_1}^{z_2} \left( \frac{\partial^2 \psi}{\partial z\, \partial \xi} - \beta^2 \psi \right) I(\xi)\, d\xi$$

$$= \frac{2\pi\beta j}{\eta} \int E^i(\xi)\rho^2 \left[ 1 + \left( \frac{d\rho}{d\xi} \right)^2 \right]^{\frac{1}{2}} \frac{1}{r} \frac{\partial \psi}{\partial r}\, d\xi, \quad (19)$$

where $E^i(\xi)$ is the tangential component of the impressed electric intensity, $\rho(z)$ is the radius of the antenna, and

$$\psi = \frac{e^{-j\beta r}}{r}, \qquad r = \{(\xi - z)^2 + [\rho(\xi)]^2\}^{\frac{1}{2}}. \quad (20)$$

---

* G. E. Albert and J. L. Synge, The general problem of antenna radiation and the fundamental integral equation with application to an antenna of revolution: Part I, *Quart. Appl. Math.*, **6**, July 1948, pp. 117–132; Part II, by J. L. Synge, pp. 133–156.

Equation 19 gives external oscillations if it is satisfied in the interval $(z_1, z_2)$, and internal oscillations if it is satisfied outside the interval $(z_1, z_2)$.

The simplest derivation of this equation is based on the equivalence theorem.* Suppose that we know the field produced by an externally impressed voltage. By the equivalence theorem this field may be calculated from certain electric and magnetic current sheets assumed to coincide with the surface of the antenna. This theorem also states that the field of these sheets is identically equal to zero in the interior of the antenna. The foregoing equation expresses this condition on the axis of the antenna. Had we actually known the field at the surface of the antenna, this equation would be merely a check on the correctness of the field; but, since we know only the electric field (and therefore the equivalent magnetic current sheet), we have instead an integral equation for the electric current.

Let the tangential component of the impressed electric intensity at $z = \xi$ be $E^i(\xi)$; the intensity produced by the antenna current will then equal $-E^i(\xi)$. In accordance with the equivalence theorem the density of the equivalent circulating magnetic current is $M_\varphi = -E^i(\xi)$. The field of this current sheet must be added to that of the electric current $I(\xi)$ in the antenna. By symmetry the radial component of the electric field vanishes on the axis, and we need to evaluate only the axial component.

The vector potential due to the electric current sheet is

$$A_z = \frac{1}{4\pi} \int I(\xi)\, \psi(\xi, z)\, d\xi. \tag{21}$$

For the scalar potential we have

$$V = \frac{1}{4\pi\varepsilon} \int q(\xi)\, \psi(\xi, z)\, d\xi, \tag{22}$$

where $q$ is the density of charge per unit length along the axis. Since $\partial I/\partial \xi = -j\omega q$,

$$V = -\frac{1}{4\pi j\omega\varepsilon} \int \frac{\partial I}{\partial \xi}\, \psi\, d\xi. \tag{23}$$

Integrating by parts and noting that the current vanishes at the ends of the antenna, we find

$$V = \frac{1}{4\pi j\omega\varepsilon} \int \frac{\partial \psi}{\partial \xi}\, I(\xi)\, d\xi. \tag{24}$$

* The derivation by Albert and Synge simultaneously includes a proof of the equivalence theorem.

Hence, the total electric intensity due to the electric current sheet is

$$E_z' = \frac{1}{4\pi j\omega\varepsilon} \int \left( \beta^2\psi - \frac{\partial^2\psi}{\partial z\,\partial\xi} \right) I(\xi)\,d\xi.\tag{25}$$

Using the formula for the field of a magnetic current element, we find that on the axis of the antenna the field due to the magnetic current sheet of density $M_\varphi = -E^i(\xi)$ is

$$E_z'' = \frac{1}{2} \int E^i(\xi)\rho^2 \left[ 1 + \left( \frac{d\rho}{d\xi} \right)^2 \right]^{\frac{1}{2}} \frac{1}{r} \frac{\partial\psi}{\partial r}\,d\xi.\tag{26}$$

Equating to zero the sum of equations 25 and 26, we obtain equation 19.

## 4.5 Integral equations and Kirchhoff's network equations

The resemblance between integral equations of the type 17 and Kirchhoff's network equations,

$$\sum_{n=1}^{n=N} Z_{mn}I_n = V_m{}^i, \qquad m = 1, 2, 3, \cdots, N,\tag{27}$$

is evident. The kernel $jG/4\pi\omega\varepsilon$ (if we divide equation 17 by $-4\pi j\omega\varepsilon$) corresponds to the transfer impedance $Z_{mn}$ in the network equations. The impressed electric intensity $E_z{}^i(z)$ in equation 17 corresponds to the voltage $V_m{}^i$ impressed on a typical mesh of the network. If we approximate equation 17 by a finite sum and multiply both sides by $\Delta z_m$, we obtain equations in the exact form 27. This analogy is not restricted to straight conductors. We can have any system of conductors, some wound into coils and some forming "capacitors," and still be able to write for them a network type of integral equation. But the equation will be very complex.

If, however, the dimensions of the conductors are small compared with $\lambda$, then the integral equations assume automatically the algebraic form 27. What happens is that the entire system of conductors can be subdivided into sections in each of which the current is substantially the same at all points, and then $I(\xi)$ can be taken outside the integral sign. If we integrate the original integral equation over each such section, the integral of the impressed intensity becomes the voltage impressed on the section. The integrals remain only as coefficients $Z_{mn}$, independent of the currents. For further details concerning the relationship between integral equations and Kirchhoff's equations, the reader is referred elsewhere.*

* J. Aharoni, *Antennae — an Introduction to Their Theory*, Clarendon Press, Oxford, 1946.

## 4.6  Ring source, Green's function, and the input impedance

Since our equations are linear, we can consider any distribution of the impressed electric intensity as due to the superposition of "delta distributions." In equations 17 and 18, for example, we may assume that $E_z{}^i(z)$ vanishes everywhere except in the interval $(\zeta - \tfrac{1}{2}s, \zeta + \tfrac{1}{2}s)$, where $s$ is infinitesimal. This represents a *ring source*. If we assume that

$$\lim \int_{\zeta - \frac{1}{2}s}^{\zeta + \frac{1}{2}s} E_z{}^i(z) \, dz = 1, \qquad s \to 0, \tag{28}$$

the corresponding solution of equations 17 and 18 is the Green's function $I(z, \zeta)$ of our problem. The solution for any given distribution of impressed electric intensity is then

$$I(z) = \int_{z_1}^{z_2} I(z, \zeta) E_z{}^i(\zeta) \, d\zeta. \tag{29}$$

The Green's function is symmetric, of course, $I(z, \zeta) = I(\zeta, z)$. At $z = \zeta$, it has a logarithmic singularity; thus,

$$I(\zeta, z) \propto \log |\zeta - z|, \tag{30}$$

as $\zeta - z$ approaches zero. Hence, for a ring source the input admittance is infinite and the input impedance vanishes. For a *ribbon source* of finite width the current (equation 29) and the admittance are infinite.

It is to be noted that, since the vector potential is finite, its contribution to the integral 28 is zero in the limit and condition 28 is equivalent to a unit discontinuity in the scalar potential,

$$V(\zeta + 0) - V(\zeta - 0) = 1. \tag{31}$$

Throughout this section we have tacitly assumed that the radius does not vanish anywhere along the antenna. In Chapter 2 we have seen that, at a point where the radius is zero, the Green's function is finite, and, hence, the input impedance is finite. In this case the ring source becomes a point source, and it is the only case in which the dimensions of the source do not enter the equations. It may be noted that it is easy to ascertain the nature of the fields in the immediate vicinity of a point source and a ring source in terms of appropriate solutions of Maxwell's differential equations; but to do the same by using integral equations is very difficult. In equations 17 and 18 the kernels and the expressions on the right-hand side are singular at the ring source at $z = \zeta$; here at least we have a warning of the unusual conditions. But in equation 19 the kernel is regular, the right-hand side is regular, and there is nothing in the equation to indicate a logarithmic singularity in its solution $I(z, \zeta)$ for a ring source at $z = \zeta$.

## 4.7  Solutions in terms of orthogonal functions

Some integral equations may be solved with the aid of orthogonal expansions, Fourier series, for example.* Consider equation 17 for the hollow cylindrical antenna, and let the antenna extend from $z = 0$ to $z = 2l$. Let

$$I(z) = \sum_{n=1}^{\infty} I_n \sin \frac{n\pi z}{2l}, \qquad E^i(z) = \sum_{n=1}^{\infty} E_n \sin \frac{n\pi z}{2l} \tag{32}$$

The sine series for $I(z)$ is chosen in order to satisfy the end conditions

$$I(0) = I(2l) = 0. \tag{33}$$

Substituting from equations 32 in equation 17, multiplying by $\sin(m\pi z/2l)$, and integrating from $z = 0$ to $z = 2l$, we obtain

$$\sum_{n=1}^{\infty} Z_{mn} I_n = -4\pi j\omega\epsilon l E_m, \qquad m = 1, 2, 3, \cdots. \tag{34}$$

$$Z_{mn} = \int_0^{2l} \int_0^{2l} \left( \frac{\partial^2 G}{\partial z^2} + \beta^2 G \right) \sin \frac{n\pi\xi}{2l} \sin \frac{m\pi z}{2l} \, d\xi \, dz.$$

Hence, the integral equation has been reduced to an infinite system of linear algebraic equations.

The evaluation of $Z_{mn}$ is difficult. If the impressed electric intensity is concentrated in a small interval — as it is in a transmitting antenna — a very large number of terms must be taken in the Fourier series for $E^i(z)$ in order to obtain a satisfactory approximation. In a receiving antenna the load is highly concentrated, and we must again take a very large number of terms.

## 4.8  Variational theorems

Schwinger found that the impedance of certain waveguide discontinuities possesses the extremal property. This property is shared by more general functions. First, let us consider the finite network equations 27 and form the following function:

$$\Phi = \sum_m \sum_n Z_{mn} I_m I_n. \tag{35}$$

---

* F. H. Murray, On the numerical calculation of the current in an antenna, *Amer. Jour. Math.*, 53, 1931, pp. 873–890.

F. B. Pidduck, *Currents in Aerials and High Frequency Networks*, Clarendon Press, Oxford, 1946.

Multiplying equations 27 by $I_m$ and summing over $m$, we find that, when these equations are satisfied,

$$\Phi = \sum_m V_m{}^i I_m. \tag{36}$$

We also find that, if we keep the $V$'s fixed,

$$\delta(\Phi - 2\sum_m V_m{}^i I_m) = 0. \tag{37}$$

To prove this we take the variation of $\Phi$ from equation 35 and note that $Z_{mn} = Z_{nm}$.

If all the $V$'s except $V_1$ vanish, the impedance to $V_1$ is

$$Z_1 = \frac{V_1{}^i}{I_1} = \frac{\Phi}{I_1{}^2}. \tag{38}$$

If we keep $I_1$ fixed,

$$\delta Z_1 = 0. \tag{39}$$

In the case of the hollow cylindrical antenna, we form the following integral analogous to the series in equation 35,

$$\Phi = \frac{j}{4\pi\omega\varepsilon} \int_{z_1}^{z_2} \int_{z_1}^{z_2} \left( \frac{\partial^2 G}{\partial z^2} + \beta^2 G \right) I(\xi)\, I(z)\, d\xi\, dz, \tag{40}$$

where $G(\xi - z, a)$ is obtained from equation 14. Since $G$ is an even function of $\xi - z$, it is a symmetric function of $\xi$ and $z$. Multiplying equation 17 by $I(z)$ and integrating over the antenna, we find that, if $I(z)$ satisfies equation 17,

$$\Phi = \int_{z_1}^{z_2} E^i(z)\, I(z)\, dz. \tag{41}$$

We also find that, if $I(z)$ is the solution of equation 17, then,

$$\delta \left[ \Phi - 2 \int_{z_1}^{z_2} E^i(z)\, I(z)\, dz \right] = 0, \tag{42}$$

where in obtaining the variation we keep $E^i(z)$ fixed.

Suppose now that $E^i(z)$ vanishes everywhere except in the input interval $(\zeta - \tfrac{1}{2}s, \zeta + \tfrac{1}{2}s)$ and is such that, in this interval,

$$I(z) = I_i = \text{constant}. \tag{43}$$

In this case the input impedance,

$$Z_i = \frac{V^i}{I_i} = \frac{\Phi}{I_i{}^2}, \qquad V^i = \int_{\zeta-\frac{1}{2}s}^{\zeta+\frac{1}{2}s} E^i(z)\, dz, \tag{44}$$

is stationary with respect to variations in $I(z)$, subject to the condition that the input current is constant.

If we substitute from equation 32 in equation 42, we obtain equation 34.

Equation 44 had been used long before its extremal property became known.  It was first obtained by the induced emf method, using the reciprocity theorem.*  There is a similar expression based on the induced emf method and the energy theorem,

$$Z_i = \frac{j}{4\pi\omega\varepsilon I_i I_i{}^*}\int_{z_1}^{z_2}\int_{z_1}^{z_2}\left(\frac{\partial^2 G}{\partial z^2} + \beta^2 G\right) I(\xi)\, I^*(z)\, d\xi\, dz, \qquad (45)$$

which has also been used frequently but which does not possess the extremal property.  When the simple sinusoidal approximation to the antenna current is used in equations 44 and 45, the results are the same.

Equation 44 is very useful when a reasonably good approximation to the antenna current is known.  One should be careful, however, not to draw unwarranted conclusions from it.  For instance, if the influence of the length of the input interval (the antenna gap) on the impedance were not known beforehand, it would be difficult to deduce this effect from equation 44.  We must be careful not to conclude that the effect is absent if we neglected it in using the equation.

## 4.9  Asymptotic solutions

Hallén has obtained important asymptotic solutions of the integrodifferential equation 18.  He solves the differential equation and then notes that, as the radius $a$ of the cylinder approaches zero, the integral tends to become proportional to $I(z)$.  The coefficient of proportionality tends to infinity and hence contains an indeterminate constant.  The choice of this constant affects the usefulness of the associated asymptotic expansion of $I(z)$ for practical values of the antenna radius.

In obtaining Hallén's asymptotic solutions it is necessary to assume that the antenna current is finite everywhere.  Hence ring sources must be explicitly excluded, and the applied electric intensity must be distributed over a finite interval.  The principal effect of the length of this interval on the antenna current and on the antenna impedance is excluded automatically by the nature of the transformations involved.  In the limit this effect disappears; but, for antennas of finite radius, the asymptotic expressions for the antenna impedance should be used only when the length of the input interval is not much smaller than the radius and when it is known from other considerations that the effect of this length is sufficiently small.  As far as the antenna current is concerned, the effect of the length of the input interval is confined to an interval

---

* P. S. Carter, Circuit relations in radiating systems and applications to antenna problems, *IRE Proc.*, **20**, June 1932, pp. 1004–1041.

comparable to the antenna radius in the immediate vicinity of the input. The ambiguity associated with neglecting the length of the input interval affects the input susceptance but not the conductance. The essential details of Hallén's method are given in the next chapter.

## REFERENCES

1. H. C. Pocklington, Electrical oscillations on wires, *Camb. Phil. Soc. Proc.*, **9**, October 25, 1897, pp. 324–332.
2. E. Hallén, Über die elektrischen Schwingungen in drahtförmigen Leitern, *Uppsala Universitets Årsskrift*, 1930, no. 1.
3. F. H. Murray, Conductors in an electromagnetic field $(E^0 e^{pt}, H^0 e^{pt})$, *Amer. Jour. Math.*, **53**, April 1931, pp. 275–288.
4. F. H. Murray, On the numerical calculation of the current in an antenna, *Amer. Jour. Math.*, **53**, October 1931, pp. 873–890.
5. L. V. King, On the radiation field of a perfectly conducting base insulated antenna over a perfectly conducting plane earth, and the calculation of radiation resistance and reactance, *Phil. Trans. Roy. Soc.* (Lond.), Ser A, **236**, November 2, 1937, pp. 381–422.
6. E. Hallén, Theoretical investigations into the transmitting and receiving qualities of antennas, *Nova Acta* (Uppsala), **11**, 1938, no. 4.
7. J. F. Carlson and A. E. Heins, The reflection of an electromagnetic plane wave by an infinite set of plates, I and II, *Quart. Appl. Math.*, **4**, January 1947, pp. 313–329, and **5**, April 1947, pp. 82–88.
8. A. E. Heins, The radiation and transmission properties of a pair of parallel plates, I and II, *Quart. Appl. Math.*, **5**, July 1948, pp. 157–166, and October 1948, pp. 215–220.
9. J. W. Miles, The diffraction of a plane wave through a grating, *Quart. Appl. Math.*, **7**, April 1949, pp. 45–64.
10. J. W. Miles, On certain integral equations in diffraction theory, *Jour. Math. and Phys.*, **28**, January 1950, pp. 223–226.
11. H. Zuhrt, Eine strenge Berechnung der Dipolantennen mit rohrförmigem Querschnitt, *Frequenz*, 4, June 1950, pp. 135–141.
12. A. E. Heins, The reflection of an electromagnetic plane wave by an infinite set of plates III, *Quart. Appl. Math.*, **8**, October 1950, pp. 281–291.
13. H. Levine and C. H. Papas, Theory of the circular diffraction antenna, *Jour. Appl. Phys.*, **31**, January 1951, pp. 29–53.
14. J. E. Storer, The impedance of an antenna over a large circular screen, *Jour. Appl. Phys.*, **22**, August 1951, pp. 1058–1066.
15. J. Aharoni, *Antennae — An Introduction to Their Theory*, Clarendon Press, Oxford, 1946.
16. F. B. Pidduck, *Currents in Aerials and High Frequency Networks*, Clarendon Press, Oxford, 1946.

# 5

## CYLINDRICAL ANTENNAS

### 5.1 Fundamental equations

In this chapter we shall present Hallén's method of obtaining asymptotic solutions of the integrodifferential equation 4–18 for hollow cylindrical antennas. Solving the differential equation for the integral, we have

$$\int_{z_1}^{z_2} G(\xi - z)\, I(\xi)\, d\xi =$$

$$Ae^{-j\beta z} + Be^{j\beta z} + \frac{j}{30} \int_{z_0}^{z} E^i(\xi) \sin \beta(\xi - z)\, d\xi, \quad (1)$$

where $z = z_0$ is a point on the antenna, and

$$G(\xi - z) = \frac{1}{2\pi} \int_0^{2\pi} r^{-1} e^{-j\beta r}\, d\varphi, \quad r = [(\xi - z)^2 + 4a^2 \sin^2 \tfrac{1}{2}\varphi]^{\frac{1}{2}}. \quad (2)$$

The arbitrary constants of integration $A$, $B$ can be determined from the boundary conditions

$$I(z_1) = 0, \qquad I(z_2) = 0, \quad (3)$$

after the general solution of equation 1 has been found. For hollow cylindrical antennas these conditions are exact. In the immediate vicinity of either end of the antenna the charge per unit length varies inversely as the square root of the distance from the end; hence, the charging current must vary directly as the square root of this distance.

The integral on the left in equation 1 equals the vector potential multiplied by $4\pi$. Using equations 1 and 4–5, we obtain

$$V = 30Ae^{-j\beta z} - 30Be^{j\beta z} + \int_{z_0}^{z} E^i(\xi) \cos \beta(\xi - z)\, d\xi. \quad (4)$$

If $E^i(\xi) = 0$ everywhere except at $\xi = \zeta$,

$$\int_{z_1}^{z_2} G(\xi - z)\,I(\xi)\,d\xi = Ae^{-j\beta z} + Be^{j\beta z}, \quad V = 30Ae^{-j\beta z} - 30Be^{j\beta z},$$
$$z_1 < z < \zeta,$$
$$= Ce^{-j\beta z} + De^{j\beta z}, \qquad = 30Ce^{-j\beta z} - 30De^{j\beta z},$$
$$\zeta < z < z_2. \tag{5}$$

The vector potential is continuous. Hence, for a unit discontinuity in the scalar potential we have the following conditions across the ring source at $z = \zeta$:

$$Ae^{-j\beta\zeta} + Be^{j\beta\zeta} = Ce^{-j\beta\zeta} + De^{j\beta\zeta},$$
$$Ce^{-j\beta\zeta} - De^{j\beta\zeta} - Ae^{-j\beta\zeta} + Be^{j\beta\zeta} = \frac{1}{30}. \tag{6}$$

In particular, if $z_1 = -l, z_2 = l, \zeta = 0$,

$$\int_{-l}^{l} G(\xi - z)\,I(\xi)\,d\xi = P\cos\beta z - \frac{j}{60}\sin\beta|z|. \tag{7}$$

If the antenna is thin and if the energy is supplied to it by a transmission line consisting of two wires perpendicular to it, the impressed intensity arises solely from the charges on the transmission line (since the vector potential due to the line currents is perpendicular to the antenna). Therefore,

$$E_z^i = -\frac{\partial V_1}{\partial z}, \tag{8}$$

where $V_1$ is the potential due to the charges on the line.

## 5.2  Properties of the kernel

The kernel (equation 2) may be expressed as follows:

$$G(\xi - z) = \frac{1}{2\pi}\int_0^{2\pi} r^{-1}\,d\varphi - \frac{1}{2\pi}\int_0^{2\pi} r^{-1}(1 - e^{-j\beta r})\,d\varphi. \tag{9}$$

If the radius $a$ of the antenna is small compared with its length, then $r \simeq |\xi - z|$, except in the vicinity of $\xi = z$. If $\beta a \ll 1$, then, in this vicinity the last integrand in equation 9 equals $j\beta$ except for small quantities of order $(\beta a)^2$. Hence, in this term we can approximate $r$ by $|\xi - z|$. The first term on the right in equation 9 may be transformed into a complete elliptic integral of the first kind. Thus, we find

$$G(\xi - z) =$$
$$\frac{k}{\pi a}\,F(\tfrac{1}{2}\pi, k) - |\xi - z|^{-1}[1 - \exp(-j\beta|\xi - z|)] + O(\beta^2 a^2), \tag{10}$$

where

$$k = 2a[(\xi - z)^2 + 4a^2]^{-\frac{1}{2}} \tag{11}$$

is the modulus of the elliptic integral $F$. As $\xi$ approaches $z$, the modulus approaches unity, and

$$F(\tfrac{1}{2}\pi, k) \to \log 4(1 - k^2)^{-\frac{1}{2}}$$
$$= \log 4[(\xi - z)^2 + 4a^2]^{\frac{1}{2}} - \log |\xi - z|. \tag{12}$$

Finally, in the immediate vicinity of $\xi = z$, $F(\tfrac{1}{2}\pi, k)$ tends to $\log 8a - \log|\xi - z|$, and

$$G(\xi - z) \to \frac{1}{\pi a} \log \frac{8a}{|\xi - z|} - j\beta. \tag{13}$$

Hence, the kernel is logarithmically infinite at $\xi = z$ *for all values of a*, and approaches infinity almost as $1/a$ when $a$ approaches zero.

If $|\xi - z| \gg a$, then,

$$G(\xi - z) = \frac{1}{2\pi} |\xi - z|^{-1} e^{-j\beta|\xi - z|} + O(a^2). \tag{14}$$

Therefore, as $a$ approaches zero, the kernel approaches values independent of $a$ everywhere except at distances from $\xi - z$ comparable to $a$.

## 5.3 Hallén's method of iteration

Hallén's method of iteration for solving equation 1 is based on the observation that, as the antenna radius approaches zero, the value of the integral on the left side is determined increasingly by the values of $I(\xi)$ in the vicinity of $\xi = z$. Hence, if $I(\xi)$ does not vary too rapidly in this vicinity, we can separate the integral into two components one of which constitutes a " principal part of the integral,"

$$\int_{z_1}^{z_2} G(\xi - z) I(\xi) \, d\xi$$
$$= I(z) \int_{z_1}^{z_2} G(\xi - z) \, d\xi - \int_{z_1}^{z_2} G(\xi - z)[I(z) - I(\xi)] \, d\xi. \tag{15}$$

The coefficient of $I(z)$ in the principal component increases as $a$ decreases. The second component is substantially independent of $a$. The decomposition of the integral into components behaving in this manner is not unique since the kernel also may be split into two components one of which is substantially independent of $a$. Hence, we can write equation 1 in the following form,

$$W(z) I(z) - S[I(z)] = f(z), \tag{16}$$

where $S$ is the following linear functional of $I(z)$:

$$S[I(z)] = W(z)\,I(z) - \int_{z_1}^{z_2} G(\xi - z)\,I(\xi)\,d\xi, \qquad (17)$$

and $f(z)$ is the right-hand side of equation 1. The function $W(z)$ is so chosen that $S[I(z)]$ is substantially independent of $a$. In particular, it is possible to choose

$$W(z) = 2\log\left(\frac{z_2 - z_1}{a}\right) + A, \qquad (18)$$

where $A$ is a rather arbitrary constant.

Let us choose a sequence of functions $I_0(z), I_1(z), \cdots$, defined by the following equations:

$$\begin{aligned} W(z)\,I_0(z) &= f(z), \\ W(z)\,I_1(z) &= S[I_0(z)], \\ W(z)\,I_2(z) &= S[I_1(z)], \end{aligned} \qquad (19)$$

$$\cdots\cdots\cdots\cdots\cdots\cdots$$

Adding, we find that the series

$$I(z) = I_0(z) + I_1(z) + I_2(z) + \cdots \qquad (20)$$

is a formal solution of equation 16. In particular, if $W$ is a constant, then,

$$I(z) = W^{-1} f(z) + W^{-2} S[f(z)] + W^{-3} S^2[f(z)] + \cdots, \qquad (21)$$

where $S^n$ denotes the $n$ times repeated operation 17.

If

$$W = W_1 + A, \qquad (22)$$

then,

$$\begin{aligned} W^{-1} &= W_1^{-1}(1 + AW_1^{-1})^{-1} = W_1^{-1} - AW_1^{-2} + A^2 W_1^{-3} - \cdots, \\ W^{-2} &= W_1^{-2}(1 + AW_1^{-1})^{-2} = W_1^{-2} - 2AW_1^{-3} + 3A^2 W_1^{-4} - \cdots, \end{aligned}$$

$$\cdots\cdots\cdots\cdots\cdots\cdots\cdots\cdots\cdots\cdots\cdots\cdots\cdots\cdots\cdots\cdots \qquad (23)$$

$$\begin{aligned} W^{-n} &= W_1^{-n}(1 + AW_1^{-1})^{-n} \\ &= W_1^{-n} - nAW_1^{-n-1} + \tfrac{1}{2}n(n-1)A^2 W_1^{-n-2} - \cdots. \end{aligned}$$

Substituting in equation 21, we find the functionals associated with the new choice of the expansion parameter $W_1$,

$$\begin{aligned} S_1[f(z)] &= S[f(z)] - Af(z), \\ S_1^2[f(z)] &= S^2[f(z)] - 2A\,S[f(z)] + A^2 f(z), \end{aligned} \qquad (24)$$

$$\cdots\cdots\cdots\cdots\cdots\cdots\cdots\cdots\cdots\cdots\cdots\cdots\cdots$$

## 5.4  Special asymptotic expansions

It has been noted that the representation of the integral equation 1 in the form 16 is not unique. The part of the integral on the left side of equation 1 which depends primarily on $a$ is expressed by $W(z)$, and $S[I(z)]$ approaches a bounded function as $a$ approaches zero. Any bounded part of $W(z)\,I(z)$ may be transferred to $S$. An obvious choice of $W$ and $S$ is suggested by equation 15. Thus,

$$W_1(z) = \int_{z_1}^{z_2} G(\xi - z)\,d\xi = \Omega(z) + \Psi(z),$$

$$\Omega(z) = \frac{1}{2\pi} \int_{z_1}^{z_2} \int_0^{2\pi} r^{-1}\,d\xi\,d\varphi, \tag{25}$$

$$\Psi(z) = \frac{1}{2\pi} \int_{z_1}^{z_2} \int_0^{2\pi} r^{-1}(e^{-j\beta r} - 1)\,d\xi\,d\varphi.$$

Except for quantities of the order $a^2$, we find

$$\Omega(z) = \log\{[(z - z_1)^2 + a^2]^{1/2} + (z - z_1)\} +$$
$$\log\{[(z_2 - z)^2 + a^2]^{1/2} + (z_2 - z)\} - 2\log a, \tag{26}$$
$$\Psi(z) = -\operatorname{Cin}\beta(z - z_1) - \operatorname{Cin}\beta(z_2 - z) - j\operatorname{Si}\beta(z - z_1) -$$
$$j\operatorname{Si}\beta(z_2 - z).$$

If $z$ is not too close to either $z = z_1$ or $z = z_2$,

$$\Omega(z) \simeq \log \frac{4(z_2 - z)(z - z_1)}{a^2}. \tag{27}$$

At either end,

$$\Omega(z_1) = \Omega(z_2) = \log \frac{2(z_2 - z_1)}{a}. \tag{28}$$

In the last term in equation 15 we can approximate $r$ by $|\xi - z|$; thus,

$$S_1[I(z)] = \int_{z_1}^{z_2} G(\xi - z)\,[I(z) - I(\xi)]\,d\xi$$

$$\simeq \int_{z_1}^{z_2} [I(z) - I(\xi)]|z - \xi|^{-1} \exp(-j\beta|z - \xi|)\,d\xi. \tag{29}$$

To examine the behavior of $\Omega(z)$ let us take $z_1 = -l$, $z_2 = l$; then, except in the vicinity of the ends,

$$\Omega(z) = \Omega + \log\left[1 - \left(\frac{z}{l}\right)^2\right], \tag{30}$$

where

$$\Omega = 2 \log \frac{2l}{a} \cdot \tag{31}$$

At each end $\Omega(z) = \frac{1}{2}\Omega + \log 2$. Hence, $\Omega(z)$ varies slowly over the greater part of the interval $(-l, l)$. Likewise $\Psi(z)$ is a slowly varying function; thus,

$$
\begin{aligned}
\Psi(0) &= -2 \operatorname{Cin} \beta l - 2j \operatorname{Si} \beta l \\
&= -2C - 2 \log \beta l + 2 \operatorname{Ci} \beta l - 2j \operatorname{Si} \beta l, \\
\Psi(-l) = \Psi(l) &= -\operatorname{Cin} 2\beta l - j \operatorname{Si} 2\beta l \\
&= -C - \log 2\beta l - j \operatorname{Si} 2\beta l,
\end{aligned}
\tag{32}
$$

where $C = 0.577 \cdots$ is Euler's constant. The difference $[W_1(z) - W_1(0)] I(z)$ is numerically less significant than $S[I(z)]$. Since the evaluation of $S[I(z)]$ is much simpler (analytically at least) when $W(z)$ is constant, it is only natural to include the difference in $S$ and choose

$$W_2(z) = W_1(0) = 2 \log \frac{2l}{a} - 2 \operatorname{Cin} \beta l - 2j \operatorname{Si} \beta l, \tag{33}$$
$$S_2[I(z)] = S_1[I(z)] + [W_1(0) - W_1(z)] I(z).$$

In his second paper Hallén expressed the second term in the series 20 and the corresponding input impedance in terms of sine and cosine integrals on the assumption that $W(z) = \Omega$. King and Blake[16] * presented tables and curves based on these expressions. Bouwkamp[4] evaluated numerically the effect of the third term in the series 20 on the input impedance and discovered that it was large for $\Omega = 10, 15, 20$. It should be noted that $\Omega = 20$ corresponds to an extremely thin antenna ($a = 2l/22026$). A comparison with the mode theory and experimental evidence[6,8] shows that Hallén's formula gives excessively high values for the first antiresonant impedance even if three terms of the series 20 are used. Gray[7] observed that choosing

$$W_3(z) = \operatorname{re} W_1(0) = \Omega + \operatorname{re} \Psi(0) \tag{34}$$

instead of $W(z) = \Omega$ was sufficient to bring Hallén's formula for the impedance into substantial agreement with the mode theory and with experimental results, even if only the first two terms of the series 20 were used. The still existing differences were reasonable in view of the fact that the theoretical approximations were obtained by entirely different methods (although to the same order of approximation), and well within the probable accuracy of experimental results.

* The numbers refer to the list of references at the end of the chapter.

King and Middleton[10] attempted to choose $W(z)$ so that the second term in equation 16 would be as nearly equal to zero as possible. Since $I(z)$ is unknown, they tried to make the second term small when $I(z)$ was replaced by its first approximation. In the case of a symmetric transmitting antenna the current approaches asymptotically the form $I_0 \sin \beta(l - |z|)$, and they chose

$$W_4(z) = [\sin \beta(l - |z|)]^{-1} \int_{-l}^{l} G(\xi - z) \sin \beta(l - |\xi|) \, d\xi. \quad (35)$$

If $l > \lambda/2$, this function becomes infinite at some points which invalidates equation 16 at these points. In any case equation 35 represents an extremely complicated function* which would make the evaluation of the various terms in the series 20 difficult. Thus, while starting with equation 35, King and Middleton used eventually a constant parameter:

$$W = W_4(0) = (\sin \beta l)^{-1} \int_{-l}^{l} G(\xi) \sin \beta(l - |\xi|) \, d\xi, \qquad l \leq \tfrac{1}{4}\lambda;$$
$$(36)$$
$$= W_4(l - \tfrac{1}{4}\lambda) = \int_{-l}^{l} G(\xi - l + \tfrac{1}{4}\lambda) \sin \beta(l - |\xi|) \, d\xi, \qquad l \geq \tfrac{1}{4}\lambda.$$

In the vicinity of the first critical length $l = \lambda/2$, this parameter is very close to Gray's parameter even though the definitions 34 and 36 are quite different. For this reason the values of the antiresonant impedance obtained by King and Middleton are comparable to those obtained by Gray and considerably smaller than the values obtained from $W = \Omega$.

Siegel and Labus evaluated the left side of equation 1 for the first approximation, $I(\xi) = I_0 \sin \beta(l - |\xi|)$, to the current in the symmetric transmitting antenna, and found that a substantial part of it contains the factor $I_0 \sin \beta(l - |z|)$. The coefficient of proportionality for $z > 0$,

$$W_5(z) =$$
$$\tfrac{1}{2}[\log 4z(l - z) - \log(\beta^2 a^4) + \text{Ci } 2\beta z + \text{Ci } 2\beta(l - z) - 2C], \quad (37)$$

if used in equation 16, will cancel in $S[I(z)]$ a major part of the contribution due to the sinusoidal component of $I(z)$. We could level this

* J. Labus, Rechnerische Ermittlung der [Impedanz von Antennen, *Hochfreq. u. Electroak.*, **41**, January 1933, pp. 17–23.

E. Siegel and J. Labus, Scheinwiderstand von Antennen, *ibid.*, **43**, May 1934, pp. 166–172.

function by taking its average value,

$$\overline{W}_5 = 2 \log \frac{2l}{a} - \text{Cin } 2\beta l - 1 - \frac{\sin 2\beta l}{2\beta l} \cdot \tag{38}$$

In the case of progressive waves on a wire extending from $z = 0$ to $z = l$, we have*

$$W_6 I_0(z) = A e^{-j\beta z},$$

$$W_6^2 I_1(z) = W_6 S[I_0(z)]$$

$$= A W_6 e^{-j\beta z} - A \int_0^l \int_0^{2\pi} (2\pi r)^{-1} e^{-j\beta r - j\beta \xi} \, d\xi \, d\varphi \tag{39}$$

$$= A e^{-j\beta z} \left[ W_6 - \text{Ei } 2j\beta(l - z) + \text{Ei } \frac{j\beta a^2}{2z} \right].$$

To make the squares of the real and imaginary parts minimum, we take

$$W_6 = \text{av} \left[ \text{Ei } 2j\beta(l - z) - \text{Ei } \frac{j\beta a^2}{2z} \right]$$

$$= 2 \log \frac{2l}{a} - \text{Cin } 2\beta l - 1 - \frac{\sin 2\beta l}{2\beta l} - j\text{Si } 2\beta l + j \frac{1 - \cos 2\beta l}{2\beta l} \cdot \tag{40}$$

This value is comparable to $\overline{W}_5$.

It should be noted that King-Middleton's expressions 36 for the expansion parameter as well as equations 38 and 40 depend on the form of the first approximation to the antenna current. Hence, different values will be obtained for transmitting and receiving antennas.

The various expansion parameters 31, 33, 34, and 38 are comparable in magnitude when $l/\lambda$ is not too large. But, as $l/\lambda$ increases, the differences increase. If $\lambda = \infty$, then $W_3 = \Omega$ and $\overline{W}_5 = \Omega - 2$. As $\lambda$ decreases, $\Omega$ remains constant while $W_3$ and $\overline{W}_5$ decrease. However, $W_3$ decreases more rapidly and eventually becomes smaller than $\overline{W}_5$. It is difficult to decide *a priori* which particular value will give the best asymptotic approximation *for relatively small values* of the expansion parameter. For really large values of $W$ there is no problem since all expansions are analytically the same and since for large $W$ we can take many terms of the series before it begins to diverge. Unfortunately, for practical antennas $\Omega$ is not very large.

The input admittance is a fluctuating function of the length of the antenna, and point-by-point comparison of different approximations is not very instructive. The following comparison is offered only to exhibit the differences due to the differences in the expansion parameter

---

* It is to be noticed that $\text{Ei}(jx) = C + \log jx - \text{Ein}(jx) = C + \log x + \frac{1}{2}j\pi - \text{Cin } x - j\text{Si } x = \text{Ci } x - j\text{Si } x + \frac{1}{2}j\pi.$

if we limit the series 20 to two terms.   We express all results for the input admittance $Y_i$ of a full-wave antenna $(2l = \lambda)$ in terms of the average characteristic impedance $K_a$ which occurs in the mode theory of antennas when $2l < 1.5\lambda$, and which equals $60(\Omega - 2)$.   The mode theory gives

$$K_a{}^2 Y_i = 199.09 + j125.41 + (29119 + j18342)K_a{}^{-1}. \qquad (41)$$

If we use equation 31 for the expansion parameter as in the King-Blake paper, we obtain

$$K_a{}^2 Y_i = 199.09 + j125.41 - (42320 + j15446)K_a{}^{-1}. \qquad (42)$$

If we use Gray's value (equation 34), we have

$$K_a{}^2 Y_i = 199.09 + j125.41 + (49405 + j18674)K_a{}^{-1}. \qquad (43)$$

And, finally, if we use the King-Middleton value (equation 36), then,

$$K_a{}^2 Y_i = 199.09 + j125.41 + (29352 + j29702)K_a{}^{-1}. \qquad (44)$$

The substantial difference between equation 42 on the one hand and equations 43 and 44 on the other may be traced to the lower values of the expansion parameter used in deriving the last two expressions.   On the whole the last expression is the closest to that given by the mode theory, although the reactive part of equation 43 is closer.   Hallén points out that, if the terms depending on $\Omega^{-2}$ are included in equation 42, the conductance becomes equal to that given by the mode theory, but the susceptance is still different.   King and Middleton find that for their expansion parameter the third term of the series 20 makes a significant contribution.   This indicates that the fourth term depending on $\Omega^{-3}$ should be computed before we could make an assertion concerning the best value of the expansion parameter.   In fact, the best value may not exist, for it is possible that one value may give the best results when only two terms of the series 20 are taken, and another value is best for three terms.   It would be desirable to study more closely the most obvious splitting of the integral, as shown in equation 15 and the corresponding expansion parameter (equation 33).   The expansion parameter plays the part of characteristic impedance in transmission line theory, and it so happens that equation 33 gives very closely the asymptotic value of the input impedance of an infinitely long antenna.   This fact is very suggestive.

For further details concerning special asymptotic expansions and their applications the reader is referred to the papers listed at the end of this chapter.

## 5.5   Approximate integral equations

Usually it is assumed that equations expressing physical problems correctly have solutions. The assumption is safe provided no *mathematical* approximations are subsequently made in the equations. Antenna theory provides examples in which such approximations lead to equations with no solutions. Thus, when the radius of a cylindrical antenna is small, the kernel in equation 7 for the Green's function is usually approximated by a simpler function,

$$\Gamma(\xi - z) = r_0^{-1}e^{-j\beta r_0}, \qquad r_0 = [(\xi - z)^2 + a^2]^{\frac{1}{2}}. \qquad (45)$$

If $|\xi - z| \gg a$, this kernel differs from the exact kernel (equation 2) by a quantity of the order of the square of the radius. The difference is large only in a small interval around $\xi = z$. Furthermore, if $I(\xi)$ is a slowly varying function, the values of the integral in equation 7 for the two kernels differ by quantities of the order of the square of the radius. Presumably it was such considerations as these that led to an assumption that equation 45 represents a reasonable approximation to $G(\xi - z)$.

However, the approximate integral equation with this value of $G$ has no solutions. For the approximate kernel the left side of equation 7 is a proper integral and is a continuous and differentiable function. On the other hand, the derivative of the right-hand side is discontinuous at $z = 0$. The nonexistence of solutions could have been anticipated from physical considerations. After substituting $\Gamma(\xi - z)$ for $G(\xi - z)$, the derivative of the integral in equation 7 represents, except for a constant factor, the exact potential on the axis of the cylinder due to a charge on its surface; the same derivative also represents the exact potential on the surface of the cylinder due to a charge on its axis. Consequently, equation 7 requires a charge distribution which would produce a potential discontinuity, and an infinite electric intensity, at a place where there is no charge whatsoever. Thus, the approximate integral equation formulates an impossible physical problem.

As $a$ approaches zero, the iterative process in Sections 5.3 and 5.4 leads to the same formal solutions of equation 7 for both kernels, $G(\xi - z)$ and $\Gamma(\xi - z)$. Since equation 7 has no solutions for $\Gamma(\xi - z)$, these expansions must be divergent.

At this place it may occur to the reader that some antenna problems can be solved synthetically by analogy with electrostatics. In electrostatics we may assume, for example, a positive charge uniformly distributed on a straight segment between $z = 0$ and $z = l$, and an equal negative charge uniformly distributed between $z = 0$ and $z = -l$. We can then calculate the potential of this charge distribution and replace one or more equipotential surfaces by conducting surfaces without affecting the field. In this way we can solve many problems of charge distribution on conductors whose potentials are given (the shapes of these conductors will be determined by the assumed charge distributions). It may seem, at first, that we can similarly assume arbitrarily some current distribution and then calculate surfaces on which the tangential components of the electric intensity vanish, thus solving some antenna problems exactly. However, we shall find that for an arbitrary current distribution there are no such surfaces.

## REFERENCES

The following are basic papers expounding Hallén's method of antenna analysis:

1. E. Hallén, Über die elektrischen Schwingungen in drahtförmigen Leitern, *Uppsala Universitets Årsskrift*, 1930, no. 1.
2. E. Hallén, Theoretical investigations into the transmitting and receiving qualities of antennae, *Nova Acta*, Uppsala, **11**, 1938, no. 4.
3. E. Hallén, Further investigations into the receiving qualities of antennae: the absorbing of transient, unperiodic radiation, *Uppsala Universitets Årsskrift*, 1939, no. 4.

The following papers discuss Hallén's theory:

4. C. J. Bouwkamp, Hallén's theory for a straight perfectly conducting wire, used as a transmitting or receiving aerial, *Physica*, **9**, July 1942, pp. 609–631.
5. L. Brillouin, The antenna problem, *Quart. Appl. Math.*, **1**, October 1943, pp. 201–214.
6. S. A. Schelkunoff, Antenna theory and experiment, *Jour. Appl. Phys.*, **15**, January 1944, pp. 54–60.
7. M. C. Gray, A modification of Hallén's solution of the antenna problem, *Jour. Appl. Phys.*, **15**, January 1944, pp. 61–65.
8. S. A. Schelkunoff, On the antenna problem, *Quart. Appl. Math.*, **1**, January 1944, pp. 354–355.
9. S. A. Schelkunoff, Concerning Hallén's integral equation for cylindrical antennas, *IRE Proc.*, December 1945, pp. 872–878.
10. R. King and D. Middleton, The cylindrical antenna; current and impedance, *Quart. Appl. Math.*, **3**, January 1946, pp. 302–335; Corrections, *ibid.*, **4**, July 1946, pp. 199–200; Addit. corrections, *ibid.*, **6**, July 1948, p. 192.
11. E. Hallén, Iterated sine and cosine integrals, *Kungl. Tekniska Högskolan*, 1947, no. 12.
12. E. Hallén, Properties of long antennas, *Cruft Laboratory Report no. 44*, Harvard University, May 25, 1948.
13. E. Hallén, Admittance diagrams for antennas and the relation between antenna theories, *Cruft Laboratory Report no. 46*, Harvard University, June 1, 1948.
14. E. Hallén, Traveling waves and unsymmetrically fed antennas, *Cruft Laboratory Report no. 49*, Harvard University, June 22, 1948.
15. E. Hallén, Properties of a long antenna, *Jour. Appl. Phys.*, December 1948, pp. 1140–1147.

The following papers are concerned with special applications of Hallén's theory:

16. R. King and F. G. Blake, Jr., The self-impedance of a symmetrical antenna, *IRE Proc.*, **30**, July 1942, pp. 335–349.

17. R. King and C. W. Harrison, Jr., The distribution of current along a symmetrical center-driven antenna, *IRE Proc.*, **31**, October 1943, pp. 548–566; Corrections, *ibid.*, December 1943, p. 697.

18. R. King, Coupled antennas and transmission lines, *IRE Proc.*, **31**, November 1943, pp. 626–640.

19. C. W. Harrison, Jr., and R. King, The radiation field of a symmetrical center-driven antenna of finite cross section, *IRE Proc.*, **31**, December 1943, pp. 693–697.

20. R. King and C. W. Harrison, Jr., The receiving antenna, *IRE Proc.*, **32**, January 1944, pp. 18–35.

21. C. W. Harrison, Jr., and R. King, The receiving antenna in a plane-polarized field of arbitrary orientation, *IRE Proc.*, **32**, January 1944, pp. 35–49.

22. R. King and C. W. Harrison, Jr., The impedance of long, short and capacitively loaded antennas with a critical discussion of the antenna problem, *Jour. Appl. Phys.*, **15**, February 1944, pp. 170–185.

23. R. King and C. W. Harrison, Jr., Mutual and self-impedance for coupled antennas, *Jour. Appl. Phys.*, **15**, June 1944, pp. 481–495.

24. D. D. King and R. King, Terminal functions for antennas, *Jour. Appl. Phys.*, **15**, February 1944, pp. 186–192.

25. C. W. Harrison, Jr., Mutual and self-impedance for collinear antennas, *IRE Proc.*, **33**, June 1945, pp. 398–408.

26. C. W. Harrison, Jr., On the distribution of current along asymmetrical antennas, *Jour. Appl. Phys.*, **16**, July 1945, pp. 402–408.

27. R. King and D. D. King, Microwave impedance measurements with application to antennas, *Jour. Appl. Phys.*, **16**, August 1945, pp. 445–453.

28. D. Middleton and R. King, The thin cylindrical antenna: A comparison of theories, *Jour. Appl. Phys.*, **17**, April 1946, pp. 273–284.

29. C. W. Harrison, Jr., A theory for three-element broadside arrays, *IRE Proc.*, **34**, April 1946, pp. 204P–209P.

30. R. King and T. W. Winternitz, The cylindrical antenna with gap, *Quart. Appl. Math.*, **5**, January 1948, pp. 403–416.

31. C. T. Tai, Coupled antennas, *IRE Proc.*, **36**, April 1948, pp. 487–500.

# 6

# NATURAL OSCILLATIONS

## 6.1 Forced and natural oscillations

Once the steady-state solution of a given antenna problem has been found, it is relatively easy to obtain the more general solution representing the response of the antenna to an impressed field varying arbitrarily with time. Throughout the preceding chapters the exponential time factor is in the form $\exp(j\omega t)$ which makes the equations more easily interpretable when the radian frequency $\omega = 2\pi f$ is real. However, there is nothing in the analysis that requires $\omega$ to be real; and, if $\omega$ is permitted to be complex, we obtain the more general exponential solutions and can use Laplace integrals to introduce an arbitrary dependence on time. While analytically $\omega$ can be complex, physically it is essentially real. For this reason we first transform our equations formally by replacing $j\omega$ with $p = \xi + j\omega$: that is, $\omega$ with $\omega - j\xi$. The real part $\xi$ of the oscillation constant $p$ is called the growth constant; its negative is the damping constant. Let $F(x, y, z)$ be some field quantity when the function representing the impressed field is of the exponential form $V \exp(pt)$, and let

$$F(x, y, z) = V\, T(x, y, z, p)e^{pt}. \tag{1}$$

Functions that are arbitrary for practical purposes may be represented by Laplace integrals of the form

$$V(t) = \frac{1}{2\pi j} \int_{(C)} S(p)e^{pt}\, dp, \tag{2}$$

where the contour of integration $(C)$ runs to the right of and parallel to the imaginary axis in the $p$ plane. For the impressed field represented by this time function, we have

$$F(x, y, z, t) = \frac{1}{2\pi j} \int_{(C)} S(p)\, T(x, y, z, p)e^{pt}\, dp. \tag{3}$$

152

As an example let us consider a perfectly conducting sphere of radius $a$, concentric with the origin of our coordinate system, and let us assume that, at the instant $t = 0$, a constant electric field of intensity $E_0$ is impressed on this sphere.    If this field is parallel to the $z$ axis, the meridian component is $E_\theta{}^i = -E_0 \sin \theta$.    The total intensity tangential to the sphere must vanish; hence, the component due to the charges and currents on the sphere is $E_\theta(a, \theta, t) = E_0 \sin \theta$ when $t > 0$.    When $t < 0$, $E_\theta(a, \theta, t) = 0$.    Therefore,

$$E_\theta(a, \theta, t) = \frac{E_0}{2\pi j} \sin \theta \int_{(C)} p^{-1} e^{pt} \, dp. \tag{4}$$

From equations 1–110 we can obtain the transfer ratio $E_\theta(r, \theta)/E_\theta(a, \theta)$ for the exponential time variation, and, then,

$$E_\theta(r, \theta, t) = \frac{E_0 a \sin \theta}{2\pi j r} \times$$

$$\int_{(C)} \frac{(pa/c)^2 + (pa/c)(a/r) + (a^2/r^2)}{p[(pa/c)^2 + (pa/c) + 1]} \exp\left[\frac{p(ct - r + a)}{c}\right] dp. \tag{5}$$

If $ct - r + a < 0$, that is, if $r - a > ct$, the contour $(C)$ may be closed with an infinite semicircle in the right half of the plane without changing the value of the integral.    Since the integrand is holomorphic inside the closed contour, we have

$$E_\theta(r, \theta, t) = 0, \qquad r - a > ct; \tag{6}$$

that is, the field is zero at points that cannot be reached in time $t$ by a disturbance traveling from the surface of the sphere with the speed $c$. If $r - a < ct$, the contour $(C)$ may be closed in the left half-plane.    The integrand is holomorphic except at $p = 0$ and two other poles given by

$$\left(\frac{pa}{c}\right)^2 + \frac{pa}{c} + 1 = 0,$$

$$p_1 = \frac{cw}{a}, \qquad p_2 = \frac{cw^*}{a}, \qquad w = -\tfrac{1}{2} + \tfrac{1}{2} j\sqrt{3}. \tag{7}$$

By the theorem of residues,

$$E_\theta(r, \theta, t) = \frac{E_0 a}{r} \left[ \frac{a^2}{r^2} + \frac{w^2 + w(a/r) + (a/r)^2}{w(w - w^*)} e^{w(ct - r + a)/a} + \right.$$

$$\left. \frac{(w^*)^2 + w^*(a/r) + (a/r)^2}{w^*(w^* - w)} e^{w^*(ct - r + a)/a} \right] \sin \theta. \tag{8}$$

Substituting from equations 7 and simplifying, we find

$$E_\theta(r, \theta, t) = \frac{E_0 a^3 \sin\theta}{r^3} + \frac{2E_0}{\sqrt{3}} \frac{a}{r} \left(1 - \frac{a}{r}\right)\left(1 + \frac{a}{r} + \frac{a^2}{r^2}\right)^{1/2} \times$$

$$e^{(r-a-ct)/2a} \cos\left[\frac{\sqrt{3}(r - a - ct)}{2a} - \vartheta\right] \sin\theta,$$

$$\cos\vartheta = \tfrac{1}{2}\sqrt{3} \left(1 + \frac{a}{r}\right)\left(1 + \frac{a}{r} + \frac{a^2}{r^2}\right)^{-1/2},$$

$$\sin\vartheta = \tfrac{1}{2} \left(1 - \frac{a}{r}\right)\left(1 + \frac{a}{r} + \frac{a^2}{r^2}\right)^{-1/2}.$$

(9)

The transient part of $E_\theta$ vanishes at the surface of the sphere at all times. It represents free or natural electric oscillations of a perfectly conducting sphere, and, except for the amplitude and phase, it can be determined directly from equations 1–110 if we impose the boundary condition $E_\theta(a, \theta) = 0$. From equations 7 we find that the damping constant is $c/2a$, and the radian frequency $\omega = c\sqrt{3}/2a$. The wavelength corresponding to this frequency is $\lambda = c/f = 4\pi a/\sqrt{3}$. It exceeds the circumference of the sphere by 15.5 percent.

## 6.2  Equivalent networks

Any well-defined electric structure has a unique input impedance; but the converse is not true. Several networks, either discrete or continuous, may have the same impedance $Z(p)$ at all frequencies; and, of course, many more may have approximately the same impedance in a limited frequency range. The problem of network analysis is: *Given a network of resistors, inductors, and capacitors or a continuous physical structure (such as an antenna), find its impedance (or admittance) function.* The problem of network synthesis is the inverse problem: *Given a physically realizable impedance function $Z(p)$, find one or more networks possessing this impedance.* The problem of network synthesis is particularly important in the design of filters and impedance corrective networks. An equivalent network for an antenna may be useful in experiments designed to test the terminal networks intended to operate with the antenna, before the antenna is actually constructed.

In the case of discrete networks the problem of analysis is almost trivial: We have to solve a system of linear algebraic equations. But the problem of synthesis is far from trivial. In the case of antennas even the analysis is formidable. Fortunately, in practical applications simple approximations often suffice, and at present at least the complete solution of the problem of obtaining networks equivalent to antennas is interesting only from the theoretical point of view.

The equations for discrete networks can be solved in general terms, and it is relatively easy to establish the criteria for the physical realizability of $Z(p)$: that is, the conditions that must be satisfied by $Z(p)$ if it is to represent the impedance of any network whose elements consist of positive resistances, inductances and capacitances.* Some of these conditions are obviously applicable to either discrete or continuous structures. For example, the zeros and poles must not lie in the right half of the complex plane; otherwise, the system would permit oscillations of increasing amplitude without the corresponding supply of energy. If complex, the zeros and poles must occur in conjugate pairs. This follows from the fact that the coefficients in $Z(p)$ are real. On the other hand, at infinity the impedance of a finite discrete network has either a simple pole or a simple zero, or else it reduces to a constant. For continuous structures the behavior of $Z(p)$ at infinity cannot be specified as simply. In this book, however, we are not concerned with the general theory of impedance functions. Our functions are physically realizable because they are obtained by the analysis of given structures and their analytic properties are exhibited.

The admittance $Y_t$ of a spherical antenna is given by equation 2–196. It is seen to be a sum of an infinite number of admittance functions. Each component admittance is proportional to the radial admittance $Y_n(pa)$ of a zonal spherical wave (equation 2–198). Each radial admittance is a rational fraction, in which the degree of the numerator equals that of the denominator. The zeros and poles are in the left half of the plane, excepting the simple zero at the origin. Hence, each component admittance is physically realizable, and the admittance of the spherical antenna may be considered as the admittance of certain finite discrete networks connected in parallel.

To derive the network structures of the radial admittances it is convenient to consider simultaneously the radial impedance of a TM wave and the radial admittance of a TE wave of the same order (see Sections 1.5 and 1.6),

$$Z_n{}^{\mathrm{TM}}(a) = -\frac{\eta\, Kn_n{}'(w)}{Kn_n(w)}\,, \qquad Y_n{}^{\mathrm{TE}}(a) = -\frac{\eta^{-1}\, Kn_n{}'(w)}{Kn_n(w)}\,, \qquad (10)$$

$$w = pa(\mu\varepsilon)^{\frac12}.$$

* Otto Brune, Synthesis of a finite two-terminal network whose driving-point impedance is a prescribed function of frequency, *Jour. Math. and Phys.*, **10**, August 1931, pp. 191–236.

The impedance of the TM wave is proportional to the admittance of the TE wave, and the corresponding networks are dual. As $w$ approaches zero, $Kn_n(w)$ approaches $Aw^{-n} \exp(-w)$. Hence,

$$Z_n{}^{\mathrm{TM}}(a) \to \frac{n}{p\varepsilon a}, \tag{11}$$

and the impedance has a simple pole at the origin. Since $n/p\varepsilon a$ is the impedance corresponding to the capacitance $\varepsilon a/n$, this part of $Z$ is physically realizable. Let us subtract it from $Z$ and simplify the remainder, using the first of the recurrence formulas for the normalized Bessel functions,*

$$w\, Kn_n{}'(w) = -n\, Kn_n(w) - w\, Kn_{n-1}(w),$$
$$w\, Kn_{n-1}{}'(w) = n\, Kn_{n-1}(w) - w\, Kn_n(w). \tag{12}$$

Thus, we have

$$-\frac{\eta\, Kn_n{}'(w)}{Kn_n(w)} - \frac{n}{p\varepsilon a} = \frac{w\, Kn_{n-1}(w)}{p\varepsilon a\, Kn_n(w)}. \tag{13}$$

Using the second recurrence formula in the denominator, and dividing both terms of the fraction by the numerator, we obtain the first of the following recurrence relations:

$$Z_n{}^{\mathrm{TM}} = \frac{n}{p\varepsilon a} + \frac{1}{(n/p\mu a) + Y_{n-1}{}^{\mathrm{TE}}},$$

$$Y_n{}^{\mathrm{TE}} = \frac{n}{p\mu a} + \frac{1}{(n/p\varepsilon a) + Z_{n-1}{}^{\mathrm{TM}}}. \tag{14}$$

The second formula is obtained by interchanging $\mu$ and $\varepsilon$.

From equations 1–110 we obtain the radial impedance of the zonal wave of the first order,

$$Z_1{}^{\mathrm{TM}} = \frac{\eta(w^2 + w + 1)}{w(w + 1)} = \frac{1}{p\varepsilon a} + \frac{1}{(1/p\mu a) + \eta^{-1}}. \tag{15}$$

Interchanging $\mu$ and $\varepsilon$,

$$Y_1{}^{\mathrm{TE}} = \frac{1}{p\mu a} + \frac{1}{(1/p\varepsilon a) + \eta}. \tag{16}$$

Equation 15 shows that $Z_1$ is the impedance of a capacitor in series with the parallel combination of an inductor and a resistor (Fig. 6.1a) Similarly $Y_1$ is the admittance of an inductor in parallel with a series combination of a capacitor and a resistor (Fig. 6.1b).

* *Applied Mathematics*, p. 412.

From equations 14 we see that $Z_n^{\text{TM}}$ is the impedance of the capacitor $\varepsilon a/n$ in series with the parallel combination of the inductor $\mu a/n$ and $Y_{n-1}^{\text{TE}}$, and that $Y_n^{\text{TE}}$ is the admittance of the inductor $\mu a/n$ in parallel with the series combination of the capacitor $\varepsilon a/n$ and $Z_{n-1}^{\text{TM}}$. Using these rules repeatedly, we obtain the network representations of the radial impedances of TM and TE waves (Fig. 6.2).

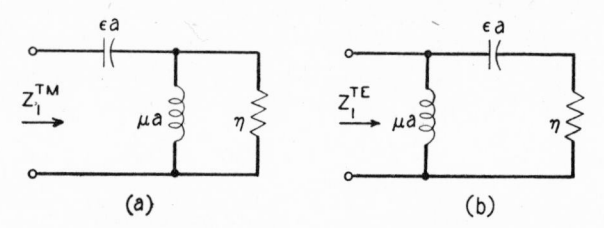

FIG. 6.1   Network representations of the radial wave impedances: (a) TM zonal wave of the first order, (b) TE zonal wave of the first order.

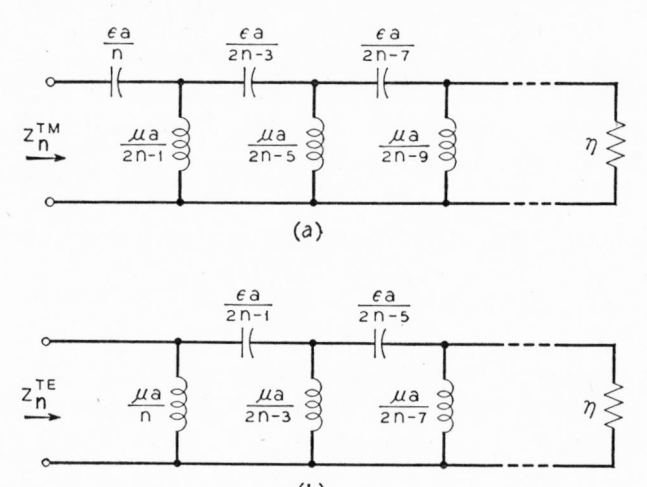

FIG. 6.2   Network representation of the radial wave impedance of the $n$th-order zonal waves [and more generally of waves in which the radial field intensity is proportional to $P_n^m(\cos\theta)\cos m\varphi$]: (a) TM waves, (b) TE waves.

If we multiply each inductance and resistance and divide each capacitance by a constant $u$, the impedance of the network is multiplied by $u$. For instance, the impedance of the network in Fig. 6.3 is $u$ times that of the network in Fig. 6.1a. Hence, the admittance (equation 2–196) of the spherical antenna may be represented by a parallel combination of networks of the type shown in Fig. 6.2a.

With the aid of such network representations Chu was able to obtain important relationships between the gain, bandwidth, and size of antennas.*

If the admittance has only simple poles in the finite part of the plane, it can be expressed (the Mittag-Leffler theorem) in the following form,

$$Y(p) = F(p) + \sum_n A_n \left( \frac{1}{p - p_n} + \frac{1}{p_n} + \frac{p}{p_n^2} + \cdots + \frac{p^{\alpha-2}}{p_n^{\alpha-1}} \right),$$

(17)

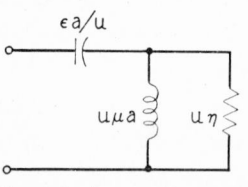

where $F(p)$ is an integral function, $p = p_n$ is a typical pole of $Y(p)$, and $\alpha$ is such that $\sum A_n p_n^{-\alpha}$ is convergent. Equation 2–203 for the admittance of the spherical antenna is of this form. In the case of finite networks we can retain in the summation only the partial fractions $A_n/(p - p_n)$ and include the remaining terms (needed only for convergence purposes) in $F(p)$; after this rearrangement the degree of $F(p)$ cannot exceed one for, if there is a pole at infinity, it must be simple. If the network is continuous and nondissipative, it is possible to obtain directly from Maxwell's equations the following expansion,†

FIG. 6.3 A network whose impedance is $u$ times that of the network in Figure 6.1a.

$$Y(j\omega) = \sum_n \frac{j\omega}{2 \mathcal{E}_n(\omega_n^2 - \omega^2)},$$

(18)

where $\omega_n$ is the natural frequency of the $n$th mode when the input terminals of the network are short-circuited and $\mathcal{E}_n$ is the energy stored in it when the current through the input terminals is unity. Similarly, for the input impedance we have

$$Z(j\omega) = \sum \frac{j\omega}{2 \mathcal{E}_n(\omega_n^2 - \omega^2)},$$

(19)

where $\omega_n$ is the natural frequency of the $n$th mode when the terminals of the network are open and $\mathcal{E}_n$ is the stored energy when the voltage across the input terminals is unity. These expansions are special cases of equation 17.

If the network is slightly dissipative, the following *approximate*

---

* L. J. Chu, Physical limitations of omni-directional antennas, *Jour. Appl. Phys.*, **19**, December 1948, pp. 1163–1175.

† E. U. Condon, Forced oscillations in cavity resonators, *Jour. Appl. Phys.*, **12**, February 1941, pp. 129–132.

expansions may be obtained,*

$$Y(j\omega) \simeq \sum_n \frac{j\omega}{2\mathfrak{S}_n(\omega_n{}^2 - \omega^2 + j\omega\omega_n Q_n{}^{-1})},$$

$$Z(j\omega) \simeq \sum_n \frac{j\omega}{2\mathfrak{S}_n(\omega_n{}^2 - \omega^2 + j\omega\omega_n Q_n{}^{-1})},$$

$$(20)$$

where the $Q_n$'s are the " quality factors " of the corresponding modes,

$$Q_n = -\frac{\omega_n}{2\xi_n}, \tag{21}$$

and $\xi_n = \mathrm{re}(p_n)$. If $P_n$ is the average dissipated or radiated power in the $n$th mode, the relative rate of energy loss is $P_n/\mathfrak{S}_n$, and the relative rate of decrease in the amplitude of the oscillations is $P_n/2\mathfrak{S}_n$. Hence,

$$\xi_n = -\frac{P_n}{2\mathfrak{S}_n}, \qquad Q_n = \frac{\omega_n\mathfrak{S}_n}{P_n}. \tag{22}$$

Each term in equation 18 represents the admittance of a series combination of an inductance and capacitance; and the entire series is the admittance of an infinite number of such simple circuits connected in parallel. Similarly, the series 19 is the impedance of an infinite number of parallel combinations of inductances and capacitances connected in series.

The approximate expansions 20 represent similar networks with small resistances added in series with series combinations of inductances and capacitances, and small conductances in parallel with parallel combinations. But it is not safe to use these approximate formulas except in the immediate vicinity of a resonance. These equations are based on the assumption that the damping constant of each natural mode is small, and they do not take into consideration the precise mechanism by which the damping is introduced. Consider, for instance, the circuits in Fig. 6.4 in which $R$ is very small and $R'$ very large compared with $(L/C)^{1/2}$. Both circuits have small damping constants, and their quality factors are equal if $RR' = L/C$. Their impedance representations in the form 20 are identical, and yet the circuits behave very differently for very low and for very high frequencies. If $R'$ is constant, the equivalent series resistance of the circuit $b$ is proportional to the square of the frequency. The input resistance of $a$ has a small constant value at all frequencies; but at high frequencies the input resistance of $b$ is very large. Near a resonance, however, one term in the expansions 21 becomes dominant and controls the *changes* in the impedance with frequency. For this reason expansions 21 are im-

* *Ibid.*

portant.  The parameters $\omega_n$, $\mathscr{E}_n$, $Q_n$ can often be obtained approximately without solving the complete boundary value problem.

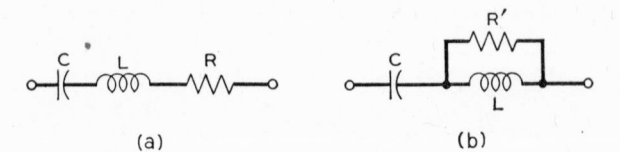

(a)                              (b)

FIG.  6.4   Two typical series resonant circuits.

If $Y(p)$ has only simple zeros $a_1$, $a_2$, $\cdots$, and simple poles $b_1$, $b_2$, $\cdots$, in addition to a zero or pole at $p = 0$, then by the Weierstrass theorem,

$$Y(p) = e^{F(p)}p^\alpha \times$$

$$\frac{\Pi(1-pa_n{}^{-1})\exp[pa_n{}^{-1}+\frac{1}{2}p^2a_n{}^{-2}+\frac{1}{3}p^3a_n{}^{-3}+\cdots+(\beta-1)^{-1}p^{\beta-1}a_n{}^{1-\beta}]}{\Pi(1-pb_n{}^{-1})\exp[pb_n{}^{-1}+\frac{1}{2}p^2b_n{}^{-2}+\frac{1}{3}p^3b_n{}^{-3}+\cdots+(\beta-1)^{-1}p^{\beta-1}b_n{}^{1-\beta}]},$$

$$(23)$$

where $F(p)$ is an integral function, $\alpha = \pm 1$, and $\beta$ is such that $\sum a_n{}^{-\beta}$ and $\sum b_n{}^{-\beta}$ are convergent.  This expression lacks the simplicity of the corresponding product expansions for finite networks, in which the exponential convergence factors are not required and $F(p) = 0$.

## 6.3   Small antennas

Consider a perfectly conducting spherical surface joined to conical surfaces extending to the origin $O$ (Fig. 6.5) where the cones are con-

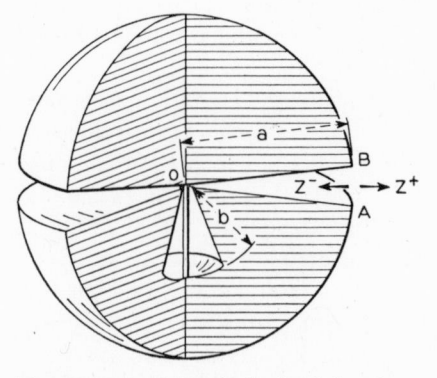

FIG.  6.5   An inductively loaded sphere.

nected in series with two other cones forming a cavity.  The condition for natural oscillations is

$$Z^+(j\omega) + Z^-(j\omega) = 0, \quad \text{or} \quad Y^+(j\omega) + Y^-(j\omega) = 0, \qquad (24)$$

where $Y^+$ is the admittance seen outward from the gap $A$, $B$ and $Y^-$ is the admittance seen inward. The former (for circularly symmetric oscillations) is given by equation 2–196 and the latter, except for a small capacitance edge effect, is

$$Y^-(j\omega) = jK_1^{-1} \frac{K_2 \sin \beta a \sin \beta b - K_1 \cos \beta a \cos \beta b}{K_2 \cos \beta a \sin \beta b + K_1 \sin \beta a \cos \beta b}, \qquad (25)$$

where $K_1$ and $K_2$ are the characteristic impedances of the conical guides seen inward from the gap.

As $\omega \to 0$, we have

$$Y^-(j\omega) \to \frac{1}{j\omega L_i}, \qquad L_i = (K_1 a + K_2 b)(\mu\varepsilon)^{\frac{1}{2}},$$
$$Y^+(j\omega) \to \frac{3\pi}{2} Y_1{}^{\mathrm{TM}} + j\omega\, C_{e,\mathrm{sh}}, \qquad (26)$$

where $L_i$ is the internal inductance of the spherical oscillator and $C_{e,\mathrm{sh}}$ is the external capacitance, representing the higher modes of external

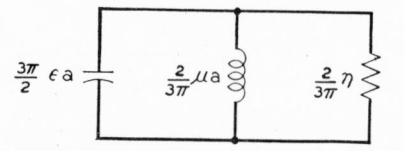

$$C_{e,\mathrm{sr}} = \frac{3\pi}{2}\epsilon a$$

$$L_i \qquad C_{e,\mathrm{sh}} \qquad L_e = \frac{2\mu a}{3\pi} \qquad R_{\mathrm{rad}} = \frac{2\eta}{3\pi} = 80$$

Fɪɢ. 6.6   Network representation of the inductively loaded sphere.

$$\frac{3\pi}{2}\epsilon a \qquad \frac{2}{3\pi}\mu a \qquad \frac{2}{3\pi}\eta$$

Fɪɢ. 6.7   A circuit equivalent to a conducting sphere oscillating in its gravest mode.

oscillations on the sphere, in shunt with the network representing the first mode. The latter network is shown in Fig. 6.3 with $u = \dfrac{2}{3\pi}$. The complete network is shown in Fig. 6.6.

If we short-circuit the cones, $L_i = 0$ and the network becomes that shown in Fig. 6.7. This network still represents correctly the gravest mode of oscillations on the sphere. Incidentally, with the values of the circuit parameters as indicated, the *energy stored in the capacitor equals the external electrostatic energy associated with the charge on the sphere, and the energy stored in the inductor equals the external magnetic energy associated with the current.*

The equivalent circuit of a small antenna can be obtained from general considerations without solving the particular antenna boundary value problem. Consider, for example, a wire of length $2l$ loaded inductively in the center. From the law of conservation of energy, we have

$$\frac{d}{dt}\left[\tfrac{1}{2}L\left(\frac{dq}{dt}\right)^2 + \frac{1}{2}\frac{q^2}{C}\right] = -P, \qquad (27)$$

where $q$ is the charge on one arm of the antenna. The first term inside the brackets represents the stored magnetic energy and the second the stored electric energy; $P$ is the rate at which the circuit loses energy by dissipation in heat or by radiation. Power lost by dissipation in heat is $R(dq/dt)^2$; but, since we are interested in radiation, we shall assume that the conductors are perfect.* In Chapter 1 we have seen that a small circuit radiates a small fraction of its stored energy, and its electrical behavior in a relatively short time interval must be determined primarily by $L$ and $C$. Hence, tentatively we neglect $P$ in equation 27 and obtain

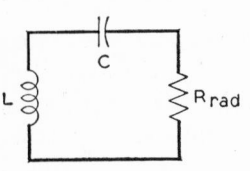

FIG. 6.8 Network representation of a small perfectly conducting antenna with the terminals short-circuited.

the natural frequency $\omega = (LC)^{-\frac{1}{2}}$. Having determined this frequency, we calculate the radiated power from the external field of the circuit. For the wire of length $2l$, for instance,

$$P = \frac{\eta}{6\pi}\beta^2 l^2 \left(\frac{dq}{dt}\right)^2 = \frac{\omega^2 \mu^2 l^2}{6\pi\eta}\left(\frac{dq}{dt}\right)^2. \qquad (28)$$

The coefficient of proportionality,

$$R_{\text{rad}} = \frac{\eta}{6\pi}\beta^2 l^2 = \frac{\omega^2 \mu^2 l^2}{6\pi\eta}, \qquad (29)$$

is called the "radiation resistance" because it plays the part of resistance in the circuit. Thus we have the equivalent circuit shown in Fig. 6.8.

The next problem is to construct a circuit whose resistance is proportional to the square of the frequency when the frequency is sufficiently low (in the present case $\beta l \ll 1$, which is the definition of a "short" wire).

---

* It must be remembered, however, that ohmic losses in small antennas are often much larger than radiation losses, and they should always be included in the complete circuit.

Consider the impedance $Z$ of a constant resistance $R'$ in parallel with an inductance $L$ so small that $\omega L \ll R'$. Then,

$$Z = \frac{j\omega L R'}{R' + j\omega L}$$

$$= j\omega L\left(1 + \frac{j\omega L}{R'}\right)^{-1} \simeq j\omega L + \frac{\omega^2 L^2}{R'} + O\left[\frac{(\omega L)^3}{R'^2}\right]. \qquad (30)$$

Hence, the circuits shown in Fig. 6.4 are equivalent when $\omega L \ll R'$, and the series resistance of the circuit $a$ is proportional to the square of the frequency. Using $R_{\text{rad}}$ for $R$, we obtain

$$\frac{\omega^2 \mu^2 l^2}{6\pi\eta} = \frac{\omega^2 L^2}{R'}, \qquad L = \mu l\left(\frac{R'}{6\pi\eta}\right)^{\frac{1}{2}}. \qquad (31)$$

This equation suggests that space may be considered as a pure resistance inductively coupled to our antenna. Equation 31 does not give this resistance and the coupling inductance uniquely. This is natural since space has no well-defined terminals, and it has to be provided with them if we wish to include it in our networks. A short wire and a small spherical antenna excite the same type of external field (the zonal wave of the first order) except in their immediate vicinities. For the spherical antenna (Fig. 6.6) the shunt resistance equals $2\eta/3\pi$. Hence, choosing $R' = 2\eta/3\pi$, we find that the coupling inductance is $\mu l/3\pi$, and the network in Fig. 6.8 is transformed into that in Fig. 6.9.

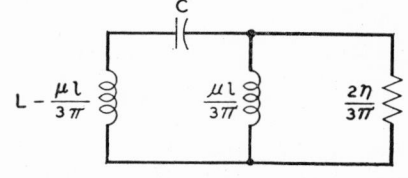

FIG. 6.9  Network representation of a short wire loaded inductively in the center.

The condition $\omega\mu l/3\pi \ll 2\eta/3\pi$, implicit in the transformation, is satisfied since it is equivalent to $\beta l \ll 2$ which is weaker than the condition $\beta l \ll 1$ required for the original network in Fig. 6.8. However, the practical range of application of these networks can be stretched.

## 6.4　Thin conductors — I

Natural electric oscillations on thin wires resemble vibrations of strings under tension, since these phenomena are basically the same. When a string with two fixed ends (Fig. 6.10$a$) is displaced from its neutral state, the restoring forces of tension tend to return it to its neutral position; but, when it does return there, it has acquired a momentum which carries it beyond the neutral position. The displaced string has potential energy which is transformed into kinetic energy when the string returns to the neutral position; the kinetic energy is gradually transformed back into potential energy as the momentum carries the string away from the neutral position. Similarly, when some electrons are displaced on a wire (Fig. 6.10b), the restoring forces of attraction between the positive and negative charges tend to pull them back; but, when the wire is once more electrically neutral, the electrons are in motion, and their electromagnetic momentum carries them on until the ends of the wires are again oppositely charged. Here the electric energy associated with the separated charges is gradually transformed into the magnetic energy associated with the moving charge, and vice versa.

In the case of strings under constant tension and with uniformly distributed mass, the various natural modes of oscillation are given by

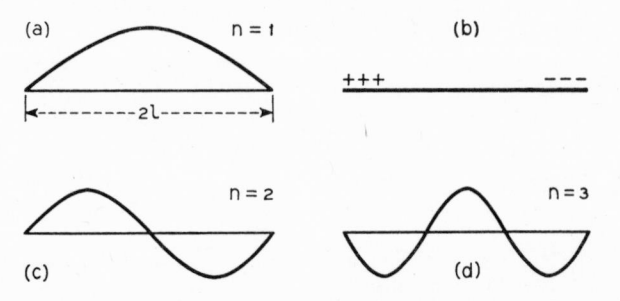

FIG. 6.10 Diagrams representing various modes of mechanical oscillation of stretched strings and electromagnetic oscillation of thin conductors.

sinusoidal displacements (Fig. 6.10a, c, d). The natural wavelengths are integral submultiples of a length which is double that of the string,

$$\lambda_n = \frac{4l}{n}, \qquad n = 1, 2, 3, \cdots. \tag{32}$$

The natural frequencies are given by

$$f_n = \frac{c}{\lambda_n}, \tag{33}$$

where $c$ is the velocity of waves on the string. If either the mass or the tension or both are not distributed uniformly, the displacements corresponding to the natural modes are distorted sine waves and the natural wavelengths deviate from equation 32.

We have a similar phenomenon in the case of oscillations of electric charge on wires. In a cylindrical wire neither the inductance nor the capacitance is uniformly distributed. At a point near the center of the wire, the electric intensity due to the moving charge is larger than it is near the ends, for in the first case the field is produced by the current on both sides of the point in question, whereas in the second case it is produced by the current on one side only. Hence, the inductance of a cylindrical wire is smaller near the ends than it is near the middle. The capacitance, on the other hand, is larger near the ends. Inasmuch as the inductance increases and the capacitance decreases with the decreasing radius of the wire, we may obtain a uniform distribution by making the wire thinner toward its ends. The optimum shape turns out to be very nearly spheroidal. The loss of power by radiation has only a second-order effect on the natural frequencies.

Abraham was the first to study quantitatively the electric oscillations on thin spheroids.* It is relatively easy to obtain the exact solutions of Maxwell's equations in terms of spheroidal functions satisfying certain ordinary linear differential equations; but the evaluation of these functions is not easy, and it constitutes the real problem. At the time Abraham did not seem to appreciate the importance of shape, for he apparently believed that his formulas applied to thin rods in general (by taking, of course, some mean value of the radius of the wire). Actually the orders of magnitude of the deviations from equation 32 are different for the spheroid and for other shapes even though in all cases the deviations are relatively small. As the radius of the wire decreases, the natural wavelengths of spheroids approach rapidly those given by equation 32; but for other shapes they approach these values slowly.

Abraham gives the following expressions for the oscillation constants corresponding to the various modes of oscillation on a thin spheroid of length $2l$ whose maximum radius is $a$,

$$pl\sqrt{\mu\varepsilon} = \frac{2\pi j - 9.74A - 47.4A^2}{4(1 + 5.6A^2)}, \qquad n = 1,$$

$$= \frac{4\pi j - 12.5A - 77.8A^2}{4(1 + 3.3A^2)}, \qquad n = 2,$$

$$= \frac{2n\pi j - (9.66 + 4\log n)A - 2(4.8 + 2\log n)^2A^2}{4[1 + n^{-1}(4.8 + 2\log n)A^2]}, \quad n > 2, \quad (34)$$

where Abraham's parameter $A$ is related to the average characteristic impedance of a thin spheroid, defined in Section 1.15, as follows:

$$A = \frac{1}{4\log(2l/a)} = \frac{30}{K_a + 83.18}, \qquad K_a = 120\log\frac{l}{a}. \quad (35)$$

* Die electrischen Schwingungen um einen stabförmigen Leiter, behandelt nach der Maxwell'schen Theorie, *Ann. d. Phys.*, **66**, October 1898, pp. 435–472.

From these expressions we may obtain the quality factors of thin spheroids:

$$Q_n = -\frac{\omega_n}{2\xi_n} = \frac{\pi(K_a + 83.18)}{292\,[1 + 146(K_a + 83.18)^{-1}]}, \qquad n = 1,$$

$$= \frac{\pi(K_a + 83.18)}{187\,[1 + 187(K_a + 83.18)^{-1}]}, \qquad n = 2,$$

$$= \frac{n\pi(K_a + 83.18)}{30(9.66 + 4\log n)\left[1 + \dfrac{15(9.6 + 4\log n)}{K_a + 83.18}\right]},$$

$$n > 2. \quad (36)$$

These quality factors for natural oscillations will differ from the corresponding quality factors in the case of forced oscillations in the terms of order $1/K_a$ in the denominator.

A few years later Marcel Brillouin published[*] his analysis of natural oscillations on spheroids of all eccentricities. His results for thin spheroids differ very substantially[†] from those given by Abraham. In 1930 Hallén obtained a general formula for the natural oscillation constants of thin conductors of arbitrary shape by a method described in the preceding chapter. His result for thin spheroids[‡] is the same as Abraham's. In 1941 Schelkunoff obtained another general formula as a byproduct of the mode theory of antennas[§] described in Chapter 2. Finally, in 1944 Page obtained the oscillation constants of spheroids for the first three modes.[||] Both Abraham and Page solve Maxwell's equations in spheroidal coordinates; but in the later stages their methods are different.

A comparison of the logarithmic decrements, $\delta = \pi/Q$, will enable us to bring out several important points. Page's and Schelkunoff's formulas give only the first order terms; these terms will be compared first. We have according to:

[*] *Propagation de l'Électricité*, vol. 1, Hermann, Paris, 1904.

[†] Léon Brillouin, Antennae for ultra-high frequencies, *Elec. Comm.*, **21**, 1944, no. 4, pp. 257–281; and **22**, 1945, no. 1, pp. 11–39.

[‡] Über die elektrischen Schwingungen in drahtförmigen Leitern, *Uppsala Universitets Årsskrift*, 1930, no. 1, p. 18.

[§] S. A. Schelkunoff, Theory of antennas of arbitrary size and shape, *Proc. IRE*, **29**, September 1941, pp. 493–521.

[||] Leigh Page, The electrical oscillations of a prolate spheroid, III, *Phys. Rev.*, **65**, February 1 and 15, 1944, pp. 98–117.

*Abraham*

$$\delta_1 = \frac{2.43}{\log(l/a) + 0.69}, \quad \delta_2 = \frac{1.56}{\log(l/a) + 0.69}, \quad \delta_3 = \frac{1.17}{\log(l/a) + 0.69};$$

*Marcel Brillouin*

$$\delta_1 = \frac{1.22}{\log(l/a) + 0.69}, \quad \delta_2 = \frac{0.77}{\log(l/a) + 0.69}, \quad \delta_3 = \frac{0.472}{\log(l/a) + 0.69};$$

*Hallén*

$$\delta_1 = \frac{2.43}{\log(l/a) + 0.69}, \quad \quad - \quad \quad \delta_3 = \frac{1.17}{\log(l/a) + 0.69};$$

*Page*

$$\delta_1 = \frac{2.43}{\log(l/a) - 0.52}, \quad \delta_2 = \frac{1.54}{\log(l/a) - 1.15}, \quad \delta_3 = \frac{1.24}{\log(l/a) + 0.94};$$

*Schelkunoff*

$$\delta_1 = \frac{2.43}{\log(l/a)}, \quad \quad - \quad \quad \delta_3 = \frac{1.17}{\log(l/a) - 0.2}.$$

The reason for the omission of the second mode in Hallén's and Schelkunoff's tables is this: Abraham, Brillouin, and Page considered

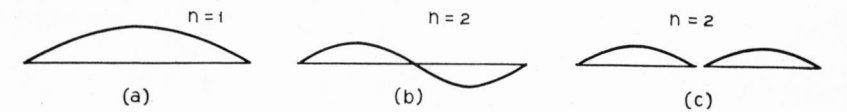

Fig. 6.11   Modes of oscillation in thin conductors: (*a*) first mode, (*b*) second mode in a continuous conductor, (*c*) second mode in a conductor broken in the center.

natural oscillations of an unbroken wire and their even modes correspond to antisymmetric current distributions (Fig. 6.11*b*); Hallén and Schelkunoff obtained their formulas as a byproduct of the theory of centrally driven antennas, and their even modes correspond to the symmetric current distributions that would exist in wires broken in the center (Fig. 6.11*c*).   Both Hallén's and Schelkunoff's methods may also be applied to the antisymmetric even oscillations.

The numerators in the formulas for the decrements can be calculated *exactly* and *unambiguously*, for they depend on the power radiated by an infinitely thin wire.   In such a wire the current distribution is exactly sinusoidal, *irrespective of its shape*, and the radiated power can easily be calculated to any number of decimal places.   The expressions given by Page for the second and third modes contain small errors; those given by Brillouin, quite large errors.

The *denominators* cannot be determined unambiguously because all these formulas give only the first terms of asymptotic expansions, valid for " large values " of $\log(l/a)$. There is no way to distinguish between " large values " of $\log(l/a)$ and " large values " of $\log(kl/a) = \log(l/a) + \log k$, where $k$ is some positive constant which may be either greater than or less than unity. Thus, the differences between the denominators are not significant without the simultaneous consideration of the higher order terms. For example, Abraham's expression for the decrement of the first mode including the second order term is

$$\delta_1 = \frac{2.43}{\log(l/a) + 0.69} + \frac{2.96}{[\log(l/a) + 0.69]^2} .$$

The " first order " term given by Page gives

$$\delta_1 = \frac{2.43}{\log(l/a) + 0.69} + \frac{2.94}{[\log(l/a) + 0.69]^2} .$$

Thus, Page's " first order approximation " is equivalent to Abraham's " second order approximation." This is an excellent illustration of a theoretically obvious fact that one first order approximation may be just as good as another second order approximation. Schelkunoff's first order term gives

$$\delta_1 = \frac{2.43}{\log(l/a) + 0.69} + \frac{1.68}{[\log(l/a) + 0.69]^2} .$$

This is better than Abraham's first order approximation but not as good as his second order approximation. Finally, for the high order modes, Abraham's second order approximation is

$$\delta_n = \frac{\log n + 2.41}{n[\log(l/a) + 0.69]} + \frac{(\log n + 2.4)^2}{2n[\log(l/a) + 0.69]^2} ,$$

whereas Schelkunoff's first order approximation is

$$\delta_n = \frac{\log n + 2.41}{n[\log(l/a) - 0.25 \log n]}$$

$$= \frac{\log n + 2.41}{n[\log(l/a) + 0.69]} + \frac{(\log n + 2.41)(\log n + 2.76)}{4n[\log(l/a) + 0.69]^2} .$$

Hence, Schelkunoff's first order term includes somewhat more than one half of Abraham's second order term.

Another important point concerns the asymptotic character of the above equations. If we were to obtain the complete series for $\delta_n$, we should find that it is a divergent series. For small values of $\log(l/a)$, the series is completely useless.   For large values of $\log(l/a)$, its terms decrease at first, but eventually they begin to increase indefinitely. As $\log(l/a)$ becomes larger, the number of terms in the first group (the group of decreasing terms) also becomes larger.   For any given value of $\log(l/a)$ there is a definite limit to the accuracy with which we can calculate $\delta_n$ from the series; and this accuracy deteriorates as $\log(l/a)$ decreases until finally the series breaks down altogether.   Although all expansions, regardless of the method by which they are obtained, are *formally identical*, in the sense that any one may be transformed into any other by a simple change of the expansion parameter, some expansions begin to deteriorate for smaller values of $\log(l/a)$ than other expansions; that is, not all expansions are equally useful when $\log(l/a)$ is relatively small — as it must be for even the thinnest practicable wires.

For higher order modes the series for $\delta$ begins to deteriorate for larger values of $\log(l/a)$.   This may be seen from Abraham's expression in which the " second order term " exceeds the first order term for sufficiently large values of $n$ as long as $l/a$ has a fixed value.   Similarly, in Schelkunoff's expression the denominator becomes negative for sufficiently large $n$.   As $n$ increases, the expressions remain equally valid only if $\log(l/a)$ is increased correspondingly.

The methods used by Abraham and by Page depend on the solution of Maxwell's equations in spheroidal coordinates and are applicable only to spheroids and near spheroids; but the spheroids may be of all eccentricities.   The methods used by Hallén and Schelkunoff are more general as far as shapes of conductors are concerned; but for computational reasons they are restricted at present to thin conductors.   For fat conductors (excluding cones) Hallén's method offers more hope.

## 6.5   Thin conductors — II

Fairly simple and general formulas for resonant wavelengths and quality factors of thin conductors may be obtained as follows.   We shall assume that the conductor may be bent (Fig. 6.12) and that

FIG.  6.12   A thin wire.

its radius may vary arbitrarily with position $s$ on the conductor.   Let the current and the charge per unit length be

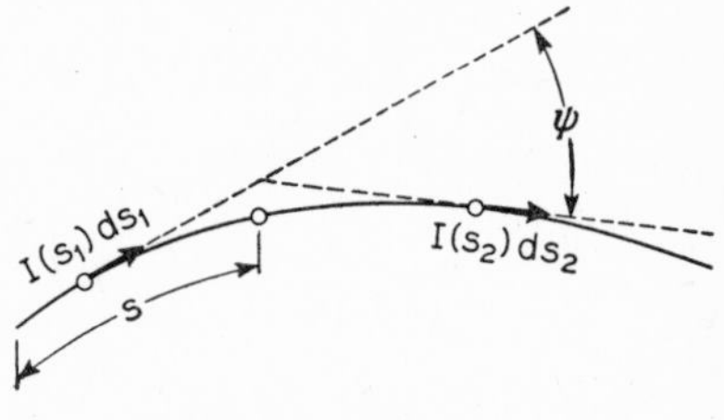

$$\widetilde{I}(s, t) = I(s)e^{-kt} \cos \omega t,$$
$$\widetilde{q}(s, t) = q(s)e^{-kt} \sin(\omega t + \vartheta),$$

(37)

where $\omega$ is a natural frequency, $k$ the corresponding damping constant, and $\vartheta$ is a phase angle approaching zero with $k$. Since

$$\frac{\partial \tilde{I}}{\partial s} = - \frac{\partial \tilde{q}}{\partial t}, \tag{38}$$

we have

$$I'(s)e^{-kt} \cos \omega t = -q(s)e^{-kt}[\omega \cos(\omega t + \vartheta) - k \sin(\omega t + \vartheta)]. \tag{39}$$

Since the bracketed expression equals

$$(\omega^2 + k^2)^{\frac{1}{2}} \cos \left( \omega t + \vartheta + \tan^{-1} \frac{k}{\omega} \right),$$

we have

$$\vartheta = -\tan^{-1} \frac{k}{\omega}, \qquad I'(s) = -(\omega^2 + k^2)^{\frac{1}{2}} q(s). \tag{40}$$

We shall assume now that the conductor is so thin that $k^2$ is negligible in comparison with $\omega^2$; then,

$$I'(s) = -\omega q(s). \tag{41}$$

Let us now consider two instants, separated approximately by one quarter of a period, such that at one instant the conductor is electrically neutral and at the other no current is flowing in it. Associated with the current at the first instant there is a certain quantity $\mathcal{E}_m$ of stored magnetic energy,

$$\mathcal{E}_m = \frac{\mu}{8\pi} \iint r^{-1} I(s_1) I(s_2) \cos \psi \, ds_1 \, ds_2, \tag{42}$$

where

$$r = \{(s_1 - s_2)^2 + [\rho(s_1)]^2\}^{\frac{1}{2}}, \tag{43}$$

and where $\rho$ is the radius of the conductor.* Similarly, at the second instant we have stored electric energy

$$\mathcal{E}_e = \frac{1}{8\pi\varepsilon} \iint r^{-1} q(s_1) \, q(s_2) \, ds_1 \, ds_2. \tag{44}$$

Substituting from equation 41, we have

$$\mathcal{E}_e = \frac{1}{8\pi\varepsilon\omega^2} \iint r^{-1} I'(s_1) I'(s_2) \, ds_1 \, ds_2. \tag{45}$$

---

* On account of the surface distribution of current the integral in equation 42 is a quadruple integral to begin with; but, as long as $I(s)$ is a slowly varying function of $s$, we may reduce it to the double integral. The assumption of a " slow variation of $I(s)$ " restricts us to the natural modes whose wavelengths are large compared with the radius.

Since $k$ is assumed to be small, the magnetic energy stored at the first instant is substantially equal to the electric energy stored at the second instant; therefore,

$$\omega^2 \mu\varepsilon = \left(\frac{2\pi}{\lambda}\right)^2 = \frac{\iint r^{-1} I'(s_1)\, I'(s_2)\, ds_1\, ds_2}{\iint r^{-1} I(s_1)\, I(s_2)\, \cos\psi\, ds_1\, ds_2} . \tag{46}$$

When the radius is small, the integrands are large in the vicinity of $s_2 = s_1$ where $r$ is small.  Hence, we shall approximate equation 46 by assuming that, in the integration with respect to $s_2$, the current $I(s_2)$ equals $I(s_1)$,

$$\omega^2 \mu\varepsilon = \left(\frac{2\pi}{\lambda}\right)^2 = \frac{\int \left(\int r^{-1}\, ds_2\right) [I'(s_1)]^2\, ds_1}{\int \left(\int r^{-1} \cos\psi\, ds_2\right) [I(s_1)]^2\, ds_1} . \tag{47}$$

For a *straight* conductor $\cos\psi = 1$.

The first parenthetical factor in the numerator equals the product of $4\pi\varepsilon$ and the potential at $s = s_1$ due to a uniformly distributed charge on the conductor; hence,

$$\int r^{-1}\, ds_2 = \frac{4\pi\varepsilon}{C(s_1)} , \tag{48}$$

where $C(s_1)$ is substantially the capacitance per unit length.  Similarly,

$$\int r^{-1} \cos\psi\, ds_2 = \frac{4\pi}{\mu} L(s_1), \tag{49}$$

where $L(s_1)$ is the inductance per unit length.  Hence, equation 47 becomes

$$\omega^2 \mu\varepsilon = \left(\frac{2\pi}{\lambda}\right)^2 = \frac{\int \varepsilon [C(s)]^{-1}\, [I'(s)]^2\, ds}{\int \mu^{-1} L(s)\, [I(s)]^2\, ds} . \tag{50}$$

In the case of a straight conductor $L(s)\, C(s) = \mu\varepsilon$, and

$$\omega^2 \mu\varepsilon = \left(\frac{2\pi}{\lambda}\right)^2 = \frac{\int L(s)\, [I'(s)]^2\, ds}{\int L(s)\, [I(s)]^2\, ds} . \tag{51}$$

Let us now consider more specifically a straight conductor and assume that $s$ is the distance from one of its ends.  The principal parts of the current and its derivative are

$$I(s) = I_0 \sin \frac{n\pi s}{2l}, \qquad \frac{dI}{ds} = \frac{n\pi}{2l} I_0 \cos \frac{n\pi s}{2l}, \qquad (52)$$

where $2l$ is the total length of the conductor. Substituting in equation 51, we obtain

$$\left(\frac{2\pi}{\lambda_n}\right)^2 = \left(\frac{n\pi}{2l}\right)^2 \frac{\int_0^{2l} L(s) \cos^2(n\pi s/2l) \, ds}{\int_0^{2l} L(s) \sin^2(n\pi s/2l) \, ds}$$

$$= \left(\frac{n\pi}{2l}\right)^2 \frac{\int_0^{2l} L(s) \, ds + \int_0^{2l} L(s) \cos(n\pi s/l) \, ds}{\int_0^{2l} L(s) \, ds - \int_0^{2l} L(s) \cos(n\pi s/l) \, ds}. \qquad (53)$$

We also have

$$L(s) \propto \log 4s(2l - s)[\rho(s)]^{-2}. \qquad (54)$$

For a spheroid

$$[\rho(s)]^2 = a^2 s(2l - s)l^{-2}, \qquad (55)$$

where $a$ is the maximum radius and $2l$ is the total length. Hence, $L(s)$ is constant, and

$$\left(\frac{2\pi}{\lambda_n}\right)^2 = \left(\frac{n\pi}{2l}\right)^2, \qquad \lambda_n = \frac{4l}{n} \; ; \qquad (56)$$

that is, there is no first order deviation of the resonant lengths from $(4l/n)$. For a cylinder, $\rho(s) = a$. Evaluating the integrals, we find

$$\lambda_n = \frac{4l}{n} \left[ 1 + \frac{\text{Si } 2n\pi}{2n\pi \left[ \log(2l/a) - 1 + \log 2 \right]} \right],$$

$$\frac{l}{\lambda_n} = \frac{n}{4} - \frac{\text{Si } 2n\pi}{8\pi \left[ \log(2l/a) - 1 + \log 2 \right]}. \qquad (57)$$

These expressions agree with those obtained by other methods except for an additive constant in conjunction with $\log(2l/a)$, which — as we have seen — cannot be fixed uniquely.

The quality factor $Q_n$ associated with the $n$th natural mode may be obtained from equation 22. To calculate its principal part, we evaluate the stored energy (equation 42) on the assumption that the current distribution is sinusoidal. We also calculate the corresponding radiated power (by the Poynting vector method or some other method) and express it in the form

$$P_n = \tfrac{1}{2} R_n I_0^2, \qquad (58)$$

where $I_0$ is the maximum amplitude of the antenna current and $R_n$ is the radiation resistance referred to a current antinode. Therefore,

$$Q_n = \frac{60\pi}{\lambda_n R_n} \int_0^{2l} \int_0^{2l} \sin\frac{n\pi s_1}{2l} \sin\frac{n\pi s_2}{2l} \frac{\cos\psi}{r}\, ds_1\, ds_2, \quad (59)$$

where $2l$ is the length of the conductor and $s$ is measured from one of its ends (or from a current node in the case of a loop).

The integral may be approximated in the same way as in passing from equation 46 to equation 47,

$$Q_n = \frac{60\pi}{\lambda_n R_n} \int_0^{2l} \left( \int_0^{2l} \frac{\cos\psi}{r}\, ds_2 \right) \sin^2\frac{n\pi s_1}{2l}\, ds_1. \quad (60)$$

Replacing the integral in parentheses by its average value, we have

$$Q_n = \frac{60\pi}{\lambda_n R_n} \left( \frac{1}{2l} \int_0^{2l} \int_0^{2l} \frac{\cos\psi}{r}\, ds_1\, ds_2 \right) \int_0^{2l} \sin^2\left(\frac{n\pi s_1}{2l}\right) ds_1$$

$$= \frac{30\pi}{\lambda_n R_n} \int_0^{2l} \int_0^{2l} \frac{\cos\psi}{r}\, ds_1\, ds_2. \quad (61)$$

Noting that at low frequencies the integral,

$$L = \frac{\mu}{4\pi} \int_0^{2l} \int_0^{2l} \frac{\cos\psi}{r}\, ds_1\, ds_2, \quad (62)$$

represents the inductance of the current filament, we have

$$Q_n = \frac{\omega_n L}{2R_n}. \quad (63)$$

In the derivation of this formula for $Q_n$, we have pointed out the various mathematical approximations. If we rely on physical reasoning, we can obtain equation 63 much more simply. Let us return to equation 22 which defines $Q_n$, and to equation 58 which gives the radiated power. If $L$ is the inductance of the conductor, the stored magnetic energy for a *uniform* current equal to $I_0$ will be $\frac{1}{2}LI_0^2$; for a sinusoidally distributed current the stored energy is one half of this value,

$$\mathcal{E}_n = \tfrac{1}{4}LI_0^2. \quad (64)$$

Substituting from equations 58 and 64 in equation 22, we obtain equation 63.

If we apply either equation 61 or 63 to a spheroid, we obtain exactly the first term of Abraham's expression. If we use equation 59, we find

$$Q_n = 30n\pi \left( \log\frac{l}{a} - \log n + \operatorname{Ci} n\pi \right) R_n^{-1}. \quad (65)$$

Substituting $l = n\lambda_n/4$, we find

$$Q_n = 30n\pi \left( \log \frac{\lambda_n}{4a} + \text{Ci } n\pi \right) R_n^{-1}. \tag{66}$$

The limit of $R_n$ as the radius approaches zero is independent of the shape of the antenna and can be calculated exactly,

$$R_n = 30 \text{ Cin } 2n\pi = 30(\log n + \log 2\pi + C - \text{Ci } 2n\pi),$$
$$n = 1, 2, 3, 4, \cdots. \tag{67}$$

These values of the radiation resistance correspond to various modes of oscillation on a continuous wire (Fig. 6.11a and b). If the wire is broken in the center, then the limit is

$$R_n' = 120 \text{ Cin } n\pi - 30 \text{ Cin } 2n\pi, \qquad n = 2, 4, 6, \cdots,$$
$$= 90(\log n + \log \pi + C - \tfrac{1}{3} \log 2) + 30(\text{Ci } 2n\pi - 4\text{Ci } n\pi), \tag{68}$$

where $n$ is the number of half-waves in the oscillation (Fig. 6.11c). In the preceding equations we have assumed that the intrinsic impedance of free space is $120\pi$ ohms (based on the velocity of $3 \times 10^8$ meters per second). In the mks system of units the permeability of free space is exactly $4\pi10^{-7}$; to find the intrinsic impedance, this value must be multiplied by the velocity of light. For the first five odd modes we have

| $n$ | 1 | 3 | 5 | 7 | 9 |
|---|---|---|---|---|---|
| $R_n$ | 73.129602 | 105.494231 | 120.766134 | 130.845547 | 138.378883 |

For the first five even modes,

| $n$ | 2 | 4 | 6 | 8 | 10 |
|---|---|---|---|---|---|
| $R_n$ | 93.430697 | 114.088669 | 126.226587 | 134.847874 | 141.537922 |

For a wire broken in the center,

| $n$ | 2 | 4 | 6 | 8 | 10 |
|---|---|---|---|---|---|
| $R_n'$ | 199.087710 | 259.634117 | 295.750339 | 321.506803 | 341.523773 |

In comparing the logarithmic decrements at the end of the preceding section, we pointed out that the numerators may be calculated exactly. These numerators are equal in fact to $R_n/30n$, where $R_n$ is given in the above tables.

# PROBLEMS

**1.** Obtain the most general solution of Maxwell's equations which is independent of the $z$ coordinate.

*Ans.* This solution is the sum of two solutions one of which is derivable from $H_z$ and the other from $E_z$. Each of the component solutions is given by series (or integrals) involving an arbitrary parameter $n$ and arbitrary sets of constants. If

$$R_n(\beta\rho) = A_n J_n(\beta\rho) + B_n N_n(\beta\rho), \qquad \Phi_n(\varphi) = C_n \cos n\varphi + D_n \sin n\varphi,$$

then one component solution is of the form,

$$H_z = \sum_n R_n(\beta\rho)\,\Phi_n(\varphi), \qquad E_\varphi = -\frac{1}{j\omega\varepsilon}\frac{dH_z}{d\rho} = j\eta\sum_n R_n{}'(\beta\rho)\,\Phi_n(\varphi),$$

$$E_\rho = \frac{1}{j\omega\varepsilon\rho}\sum_n R_n(\beta\rho)\,\Phi_n{}'(\varphi).$$

The other is of the form,

$$E_z = \sum_n R_n(\beta\rho)\,\Phi_n(\varphi), \qquad H_\varphi = \frac{1}{j\omega\mu}\frac{dE_z}{d\rho} = -j\eta^{-1}\sum_n R_n{}'(\beta\rho)\,\Phi_n(\varphi),$$

$$H_\rho = \frac{j}{\omega\mu\rho}\sum_n R_n(\beta\rho)\,\Phi_n{}'(\varphi).$$

**2.** Calculate the field such that the components of $E$ tangential to a cylinder of radius $a$ assume given values $E_z(a,\varphi)$, $E_\varphi(a,\varphi)$. In addition the field is required to be finite inside the cylinder and to vary as $\rho^{-\frac{1}{2}}\exp(-j\beta\rho)$ at infinity.

*Ans.*

$$E_z{}^-(\rho,\varphi) = \sum_{n=0}^{\infty} (E_{z,n}{}^{(1)}\cos n\varphi + E_{z,n}{}^{(2)}\sin n\varphi)\,\frac{J_n(\beta\rho)}{J_n(\beta a)}\,, \qquad \rho \le a,$$

$$E_z{}^+(\rho,\varphi) = \sum_{n=0}^{\infty} (E_{z,n}{}^{(1)}\cos n\varphi + E_{z,n}{}^{(2)}\sin n\varphi)\,\frac{J_n(\beta\rho) - j\,N_n(\beta\rho)}{J_n(\beta a) - j\,N_n(\beta a)}\,, \qquad \rho \ge a,$$

$$E_\varphi{}^-(\rho,\varphi) = \sum_{n=0}^{\infty} (E_{\varphi,n}{}^{(1)}\cos n\varphi + E_{\varphi,n}{}^{(2)}\sin n\varphi)\,\frac{J_n{}'(\beta\rho)}{J_n{}'(\beta a)}\,,$$

$$E_\varphi{}^+(\rho,\varphi) = \sum_{n=0}^{\infty} (E_{\varphi,n}{}^{(1)}\cos n\varphi + E_{\varphi,n}{}^{(2)}\sin n\varphi)\,\frac{J_n{}'(\beta\rho) - j\,N_n{}'(\beta\rho)}{J_n{}'(\beta a) - j\,N_n{}'(\beta a)}\,,$$

where

$$E_{z,0}{}^{(1)} = \frac{1}{2\pi}\int_0^{2\pi} E_z(a,\varphi)\,d\varphi, \qquad E_{z,n}{}^{(1)} = \frac{1}{\pi}\int_0^{2\pi} E_z(a,\varphi)\cos n\varphi\,d\varphi,$$

$$E_{z,0}{}^{(2)} = 0, \qquad E_{z,n}{}^{(2)} = \frac{1}{\pi}\int_0^{2\pi} E_z(a,\varphi)\sin n\varphi\,d\varphi,$$

with similar equations for $E_{\varphi,n}{}^{(1)}$ and $E_{\varphi,n}{}^{(2)}$.

$$H_\varphi{}^-(\rho,\varphi) = \sum_{n=0}^{\infty} Y_{\text{TE},n}{}^-(E_{z,n}{}^{(1)}\cos n\varphi + E_{z,n}{}^{(2)}\sin n\varphi)\,\frac{J_n{}'(\beta\rho)}{J_n{}'(\beta a)}\,,$$

$$Y_{\text{TE},n}{}^- = -\frac{j\,J_n{}'(\beta a)}{\eta\,J_n(\beta a)}\,,$$

$$H_\varphi^+(\rho, \varphi) = -\sum_{n=0}^\infty Y_{TE,n}^+(E_{z,n}^{(1)} \cos n\varphi + E_{z,n}^{(2)} \sin n\varphi) \frac{J_n'(\beta\rho) - j N_n'(\beta\rho)}{J_n'(\beta a) - j N_n'(\beta a)},$$

$$Y_{TE,n}^+ = j\eta^{-1} \frac{J_n'(\beta a) - j N_n'(\beta a)}{J_n(\beta a) - j N_n(\beta a)},$$

$$H_z^-(\rho, \varphi) = -\sum_{n=0}^\infty Y_{TM,n}^-(E_{\varphi,n}^{(1)} \cos n\varphi + E_{\varphi,n}^{(2)} \sin n\varphi) \frac{J_n(\beta\rho)}{J_n(\beta a)},$$

$$Y_{TM,n}^- = \frac{j J_n(\beta a)}{\eta J_n'(\beta a)},$$

$$H_z^+(\rho, \varphi) = \sum_{n=0}^\infty Y_{TM,n}^+(E_{\varphi,n}^{(1)} \cos n\varphi + E_{\varphi,n}^{(2)} \sin n\varphi) \frac{J_n(\beta\rho) - j N_n(\beta\rho)}{J_n(\beta a) - j N_n(\beta a)},$$

$$Y_{TM,n}^+ = -j\eta^{-1} \frac{J_n(\beta a) - j N_n(\beta a)}{J_n'(\beta a) - j N_n'(\beta a)},$$

$$H_\rho = \frac{j}{\omega\mu\rho} \frac{\partial E_z}{\partial \varphi}, \qquad E_\rho = -\frac{j}{\omega\epsilon\rho} \frac{\partial H_z}{\partial \varphi}.$$

**3.** Show that the field obtained in the preceding problem requires an electric current sheet on the surface of the cylinder of radius $a$. Calculate the components of the linear current density.

Ans. $C_z(a, \varphi) = H_\varphi^+(a, \varphi) - H_\varphi^-(a, \varphi)$

$$= -\sum_{n=0}^\infty (Y_{TE,n}^+ + Y_{TE,n}^-)(E_{z,n}^{(1)} \cos n\varphi + E_{z,n}^{(2)} \sin n\varphi),$$

$C_\varphi(a, \varphi) = H_z^-(a, \varphi) - H_z^+(a, \varphi)$

$$= -\sum_{n=0}^\infty (Y_{TM,n}^+ + Y_{TM,n}^-)(E_{\varphi,n}^{(1)} \cos n\varphi + E_{\varphi,n}^{(2)} \sin n\varphi).$$

Note that, if $C_{z,n}^{(1)}$, $C_{z,n}^{(2)}$, $C_{\varphi,n}^{(1)}$, $C_{\varphi,n}^{(2)}$ are the Fourier components of the current density, then,

$$E_{z,n}^{(1)} = -\frac{C_{z,n}^{(1)}}{Y_{TE,n}^+ + Y_{TE,n}^-},$$

$$E_{\varphi,n}^{(1)} = -\frac{C_{\varphi,n}^{(1)}}{Y_{TM,n}^+ + Y_{TM,n}^-}, \qquad \text{etc.,}$$

$$Y_{TE,n}^+ + Y_{TE,n}^- = \frac{2}{\eta\pi\beta a \, J_n(J_n - jN_n)},$$

$$Y_{TM,n}^+ + Y_{TM,n}^- = \frac{2}{\eta\pi\beta a J_n'(J_n' - jN_n')}.$$

**4.** Calculate the field of a given cylindrical current sheet of radius $a$ (axially uniform) in the presence of a perfectly conducting coaxial cylinder of radius $b < a$.

*Ans.* The field is the sum of the field given in Problem 2 and the following field reflected from the cylinder.

$$E_z^r(\rho, \varphi) = - \sum_{n=0}^{\infty} (E_{z,n}^{(1)} \cos n\varphi + E_{z,n}^{(2)} \sin n\varphi) \frac{J_n(\beta b)[J_n(\beta \rho) - j N_n(\beta \rho)]}{J_n(\beta a)[J_n(\beta b) - j N_n(\beta b)]},$$

$$E_\varphi^r(\rho, \varphi) = - \sum_{n=0}^{\infty} (E_{\varphi,n}^{(1)} \cos n\varphi + E_{\varphi,n}^{(2)} \sin n\varphi) \frac{J_n'(\beta b)[J_n'(\beta \rho) - j N_n'(\beta \rho)]}{J_n'(\beta a)[J_n'(\beta b) - j N_n'(\beta b)]},$$

$$H_\varphi^r(\rho, \varphi) = \sum_{n=0}^{\infty} j\eta^{-1}(E_{z,n}^{(1)} \cos n\varphi + E_{z,n}^{(2)} \sin n\varphi) \frac{J_n(\beta b)[J_n'(\beta \rho) - j N_n'(\beta \rho)]}{J_n(\beta a)[J_n(\beta b) - j N_n(\beta b)]},$$

$$H_z^r(\rho, \varphi) = \sum_{n=0}^{\infty} j\eta^{-1}(E_{\varphi,n}^{(1)} \cos n\varphi + E_{\varphi,n}^{(2)} \sin n\varphi) \frac{J_n'(\beta b)[J_n(\beta \rho) - j N_n(\beta \rho)]}{J_n'(\beta a)[J_n'(\beta b) - j N_n'(\beta b)]},$$

where $E_{z,n}^{(1)}$, $E_{z,n}^{(2)}$, etc., are expressed in terms of the current density as in Problem 3. The radial components are obtained by differentiating the tangential components as in Problem 2.

**5.** Calculate the field such that the components of $H$ tangential to a cylinder of radius $a$ assume given values $H_z(a, \varphi)$, $H_\varphi(a, \varphi)$. The field is required to remain finite inside the cylinder and vary as $\rho^{-\frac{1}{2}} \exp(-j\beta\rho)$ at infinity.

*Ans.*

$$H_z^-(\rho, \varphi) = \sum_{n=0}^{\infty} (H_{z,n}^{(1)} \cos n\varphi + H_{z,n}^{(2)} \sin n\varphi) \frac{J_n(\beta \rho)}{J_n(\beta a)},$$

$$H_z^+(\rho, \varphi) = \sum_{n=0}^{\infty} (H_{z,n}^{(1)} \cos n\varphi + H_{z,n}^{(2)} \sin n\varphi) \frac{J_n(\beta \rho) - j N_n(\beta \rho)}{J_n(\beta a) - j N_n(\beta a)},$$

$$H_\varphi^-(\rho, \varphi) = \sum_{n=0}^{\infty} (H_{\varphi,n}^{(1)} \cos n\varphi + H_{\varphi,n}^{(2)} \sin n\varphi) \frac{J_n'(\beta \rho)}{J_n'(\beta a)},$$

$$H_\varphi^+(\rho, \varphi) = \sum_{n=0}^{\infty} (H_{\varphi,n}^{(1)} \cos n\varphi + H_{\varphi,n}^{(2)} \sin n\varphi) \frac{J_n'(\beta \rho) - j N_n'(\beta \rho)}{J_n'(\beta a) - j N_n'(\beta a)};$$

$$H_{z,0}^{(1)} = \frac{1}{2\pi} \int_0^{2\pi} H_z(a, \varphi)\, d\varphi, \qquad H_{z,n}^{(1)} = \frac{1}{\pi} \int_0^{2\pi} H_z(a, \varphi) \cos n\varphi\, d\varphi,$$

$$H_{z,0}^{(2)} = 0, \qquad\qquad\qquad H_{z,n}^{(2)} = \frac{1}{\pi} \int_0^{2\pi} H_z(a, \varphi) \sin n\varphi\, d\varphi;$$

$$E_\varphi^-(\rho, \varphi) = - \sum_{n=0}^{\infty} Z_{\mathrm{TM},n}^-(H_{z,n}^{(1)} \cos n\varphi + H_{z,n}^{(2)} \sin n\varphi) \frac{J_n'(\beta \rho)}{J_n'(\beta a)},$$

$$E_\varphi^+(\rho, \varphi) = \sum_{n=0}^{\infty} Z_{\mathrm{TM},n}^+(H_{z,n}^{(1)} \cos n\varphi + H_{z,n}^{(2)} \sin n\varphi) \frac{J_n'(\beta \rho) - j N_n'(\beta \rho)}{J_n'(\beta a) - j N_n'(\beta a)},$$

$$E_z^-(\rho, \varphi) = \sum_{n=0}^{\infty} Z_{\mathrm{TE},n}^-(H_{\varphi,n}^{(1)} \cos n\varphi + H_{\varphi,n}^{(2)} \sin n\varphi) \frac{J_n(\beta \rho)}{J_n(\beta a)},$$

$$E_z^+(\rho, \varphi) = - \sum_{n=0}^{\infty} Z_{\mathrm{TE},n}^+ (H_{\varphi,n}^{(1)} \cos n\varphi + H_{\varphi,n}^{(2)} \sin n\varphi) \frac{J_n(\beta\rho) - j N_n(\beta\rho)}{J_n(\beta a) - j N_n(\beta a)} ,$$

where the radial wave impedances $Z_{\mathrm{TM},n}$ and $Z_{\mathrm{TE},n}$ of the various modes are the reciprocals of the corresponding wave admittances $Y_{\mathrm{TM},n}$ and $Y_{\mathrm{TE},n}$ given in Problem 2. The radial components of $E$ and $H$ are determined by differentiation with respect to $\varphi$ as in Problem 2.

**6.** In the preceding problem the field is such that the electric intensity tangential to the cylinder $\rho = a$ is discontinuous. This implies a source of the field in the form of a cylindrical magnetic current sheet (or double electric current sheet). The linear density of the magnetic current sheet equals the discontinuity in $E_{\mathrm{tan}}$; thus,

$$M_\varphi(a, \varphi) = E_z^+(a, \varphi) - E_z^-(a, \varphi), \qquad M_z(a, \varphi) = E_\varphi^-(a, \varphi) - E_\varphi^+(a, \varphi).$$

Express these quantities in terms of $H$ at the surface of the cylinder.

*Ans.*

$$M_{z,n}^{(1,2)}(a, \varphi) = - (Z_{\mathrm{TM},n}^+ + Z_{\mathrm{TM},n}^-) H_{z,n}^{(1,2)} = - \frac{2\eta H_{z,n}^{(1,2)}}{\pi \beta a \, J_n(J_n - jN_n)} ,$$

$$M_{\varphi,n}^{(1,2)}(a, \varphi) = - (Z_{\mathrm{TE},n}^+ + Z_{\mathrm{TE},n}^-) H_{\varphi,n}^{(1,2)} = - \frac{2\eta H_{\varphi,n}^{(1,2)}}{\pi \beta a \, J_n'(J_n' - jN_n')} .$$

**7.** Note that the answers to the preceding problems may be expressed compactly in terms of the following transfer ratios and wave impedances and admittances:

$$S_n^-(\beta\rho, \beta a) = \frac{J_n(\beta\rho)}{J_n(\beta a)} , \qquad\qquad S_n^+(\beta\rho, \beta a) = \frac{J_n(\beta\rho) - j N_n(\beta\rho)}{J_n(\beta a) - j N_n(\beta a)} ;$$

$$T_n^-(\beta\rho, \beta a) = \frac{J_n'(\beta\rho)}{J_n'(\beta a)} , \qquad\qquad T_n^+(\beta\rho, \beta a) = \frac{J_n'(\beta\rho) - j N_n'(\beta\rho)}{J_n'(\beta a) - j N_n'(\beta a)} ;$$

$$Z_{\mathrm{TM},n}^-(\beta a) = -j\eta \frac{J_n'(\beta a)}{J_n(\beta a)} , \qquad\qquad Z_{\mathrm{TM},n}^+(\beta a) = j\eta \frac{J_n'(\beta a) - j N_n'(\beta a)}{J_n(\beta a) - j N_n(\beta a)} ;$$

$$Z_{\mathrm{TE},n}^-(\beta a) = j\eta \frac{J_n(\beta a)}{J_n'(\beta a)} , \qquad\qquad Z_{\mathrm{TE},n}^+(\beta a) = -j\eta \frac{J_n(\beta a) - j N_n(\beta a)}{J_n'(\beta a) - j N_n'(\beta a)} ;$$

$$Y_{\mathrm{TM},n}^-(\beta a) = j\eta^{-1} \frac{J_n(\beta a)}{J_n'(\beta a)} , \qquad\qquad Y_{\mathrm{TM},n}^+(\beta a) = -j\eta^{-1} \frac{J_n(\beta a) - j N_n(\beta a)}{J_n'(\beta a) - j N_n'(\beta a)} ;$$

$$Y_{\mathrm{TE},n}^-(\beta a) = -j\eta^{-1} \frac{J_n'(\beta a)}{J_n(\beta a)} , \qquad\qquad Y_{\mathrm{TE},n}^+(\beta a) = j\eta^{-1} \frac{J_n'(\beta a) - j N_n'(\beta a)}{J_n(\beta a) - j N_n(\beta a)} ;$$

$$Z_{\mathrm{TM}} Z_{\mathrm{TE}} = \eta^2, \qquad\qquad Y_{\mathrm{TM}} Y_{\mathrm{TE}} = \eta^{-2}.$$

In addition, we need the Fourier coefficients of a typical boundary function $F(\varphi)$,

$$F_0^{(1)} = \frac{1}{2\pi} \int_0^{2\pi} F(\varphi) \, d\varphi, \qquad\qquad F_n^{(1)} = \frac{1}{\pi} \int_0^{2\pi} F(\varphi) \cos n\varphi \, d\varphi,$$

$$F_0^{(2)} = 0, \qquad\qquad\qquad\qquad F_n^{(2)} = \frac{1}{\pi} \int_0^{2\pi} F(\varphi) \sin n\varphi \, d\varphi.$$

Problems involving fields inside a wedge formed by perfectly conducting half-planes $\varphi = 0$ and $\varphi = \psi$ require similar Fourier coefficients,

$$F_0^{(1)} = \frac{1}{\psi} \int_0^\psi F(\varphi)\, d\varphi, \qquad F_n^{(1)} = \frac{2}{\psi} \int_0^\psi F(\varphi) \cos n\varphi\, d\varphi,$$

$$F_0^{(2)} = 0, \qquad\qquad F_n^{(2)} = \frac{2}{\psi} \int_0^\psi F(\varphi) \sin n\varphi\, d\varphi,$$

where $n = 2m\pi/\psi$, $m = 0, 1, 2, 3, \cdots$.

Some problems involve the sums of the wave impedances (or wave admittances), looking in opposite directions. These sums may be simplified; thus,

$$[Z_{\mathrm{TM},n}^+(\beta a) + Z_{\mathrm{TM},n}^-(\beta a)]^{-1} = \frac{\pi \beta a}{2\eta} J_n(\beta a)[J_n(\beta a) - j\, N_n(\beta a)],$$

$$[Z_{\mathrm{TE},n}^+(\beta a) + Z_{\mathrm{TE},n}^-(\beta a)]^{-1} = \frac{\pi \beta a}{2\eta} J_n'(\beta a)[J_n'(\beta a) - j\, N_n'(\beta a)],$$

$$Z_{\mathrm{TM}}^+ + Z_{\mathrm{TM}}^- = \eta^2(Y_{\mathrm{TE}}^+ + Y_{\mathrm{TE}}^-), \quad Z_{\mathrm{TE}}^+ + Z_{\mathrm{TE}}^- = \eta^2(Y_{\mathrm{TM}}^+ + Y_{\mathrm{TM}}^-).$$

To obtain the real and imaginary parts of the wave impedances we may conveniently use the following identities:

$$\frac{J_n - jN_n}{J_n' - jN_n'} = \frac{J_n J_n' + N_n N_n' + j(2/\pi\beta a)}{(J_n')^2 + (N_n')^2},$$

$$\frac{J_n' - jN_n'}{J_n - jN_n} = \frac{J_n J_n' + N_n N_n' - j(2/\pi\beta a)}{(J_n)^2 + (N_n)^2}.$$

**8.** Solve Problems 2 and 3 for a typical wedge.

*Ans.*

$$E_z^-(\rho, \varphi) = \sum_n E_{z,n}^{(2)}\, S_n^-(\beta\rho, \beta a) \sin n\varphi,$$

$$E_z^+(\rho, \varphi) = \sum_n E_{z,n}^{(2)}\, S_n^+(\beta\rho, \beta a) \sin n\varphi,$$

$$E_\varphi^-(\rho, \varphi) = \sum_n E_{\varphi,n}^{(1)}\, T_n^-(\beta\rho, \beta a) \cos n\varphi,$$

$$E_\varphi^+(\rho, \varphi) = \sum_n E_{\varphi,n}^{(1)}\, T_n^+(\beta\rho, \beta a) \cos n\varphi,$$

$$H_\varphi^-(\rho, \varphi) = \sum_n Y_{\mathrm{TE},n}^-(\beta a) E_{z,n}^{(2)}\, T_n^-(\beta\rho, \beta a) \sin n\varphi,$$

$$H_\varphi^+(\rho, \varphi) = -\sum_n Y_{\mathrm{TE},n}^+(\beta a) E_{z,n}^{(2)}\, T_n^+(\beta\rho, \beta a) \sin n\varphi,$$

$$H_z^-(\rho, \varphi) = -\sum_n Y_{\mathrm{TM},n}^-(\beta a) E_{\varphi,n}^{(1)} S_n^-(\beta\rho, \beta a) \cos n\varphi,$$

$$H_z^+(\rho, \varphi) = \sum_n Y_{\mathrm{TM},n}^+(\beta a) E_{\varphi,n}^{(1)}\, S_n^+(\beta\rho, \beta a) \cos n\varphi,$$

where $n = 2m\pi/\psi$, $m = 0, 1, 2, 3, \cdots$. The radial components may be obtained by differentiation with respect to $\varphi$ as in Problem 2.

The answer to Problem 3 for the wedge is the same as that for free space.

**9.** Solve Problem 4 for the wedge.

*Ans.* The field is the sum of the field obtained in Problem 8 in which the coefficients are expressed in terms of the Fourier coefficients for the current density and the following reflected field:

$$E_z{}^r(\rho, \varphi) = -\sum_n E_{z,n}{}^{(2)} S_n{}^-(\beta b, \beta a) S_n{}^+(\beta \rho, \beta b) \sin n\varphi,$$

$$H_\varphi{}^r(\rho, \varphi) = \sum_n E_{z,n}{}^{(2)} S_n{}^-(\beta b, \beta a) S_n{}^+(\beta a, \beta b) Y_{TE,n}{}^+(\beta \rho) \sin n\varphi,$$

$$E_\varphi{}^r(\rho, \varphi) = -\sum_n E_{\varphi,n}{}^{(1)} T_n{}^-(\beta b, \beta a) T_n{}^+(\beta \rho, \beta b) \cos n\varphi,$$

$$H_z{}^r(\rho, \varphi) = -\sum_n E_{\varphi,n}{}^{(1)} T_n{}^-(\beta b, \beta a) T_n{}^+(\beta a, \beta b) Y_{TM,n}{}^+(\beta \rho) \cos n\varphi.$$

**10.** Solve Problems 5 and 6 for the wedge.

*Ans.* $H_z{}^-(\rho, \varphi) = \sum_n H_{z,n}{}^{(1)} S_n{}^-(\beta \rho, \beta a) \cos n\varphi,$

$$H_z{}^+(\rho, \varphi) = \sum_n H_{z,n}{}^{(1)} S_n{}^+(\beta \rho, \beta a) \cos n\varphi,$$

$$E_\varphi{}^-(\rho, \varphi) = -\sum_n Z_{TM,n}{}^-(\beta a) H_{z,n}{}^{(1)} T_n{}^-(\beta \rho, \beta a) \cos n\varphi,$$

$$E_\varphi{}^+(\rho, \varphi) = \sum_n Z_{TM,n}{}^+(\beta a) H_{z,n}{}^{(1)} T_n{}^+(\beta \rho, \beta a) \cos n\varphi;$$

$$H_\varphi{}^-(\rho, \varphi) = \sum_n H_{\varphi,n}{}^{(2)} T_n{}^-(\beta \rho, \beta a) \sin n\varphi,$$

$$H_\varphi{}^+(\rho, \varphi) = \sum_n H_{\varphi,n}{}^{(2)} T_n{}^+(\beta \rho, \beta a) \sin n\varphi,$$

$$E_z{}^-(\rho, \varphi) = \sum_n Z_{TE,n}{}^-(\beta a) H_{\varphi,n}{}^{(2)} S_n{}^-(\beta \rho, \beta a) \sin n\varphi,$$

$$E_z{}^+(\rho, \varphi) = -\sum_n Z_{TE,n}{}^+(\beta a) H_{\varphi,n}{}^{(2)} S_n{}^+(\beta \rho, \beta a) \sin n\varphi.$$

The solution of Problem 6 for the wedge is identical in form with that for free space.

**11.** Calculate the Fourier coefficients of a typical boundary layer function defined by

$$F(\varphi) = 0, \qquad\qquad 0 \leq \varphi < \varphi_1,$$

$$= \frac{1}{\varphi_2 - \varphi_1}, \qquad \varphi_1 < \varphi < \varphi_2,$$

$$= 0, \qquad\qquad \varphi_2 < \varphi \leq \psi,$$

for the wedge between $\varphi = 0$ and $\varphi = \psi$.

*Ans.* $F_0{}^{(1)} = \dfrac{1}{\psi}, \qquad F_n{}^{(1)} = \dfrac{2}{\psi} \dfrac{\sin \frac{1}{2}n(\varphi_2 - \varphi_1)}{\frac{1}{2}n(\varphi_2 - \varphi_1)} \cos \frac{1}{2}n(\varphi_1 + \varphi_2),$

$$F_n{}^{(2)} = \frac{2}{\psi} \frac{\sin \frac{1}{2}n(\varphi_2 - \varphi_1)}{\frac{1}{2}n(\varphi_2 - \varphi_1)} \sin \frac{1}{2}n(\varphi_1 + \varphi_2),$$

where $n = 2m\pi/\psi$, $m = 0, 1, 2, 3 \cdots$.

**12.** Calculate the Fourier coefficients of a typical boundary layer function defined by

$$F(\varphi) = 0, \qquad\qquad 0 \le \varphi < \varphi_1,$$

$$= \frac{1}{\varphi_2 - \varphi_1}, \qquad \varphi_1 < \varphi < \varphi_2,$$

$$= 0, \qquad\qquad \varphi_2 < \varphi \le 2\pi,$$

for free space.

*Ans.* The same as in the preceding problem with $\psi = 2\pi$.

**13.** Consider a perfectly conducting half-plane, $\varphi = 0$. At distance $a$ from the edge there is an infinitesimal slot parallel to the edge. Let the voltage impressed across the slot be $V_0$. Calculate the field and then the current in the plane.

*Ans.*

$$H_z^-(\rho, \varphi) = -\beta\eta^{-1}V_0\sum_n[J_n(\beta a) - j\,N_n(\beta a)]\,J_n(\beta\rho)\,\cos n\varphi, \qquad n = \tfrac{1}{2}, \tfrac{3}{2}, \tfrac{5}{2}, \cdots$$

$$H_z^+(\rho, \varphi) = -\beta\eta^{-1}V_0\sum_n J_n(\beta a)[J_n(\beta\rho) - j\,N_n(\beta\rho)]\,\cos n\varphi,$$

$$E_\varphi^-(\rho, \varphi) = -j\beta V_0\sum_n[J_n(\beta a) - j\,N_n(\beta a)]\,J_n'(\beta\rho)\,\cos n\varphi,$$

$$E_\varphi^+(\rho, \varphi) = j\beta V_0\sum_n J_n(\beta a)[J_n'(\beta\rho) - j\,N_n'(\beta\rho)]\,\cos n\varphi,$$

$$E_\rho^-(\rho, \varphi) = -j\rho^{-1}V_0\sum_n n[J_n(\beta a) - j\,N_n(\beta a)]\,J_n(\beta\rho)\,\sin n\varphi,$$

$$E_\rho^+(\rho, \varphi) = -j\rho^{-1}V_0\sum_n n J_n(\beta a)[J_n(\beta\rho) - j\,N_n(\beta\rho)]\,\sin n\varphi,$$

$$C_\rho^-(\rho) = H_z^-(\rho, 0) - H_z^-(\rho, 2\pi) = -2\beta\eta^{-1}V_0\sum_n[J_n(\beta a) - j\,N_n(\beta a)]\,J_n(\beta\rho),$$

$$C_\rho^+(\rho) = H_z^+(\rho, 0) - H_z^+(\rho, 2\pi) = -2\beta\eta^{-1}V_0\sum_n J_n(\beta a)[J_n(\beta\rho) - j\,N_n(\beta\rho)].$$

**14.** Calculate the field produced by an electric current filament $I$ parallel to the edge of a wedge formed by half-planes, $\varphi = 0$, $\varphi = \psi$, and passing through the point $(\rho_0, \varphi_0)$ where $0 < \varphi_0 < \psi$ and $0 < \psi \le 2\pi$.

*Ans.*

$$E_z^-(\rho, \varphi) = -\frac{\pi\beta\eta I}{\psi}\sum_n[J_n(\beta\rho_0) - j\,N_n(\beta\rho_0)]\,J_n(\beta\rho)\,\sin n\varphi_0 \sin n\varphi,$$

$$E_z^+(\rho, \varphi) = -\frac{\pi\beta\eta I}{\psi}\sum_n J_n(\beta\rho_0)[J_n(\beta\rho) - j\,N_n(\beta\rho)]\,\sin n\varphi_0 \sin n\varphi,$$

where $n = m\pi/\psi$, $m = 1, 2, 3, \cdots$. The remaining components of the field may be obtained from

$$H_\varphi = \frac{1}{j\omega\mu}\frac{\partial E_z}{\partial\rho}, \qquad H_\rho = \frac{j}{\omega\mu\rho}\frac{\partial E_z}{\partial\varphi}.$$

**15.** Calculate the field produced by a magnetic current filament (a solenoidal electric current filament) $V$ parallel to the edge of the wedge defined in the preceding problem.

$Ans.$ $\quad H_z^-(\rho, \varphi) = -\dfrac{\pi\beta\eta^{-1}V}{2\psi} \{[J_0(\beta\rho_0) - j\,N_0(\beta\rho_0)]\,J_0(\beta\rho) +$

$$2\sum_n [J_n(\beta\rho_0) - j\,N_n(\beta\rho_0)]\,J_n(\beta\rho)\cos n\varphi_0 \cos n\varphi\},$$

$H_z^+(\rho, \varphi) = -\dfrac{\pi\beta\eta^{-1}V}{2\psi} \{J_0(\beta\rho_0)[J_0(\beta\rho) - j\,N_0(\beta\rho)] +$

$$2\sum_n J_n(\beta\rho_0)[J_n(\beta\rho) - j\,N_n(\beta\rho)]\cos n\varphi_0 \cos n\varphi\},$$

where $n = m\pi/\psi,\ m = 1, 2, 3, \cdots$. The components of $E$ may be obtained from

$$E_\varphi = \frac{j}{\omega\varepsilon}\frac{\partial H_z}{\partial\rho}, \qquad E_\rho = \frac{1}{j\omega\varepsilon\rho}\frac{\partial H_z}{\partial\varphi}.$$

**16.** Using the results of the preceding problems, obtain the field of a plane wave coming toward the wedge from the direction given by $\varphi = \varphi_0$. Consider two

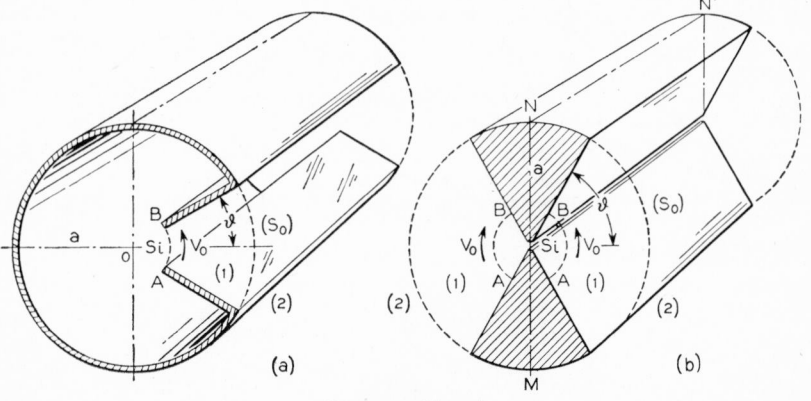

PROBLEM FIG. 1

cases: (1) $E$ is parallel to the edge; (2) $H$ is parallel to the edge. Let $E_0$ and $H_0$ be the intensities of a plane wave at the edge on the assumption that the wedge is absent.

$Ans.$ $\quad E_z = \dfrac{4\pi}{\psi} E_0 \sum_n e^{jn\pi/2} J_n(\beta\rho)\sin n\varphi_0 \sin n\varphi,\quad$ if $E$ is parallel to the edge,

$$H_z = \frac{2\pi}{\psi} H_0[J_0(\beta\rho) + 2\sum_n e^{jn\pi/2} J_n(\beta\rho)\cos n\varphi_0 \cos n\varphi],\quad \text{if } H \text{ is parallel}$$

to the edge.

**17.** Problem Figs. 1$a$, $b$ show two infinitely long wedge antennas. Assume that the boundaries are perfectly conducting and that the voltage is impressed between the edges, $A$, $B$ uniformly in the axial direction. In this case the nonvanishing components of $E$ and $H$ are $E_\varphi$, $E_\rho$, $H_\varphi$. At first let us consider the low-frequency case in which the solution may be expressed in terms of elementary functions. This will illustrate the pattern of the general solution which differs from the essentially static case largely in the type of functions involved.

At very low frequencies the magnetic field is small, and in the limiting case of zero frequency it vanishes. The electric intensity may then be derived from a static potential. Consider the double wedge (Fig. 1b), and assume that the potentials of the upper and lower wedges are, respectively, $\frac{1}{2}V_0$ and $-\frac{1}{2}V_0$. Show that the general forms of the potential function in the antenna region and in free space are, respectively:

$$V = \frac{V_0}{2\vartheta}\,\varphi + \sum_n \left[ a_n \left(\frac{\rho}{a}\right)^n + C_n \left(\frac{a}{\rho}\right)^n \right] \sin n\varphi, \qquad n = \frac{m\pi}{\vartheta},$$

$$m = 1, 2, 3, \cdots,$$

and $\quad V = \sum_k b_k \left(\frac{a}{\rho}\right)^k \sin k\varphi, \qquad k = 1, 3, 5, \cdots.$

Explain why $C_n$ must equal zero when the distance between the edges of the wedges is vanishingly small.

**18.** Obtain the fields around the wedges.

*Ans.* If $-\frac{1}{2}\pi < \varphi < \frac{1}{2}\pi$, then, in the antenna region,

$$\rho E_\varphi = -\frac{V_0}{2\vartheta} - \sum_n n a_n \left(\frac{\rho}{a}\right)^n \cos n\varphi,$$

$$\rho E_\rho = -\sum_n n a_n \left(\frac{\rho}{a}\right)^n \sin n\varphi, \qquad n = \frac{\pi}{\vartheta}, \frac{2\pi}{\vartheta}, \cdots,$$

whereas, in free space,

$$\rho E_\varphi = -\sum_k k b_k \left(\frac{a}{\rho}\right)^k \cos k\varphi,$$

$$\rho E_\rho = -\sum_k k b_k \sin k\varphi, \qquad k = 1, 3, 5, \cdots.$$

If $|\varphi| > \frac{1}{2}\pi$, the field is obtained from the above by symmetry.

**19.** Express the $b$ coefficients in terms of the $a$ coefficients and vice versa. Obtain independent sets of equations.

*Ans.* $\quad b_k = \frac{2V_0}{\pi k} + \frac{4}{\pi} \sin k\vartheta \sum_n a_n n (k^2 - n^2)^{-1} \cos n\vartheta,$

$$a_n = -\frac{4}{\pi} \cos n\vartheta \sum_k b_k k (k^2 - n^2)^{-1} \sin k\vartheta.$$

**20.** Find the charge on the upper wedge per unit length of the wedge.

*Ans.* $q = \frac{\varepsilon V_0}{\vartheta} \log \frac{a}{\rho_i} + 2\varepsilon \sum_n (1 - \rho_i{}^n a^{-n}) a_n \cos n\vartheta + 2\varepsilon \sum_k b_k \cos k\vartheta.$

The first sum represents the effect of the discontinuity on the charge distribution on the plane surfaces of the wedge and the second sum gives the charge on the cylindrical surface.

**21.** Obtain the initial approximations to the $a$'s and $b$'s.

*Ans.*  $b_k = \dfrac{2V_0}{\pi k}$,     $k = 1, 3, 5, \cdots$,

$$a_n = (-)^{m+1}\frac{8}{\pi^2}V_0\sum_k\left[k^2 - \left(\frac{m\pi}{\vartheta}\right)^2\right]^{-1}\sin k\vartheta, \quad n = m\pi/\vartheta,$$

$$m = 1, 2, 3, \cdots.$$

**22.** Eliminate the $a$'s from the equations in Problem 19.

*Ans.*  $b_k = \dfrac{2V_0}{\pi k} - \dfrac{16}{\pi^2}\sin k\vartheta \displaystyle\sum_{n,\ \alpha}\frac{n\alpha\cos^2 n\vartheta\sin \alpha\vartheta}{(k^2 - n^2)(\alpha^2 - n^2)}\,b_\alpha,$

$$k,\alpha = 1, 3, 5, \cdots, \qquad n = \frac{\pi}{\vartheta}, \frac{2\pi}{\vartheta}, \frac{3\pi}{\vartheta}, \cdots.$$

If we neglect those terms in the double sum for which $\alpha \neq k$, then,

$$b_k = \frac{2V_0}{\pi k}\left[1 + \frac{16}{\pi^2}\sin^2 k\vartheta \sum_n nk(k^2 - n^2)^{-2}\right]^{-1}.$$

**23.** In the general case (as far as the frequency is concerned) the boundary conditions are:

A. At infinity $E_\varphi$, $H_\varphi$ vary as $\rho^{-\frac{1}{2}}\exp(-j\beta\rho)$.

B. In the antenna region the radial component of $E$ vanishes at the surface of the wedge; that is, for the antenna in Fig. 1a, $E_\rho(\vartheta) = E_\rho(-\vartheta) = 0$ and for the antenna in Fig. 1b, $E_\rho(\vartheta) = E_\rho(-\vartheta) = E_\rho(\frac{1}{2}\pi+\vartheta) = E_\rho(-\frac{1}{2}\pi - \vartheta) = 0$.

C. On the output boundary cylinder $S_0$, $E_\varphi(a) = 0$ when $|\varphi| > \vartheta$ for the antenna in Fig. 1a, and $E_\varphi(a) = 0$ when $\vartheta < |\varphi| < \frac{1}{2}\pi + \vartheta$ for the antenna in Fig. 1b. Over the rest of the boundary $E_\varphi$ and $H_z$ are continuous.

D. At the input boundary cylinder $S_i$, $E_\varphi$ is given.

E. From symmetry considerations in Fig. 1b, we find the additional condition that the central plane $MN$ has in effect the boundary properties of a perfect magnetic conductor since

$$E_\varphi(\tfrac{1}{2}\pi) = E_\varphi(-\tfrac{1}{2}\pi) = 0 \quad\text{and}\quad H_z(\tfrac{1}{2}\pi) = H_z(-\tfrac{1}{2}\pi) = 0.$$

Obtain the proper values for $n$ (see Problem 1) and the corresponding angular wave functions for the wedge antenna in Fig. 1a.

*Ans.* The symmetric case: in the antenna region $n = m\pi/\vartheta$, $m = 0, 1, 2,\cdots$, and $\Phi_m(\varphi) = \cos(m\pi\varphi/\vartheta)$; in free space $n = 0, 1, 2,\cdots$, and $\Phi_n(\varphi) = \cos n\varphi$. The antisymmetric case: in the antenna region $n = (2m + 1)\pi/2\vartheta$, $m = 0, 1, 2,\cdots$, $\Phi_m(\varphi) = \sin[(2m + 1)\pi\varphi/2\vartheta]$; in free space $n = 0, 1, 2,\cdots$, $\Phi_n(\varphi) = \sin n\varphi$.

**24.** Obtain the angular wave functions for the wedge antenna in Fig. 1b.

*Ans.* The symmetric case: $\Phi_n(\varphi) = \cos n\varphi$, where $n = m\pi/\vartheta$, $m = 0, 1, 2,\cdots$, in the antenna region and $n = 1, 3, 5,\cdots$, in free space. The antisymmetric case: $\Phi_n(\varphi) = \sin n\varphi$, where $n = (2m + 1)\pi/2\vartheta$, $m = 0, 1, 2,\cdots$, in the antenna region and $n = 2, 4, 6,\cdots$, in free space.

**25.** Show that the transverse voltage

$$V(\rho) = \int_{-\vartheta}^{\vartheta} \rho\, E_\varphi(\rho, \varphi)\, d\varphi$$

across the wedge depends only on the principal wave (the wave corresponding to $n = 0$). Show that, as the radius $\rho_i$ of the input region approaches zero, the transverse voltage $V(\rho_i)$ approaches a limit.

**26.** Obtain the field in the antenna region for the case in which the radius of the input region is very small. Let $V_0$ be the impressed voltage.

*Ans.*

$$H_z^- = a_0\, J_0(\beta\rho) + V_0\left(\frac{j\pi\beta}{4\vartheta\eta}\right) N_0(\beta\rho) + \sum_n A_n\, J_n(\beta\rho)\cos n\varphi,$$

$$n = \frac{m\pi}{\vartheta}, \qquad\qquad\qquad m = 1,2,3,\cdots,$$

$$E_\varphi^- = j\eta a_0\, J_0'(\beta\rho) - V_0\left(\frac{\pi\beta}{4\vartheta}\right) N_0'(\beta\rho) + j\eta\sum_n A_n\, J_n'(\beta\rho)\cos n\varphi,$$

$$E_\rho^- = \frac{1}{j\omega\varepsilon\rho}\sum_n nA_n\, J_n(\beta\rho)\sin n\varphi,$$

**27.** Obtain the field in the free space region.

*Ans.* 
$$H_z^+ = \sum_n B_n\, [J_n(\beta\rho) - j\, N_n(\beta\rho)]\cos n\varphi,$$

$$E_\varphi^+ = j\eta\sum_n B_n\, [J_n'(\beta\rho) - j\, N_n'(\beta\rho)]\cos n\varphi,$$

$$E_\rho^+ = -\frac{1}{j\omega\varepsilon\rho}\sum_n nB_n\, [J_n(\beta\rho) - j\, N_n(\beta\rho)]\sin n\varphi,$$

where, in the case shown in Fig. 1*a*, $n = 0, 1, 2, 3,\cdots$, and, in Fig. 1*b*, $n = 1, 3, 5,\cdots$.

**28.** Express the $B$ coefficients in terms of the $A$ coefficients (Problems 26 and 27) for the case in Fig. 1*a*. Let the radius of $S_0$ be $a$.

*Ans.* If $n \neq 0$,

$$j\eta\pi B_n[J_n'(\beta a) - j\, N_n'(\beta a)] = \int_{-\pi}^{\pi} E_\varphi^+ \cos n\varphi\, d\varphi \quad = \int_{-\vartheta}^{\vartheta} E_\varphi^- \cos n\varphi\, d\varphi$$

$$= \frac{2}{n}\left[j\eta a_0\, J_0'(\beta a) - V_0\frac{\pi\beta}{4\vartheta}\, N_0'(\beta a)\right]\sin n\vartheta +$$

$$j\eta\sum_\alpha A_\alpha\, J_\alpha'(\beta a)\int_{-\vartheta}^{\vartheta}\cos \alpha\varphi\cos n\varphi\, d\varphi$$

$$= \frac{2}{n}\left[j\eta a_0\, J_0'(\beta a) - V_0\frac{\pi\beta}{4\vartheta}\, N_0'(\beta a)\right]\sin n\vartheta -$$

$$2j\eta\sum_\alpha n(\alpha^2 - n^2)^{-1}A_\alpha\, J_\alpha'(\beta a)\sin n\vartheta\cos \alpha\vartheta,$$

where the summation is extended over the set $\alpha = \pi/\vartheta,\, 2\pi/\vartheta,\, 3\pi/\vartheta \cdots$,

$$2j\eta\pi B_0[J_0{}'(\beta a) - j\, N_0{}'(\beta a)] = \int_{-\pi}^{\pi} E_\varphi{}^+\, d\varphi = \int_{-\vartheta}^{\vartheta} E_\varphi{}^-\, d\varphi$$

$$= 2\vartheta \left[ j\eta a_0\, J_0{}'(\beta a) - V_0 \frac{\pi\beta}{4\vartheta}\, N_0{}'(\beta a) \right].$$

**29.** Express the $A$ coefficients in terms of the $B$ coefficients (Problems 26 and 27) for the case in Fig. 1$b$.

*Ans.*

$$2\vartheta a_0\, J_0(\beta a) + \frac{j\pi\beta}{2\eta}\, V_0\, N_0(\beta a)$$

$$= 2\vartheta B_0[J_0(\beta a) - j\, N_0(\beta a)] + 2 \sum_{n=1,2,3,\ldots} n^{-1}B_n[J_n(\beta a) - j\, N_n(\beta a)]\sin n\vartheta,$$

$$\vartheta A_\alpha\, J_\alpha(\beta a) = 2 \sum_{n=1,2,3,\ldots} n(n^2 - \alpha^2)^{-1}B_n[J_n(\beta a) - j\, N_n(\beta a)]\sin n\vartheta \cos \alpha\vartheta,$$

$$\alpha = \frac{\pi}{\vartheta},\, \frac{2\pi}{\vartheta},\, \ldots .$$

From the equations in Problems 28 and 29 we can eliminate either the $A$'s or the $B$'s and obtain an infinite set of linear equations for either of the two sets of coefficients. If the conditions are such that the $A$'s are small, we can obtain the $B$'s by first neglecting the $A$'s. Then we can calculate the $A$'s and recalculate the $B$'s, etc.

**30.** Calculate the input admittance per unit length of the dihedral horn in Fig. 1$a$ for the case in which the $A$'s may be neglected. Let $b$ be the radius of the input boundary.

*Ans.*  $Y_i = -\dfrac{a_0}{V_0}\, J_0(\beta b) - \dfrac{j\pi\beta}{4\vartheta\eta}\, N_0(\beta b)$,

where

$$\frac{a_0}{V_0} = -\frac{j\pi\beta}{4\vartheta\eta}\, \frac{S_1}{S_2},$$

$$S_1 = N_0(\beta a) - \frac{\vartheta}{\pi}\, \frac{J_0(\beta a) - j\, N_0(\beta a)}{J_0{}'(\beta a) - j\, N_0{}'(\beta a)}\, N_0{}'(\beta a) -$$

$$\frac{2\vartheta}{\pi} \sum_{n=1,2,\ldots} \frac{\sin^2 n\vartheta}{n^2\vartheta^2}\, \frac{J_n(\beta a) - j\, N_n(\beta a)}{J_n{}'(\beta a) - j\, N_n{}'(\beta a)}\, N_0{}'(\beta a),$$

$$S_2 = J_0(\beta a) - \frac{\vartheta}{\pi}\, \frac{J_0(\beta a) - j\, N_0(\beta a)}{J_0{}'(\beta a) - j\, N_0{}'(\beta a)}\, J_0{}'(\beta a) -$$

$$\frac{2\vartheta}{\pi} \sum_{n=1,2,\ldots} \frac{\sin^2 n\vartheta}{n^2\vartheta^2}\, \frac{J_n(\beta a) - j\, N_n(\beta a)}{J_n{}'(\beta a) - j\, N_n{}'(\beta a)}\, J_0{}'(\beta a).$$

**31.** Show that, as $\beta a \to \infty$, the ratio $S_1/S_2 \to -j$ and that, consequently, the input impedance of the dihedral horn becomes independent of $\beta a$.

**32.** Obtain a set of equations for the $A$'s alternative to that in Problem 29.

*Ans.*

$$\vartheta A_\alpha \, J_\alpha{}'(\beta a) = 2 \sum_{n=1,2,\ldots} n(n^2 - \alpha^2)^{-1} B_n[J_n{}'(\beta a) - j\,N_n{}'(\beta a)] \sin n\vartheta \cos \alpha\vartheta.$$

Note that these equations are not independent of those in Problem 28 and, hence, are not sufficient for calculation of the $A$'s and $B$'s without the equations in Problem 29. They are useful as supplementary equations at points where $J_\alpha(\beta a)$ vanishes. Thus, from the two sets of equations for the $A$'s, we may obtain

$$\vartheta A_\alpha[J_\alpha(\beta a) + j\,J_\alpha{}'(\beta a)]$$

$$= 2 \sum_{n=1,2,\ldots} n(n^2 - \alpha^2)^{-1} B_n[(J_n + N_n{}') + j(J_n{}' - N_n)] \sin n\vartheta \cos \alpha\vartheta.$$

In this set of equations the coefficients of the $A_\alpha$'s cannot vanish.

**33.** Consider $N + 1$ thin cones with their axes along $(\theta_1, \varphi_1)$, $(\theta_2, \varphi_2), \cdots$, $(\theta_N, \varphi_N)$, and $(\pi, 0)$. The cone angles are $\psi_1, \psi_2, \cdots, \psi_n$, and $\psi_0$. The currents in the first $N$ cones are $I_1, I_2, \cdots, I_N$, and the transverse voltages between these cones and the "ground cone" along $(\pi, 0)$ are $V_1, V_2, \cdots, V_N$. Show that, for progressive waves,

$$V_m = \sum_{n=1}^{N} K_{mn} I_n,$$

where

$$K_{mn} = \frac{\eta}{2\pi} \log(\cos \tfrac{1}{2}\theta_m \cos \tfrac{1}{2}\theta_n \csc \tfrac{1}{2}\vartheta_{mn} \csc \tfrac{1}{2}\psi_0), \qquad n \neq m,$$

$$= \frac{\eta}{2\pi} \log(\cos^2 \tfrac{1}{2}\theta_m \csc \tfrac{1}{2}\psi_m \csc \tfrac{1}{2}\psi_0), \qquad n = m,$$

where $\vartheta_{mn}$ is the angle between the axes of the $m$th and $n$th cones.

**34.** Prove that, either in free space or in a region bounded by perfectly conducting cones emerging from a common apex, the transverse fields of TM and TE modes are orthogonal; that is,

$$\iint (E_{\theta,\text{TM}}E_{\theta,\text{TE}} + E_{\varphi,\text{TM}}E_{\varphi,\text{TE}}) \, d\Omega = 0,$$

$$\iint (H_{\theta,\text{TM}}H_{\theta,\text{TE}} + H_{\varphi,\text{TM}}H_{\varphi,\text{TE}}) \, d\Omega = 0.$$

These equations may be used to determine the field from the electric or magnetic intensities tangential to a given sphere (see Section 1.10). Thus, if $e_\theta, e_\varphi$ are the normalized components of the transverse electric intensity of a typical TM or TE mode so that

$$\iint (e_\theta{}^2 + e_\varphi{}^2) \, d\Omega = 1,$$

then the corresponding components of a given transverse field $E_\theta$, $E_\varphi$ are $Ae_\theta$, $Ae_\varphi$ where

$$A = \iint (E_\theta e_\theta + E_\varphi e_\varphi)\, d\Omega.$$

**35.** Show that, in the case of two cones, not necessarily coaxial, equation 2–54 for the normalized terminal admittance must be replaced by

$$KY_t = \frac{(\eta K)^{\frac{1}{2}}}{V_0(l)} \iint l\, \vec{H}_t \cdot \vec{h}_0\, d\Omega,$$

where $\vec{h}_0$ represents the normalized distribution pattern for the magnetic intensity of the TEM mode; that is,

$$\iint \vec{h}_0 \cdot \vec{h}_0\, d\Omega = 1.$$

**36.** Consider a sinusoidal current filament extending from $z = z_1$ to $z = z_2$. Let $r_1$ and $r_2$ be the distances from the ends of the filament and a typical point. Let $\theta_1$ and $\theta_2$ be the angles between the vectors drawn from the ends of the filament to this point and the filament. Show that, except for the electric intensities of the end charges,

$$4\pi j\omega\varepsilon E_z = I'(z_1)r_1^{-1}e^{-i\beta r_1} - I'(z_2)r_2^{-1}e^{-i\beta r_2},$$

$$4\pi j\omega\varepsilon E_\rho = I'(z_2)e^{-i\beta r_2}\cos\theta_2 - I'(z_1)e^{-i\beta r_1}\cos\theta_1 - j\beta\, I(z_2)e^{i\beta r_2} + j\beta\, I(z_1)e^{-i\beta r_1}.$$

The retarded potentials of the end charges are

$$V_1 = -\frac{I(z_1)e^{-i\beta r_1}}{4\pi j\omega\varepsilon r_1}, \qquad V_2 = \frac{I(z_2)e^{-i\beta r_2}}{4\pi j\omega\varepsilon r_2}.$$

Show also that

$$4\pi j\beta\rho H_\varphi = I'(z_2)e^{-i\beta r_2} - I'(z_1)e^{-i\beta r_1} - j\beta\, I(z_2)e^{-i\beta r_2}\cos\theta_2 + j\beta\, I(z_1)e^{-i\beta r_1}\cos\theta_1.$$

**37.** Consider a circular disk in an impressed field which is a function of the distance from the center of the disk. Obtain the differential equations connecting the scalar and vector potentials.

$Ans.$ $\quad \dfrac{dV}{d\rho} = -j\omega\mu A_\rho + E^i(\rho), \qquad \dfrac{d}{d\rho}(\rho A_\rho) = -j\omega\varepsilon\rho V;$

hence, $\qquad \rho^2 \dfrac{d^2 A_\rho}{d\rho^2} + \rho\dfrac{dA_\rho}{d\rho} - A_\rho + \beta^2\rho^2 A_\rho = -j\omega\varepsilon\rho^2 E^i(\rho),$

$$\rho\frac{d^2 V}{d\rho^2} + \frac{dV}{d\rho} + \beta^2\rho V = -\frac{d}{d\rho}\left[\rho E^i(\rho)\right].$$

**38.** Obtain the Green's function for the preceding problem (the response to a concentrated radial voltage at $\rho = \rho_0$).

$Ans.$

$V = P\, J_0(\beta\rho), \qquad\qquad\qquad\qquad\qquad\qquad\qquad \rho < \rho_0,$

$\quad = P\, J_0(\beta\rho) + \tfrac{1}{2}\pi\beta\rho_0 V_0[J_1(\beta\rho_0)\, N_0(\beta\rho) - N_1(\beta\rho_0)\, J_0(\beta\rho)], \qquad \rho > \rho_0;$

$A_\rho = -j\eta^{-1}P\, J_1(\beta\rho),$ $\rho < \rho_0;$

$= -j\eta^{-1}P\, J_1(\beta\rho) + \tfrac{1}{2}j\eta^{-1}\beta\rho_0 V_0[N_1(\beta\rho_0)\, J_1(\beta\rho) - J_1(\beta\rho_0)\, N_1(\beta\rho)],\ \rho > \rho_0;$

where $P$ is determined by the condition that the radial current at the edge of the disk vanishes. In the first approximation,

$$P = \frac{\beta\rho_0 V_0[N_1(\beta\rho_0)\, J_1(\beta a) - J_1(\beta\rho_0)\, N_1(\beta a)]}{2J_1(\beta a)},$$

where $a$ is the radius of the disk.

**39.** Consider natural oscillations of an infinitely thin perfectly conducting plane plate of arbitrary shape. Show that the scalar electric potential $V$ and both Cartesian components $A_x$, $A_y$ of the vector potential satisfy the two-dimensional wave equation,

$$\frac{\partial^2 W}{\partial x^2} + \frac{\partial^2 W}{\partial y^2} = p^2\mu\varepsilon W,$$

where $p$ is one of the natural oscillation constants.

**40.** Show that, if the plate described in the preceding problem is driven by a given field, $E_x^i(x, y)$, $E_y^i(x, y)$, then,

$$\frac{\partial V}{\partial x} = -j\omega\mu A_x - E_x^i(x, y), \qquad \frac{\partial V}{\partial y} = -j\omega\mu A_y - E_y^i(x, y).$$

$$\frac{\partial A_x}{\partial x} + \frac{\partial A_y}{\partial y} = -j\omega\varepsilon V.$$

Hence,

$$\frac{\partial^2 V}{\partial x^2} + \frac{\partial^2 V}{\partial y^2} = -\beta^2 V + \frac{\partial E_x^i}{\partial x} + \frac{\partial E_y^i}{\partial y}.$$

**41.** Consider an infinitely long, perfectly conducting strip of width $2a$. Let the strip be in the $xz$ plane between the lines $x = -a$ and $x = a$. Assume that the impressed electric intensity is parallel to the $x$ axis and is uniform in the $z$ direction. Obtain an integral equation for the linear current density $C(x)$.

$$\int_{-a}^{a} C(\xi)\, K_0(j\beta|x - \xi|)\, d\xi$$

$$= A\cos\beta x + B\sin\beta x - 2\pi j\eta^{-1}\int_{x_0}^{x} E_x^i(\xi)\sin\beta(\xi - x)\, d\xi, \qquad -a < x < a,$$

where $A$ and $B$ determined by the end conditions $C(-a) = C(a) = 0$.

**42.** In the preceding problem assume an infinitely narrow slot along the $z$ axis and a voltage $V_0$ across it. Obtain an integral equation for the current density.

*Ans.* $\displaystyle\int_{-a}^{a} C(\xi)\, K_0(j\beta|x - \xi|)\, d\xi = A\cos\beta x - j\pi\eta^{-1}V_0\sin\beta|x|.$

**43.** Obtain an integral equation for the case in which the strip of Problem 41 is in a uniform field of intensity $E_0$ parallel to the $z$ axis.

*Ans.* $\displaystyle\int_{-a}^{a} C(\xi)\, K_0(j\beta|\xi - x|)\, d\xi = \frac{2\pi E_0}{j\omega\mu}, \qquad -a < x < a.$

**44.** From Manneback's solution for waves on a semi-infinite perfectly conducting wire of infinitesimal radius show that, when the radius is finite, the current at large distances from the end is

$$I(r) = Ae^{-i\beta r}\left(2\log\frac{2r}{a} - 1\right)^{-\frac{1}{2}}.$$

Hence the energy is slowly diverging from the wire. Thus the power flow within a cylinder of radius $b$, coaxial with the wire, varies inversely as $2\log(2r/a) - 1$. Further analysis would show that the distance $r$ is " large " if it is comparable to or larger than $\lambda/2$.

# APPENDIX I

## Integrals in Antenna Theory

In Fig. 1, let

$$r = \sqrt{\rho^2 + z^2}, \qquad r_1 = \sqrt{\rho^2 + z_1^2}, \qquad r_2 = \sqrt{\rho^2 + z_2^2};$$

then,

$$\int_{z_1}^{z_2} \frac{\cos \beta(r + z)}{r} \, dz = \text{Ci } \beta(r_2 + z_2) - \text{Ci } \beta(r_1 + z_1),$$

$$\int_{z_1}^{z_2} \frac{\sin \beta(r + z)}{r} \, dz = \text{Si } \beta(r_2 + z_2) - \text{Si } \beta(r_1 + z_1).$$

Changing $z$ to $-z$,

$$\int_{z_1}^{z_2} \frac{\cos \beta(r - z)}{r} \, dz = \text{Ci } \beta(r_1 - z_1) - \text{Ci } \beta(r_2 - z_2),$$

$$\int_{z_1}^{z_2} \frac{\sin \beta(r - z)}{r} \, dz = \text{Si } \beta(r_1 - z_1) - \text{Si } \beta(r_2 - z_2).$$

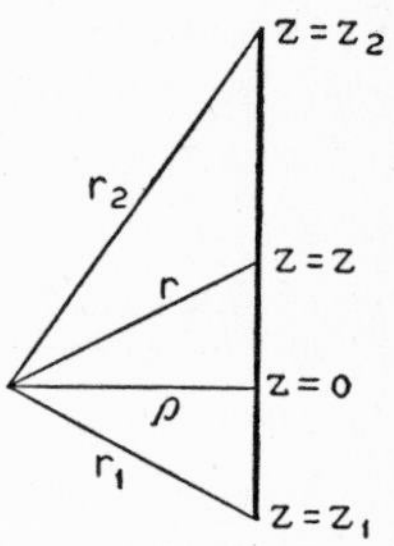

Fig. 1.

To prove the above, we introduce a new variable of integration,

$$t = r + z, \qquad dt = \frac{z \, dz}{r} + dz = \frac{(z + r) \, dz}{r} = \frac{t \, dz}{r}, \qquad \frac{dt}{t} = \frac{dz}{r} \cdot$$

Also note that

$$\int \frac{\sin \beta t}{t} \, dt = \int \frac{\sin \beta t}{\beta t} \, d(\beta t) = \text{Si } \beta t, \quad \text{etc.}$$

If $\beta$ is vanishingly small, the cosine integrals become

$$\int_{z_1}^{z_2} \frac{dz}{\sqrt{\rho^2 + z^2}} = \log \frac{r_2 + z_2}{r_1 + z_1}, \qquad \int_{-l}^{l} \frac{dz}{\sqrt{\rho^2 + z^2}} = 2 \log \frac{\sqrt{\rho^2 + l^2} + l}{\rho} \cdot$$

Also,

$$\int_{z_1}^{z_2} \frac{d\xi}{\sqrt{(\xi - z)^2 + \rho^2}}$$

$$= \log \frac{[z_2 - z + \sqrt{(z_2 - z)^2 + \rho^2}] [z - z_1 + \sqrt{(z - z_1)^2 + \rho^2}]}{\rho^2} \cdot$$

191

Let $r_1$ and $r_2$ be the distances from points 1 and 2 (Fig. 2). Similarly, let $r_{mn}$ be the distance between points $m$ and $n$. The following integrals are taken along the straight line passing through point 2 between points 3 and 4:

$$\int_{(3,4)} \frac{\cos \beta(r_1 + r_2 - r_{12} \cos \vartheta)}{r_1} dr_2$$

$$= \text{Ci } \beta(r_{14} + r_{24} - r_{12} \cos \vartheta) - \text{Ci } \beta(r_{13} + r_{23} - r_{12} \cos \vartheta),$$

$$\int_{(3,4)} \frac{\sin \beta(r_1 + r_2 - r_{12} \cos \vartheta)}{r_1} dr_2$$

$$= \text{Si } \beta(r_{14} + r_{24} - r_{12} \cos \vartheta) - \text{Si } \beta(r_{13} + r_{23} - r_{12} \cos \vartheta),$$

$$\int_{(3,4)} \frac{\cos \beta(r_1 - r_2 + r_{12} \cos \vartheta)}{r_1} dr_2$$

$$= \text{Ci } \beta(r_{13} - r_{23} + r_{12} \cos \vartheta) - \text{Ci } \beta(r_{14} - r_{24} + r_{12} \cos \vartheta),$$

$$\int_{(3,4)} \frac{\sin \beta(r_1 - r_2 + r_{12} \cos \vartheta)}{r_1} dr_2$$

$$= \text{Si } \beta(r_{13} - r_{23} + r_{12} \cos \vartheta) - \text{Si } \beta(r_{14} - r_{24} + r_{12} \cos \vartheta).$$

To prove these results, use the following substitutions,

$$\beta(r_1 + r_2 - r_{12} \cos \psi) = t \quad \text{and} \quad \beta(r_1 - r_2 + r_{12} \cos \psi) = t, \quad \text{respectively.}$$

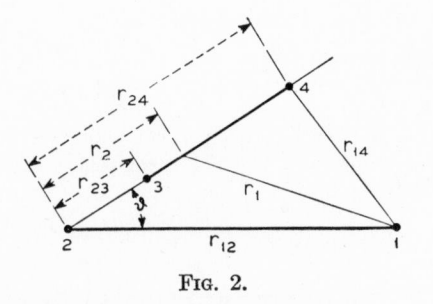

FIG. 2.

In the more general case of two inclined coplanar segments (Fig. 3), the exponential integrals may be expressed in terms of certain combinations of various distances typified by

$$t_{14} = r_{14} + s_1' - s_4'' \cos \vartheta, \qquad t_{41} = r_{41} + s_4'' - s_1' \cos \vartheta.$$

Note that $r_{14} = r_{41}$ is an essentially positive quantity while $s_1'$ and $s_4''$ may be either positive or negative. Typical exponential integrals associated with inclined segments are

$$\int_{(1-2)} \frac{e^{-j\beta(r_4+s')}}{r_4} \, ds' = e^{-j\beta s_4''\cos\vartheta} \, [\text{Ei}(-j\beta t_{24}) - \text{Ei}(-j\beta t_{14})],$$

$$\int_{(3-4)} \frac{e^{-j\beta(r_1+s'')}}{r_1} \, ds'' = e^{-j\beta s_1'\cos\vartheta} \, [\text{Ei}(-j\beta t_{41}) - \text{Ei}(-j\beta t_{31})].$$

These integrals are evaluated by introducing new variables of integration, $r_4 + s' - s_4''\cos\vartheta$ and $r_1 + s'' - s_1'\cos\vartheta$. The integral involv-

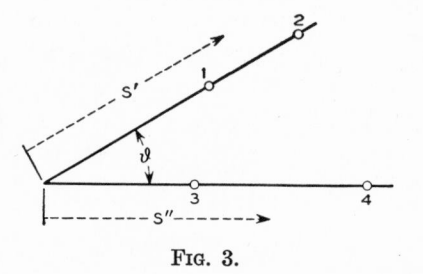

FIG. 3.

ing $r_4 - s'$ may be reduced to the first of the above integrals by reversing the sign of the variable of integration $s'$ and changing $\vartheta$ to $\pi - \vartheta$. Thus,

$$\int_{(1-2)} \frac{e^{-j\beta(r_4-s')}}{r_4} \, ds' = e^{j\beta s_4''\cos\vartheta} \, [\text{Ei}(-j\beta t_{14}) - \text{Ei}(-j\beta t_{24})].$$

A typical double integral of the exponential type is

$$\int_{(1-2)} \int_{(3-4)} \frac{e^{-j\beta(r+s'+s'')}}{r} \, ds' \, ds''$$

$$= \frac{j}{\beta(1+\cos\vartheta)} \{ e^{-j\beta(1+\cos\vartheta)s_2'}[\text{Ei}(-j\beta t_{42}) - \text{Ei}(-j\beta t_{32})] -$$

$$e^{-j\beta(1+\cos\vartheta)s_1'}[\text{Ei}(-j\beta t_{41}) - \text{Ei}(-j\beta t_{31})] +$$

$$e^{-j\beta(1+\cos\vartheta)s_4''}[\text{Ei}(-j\beta t_{24}) - \text{Ei}(-j\beta t_{14})] -$$

$$e^{-j\beta(1+\cos\vartheta)s_3''}[\text{Ei}(-j\beta t_{23}) - \text{Ei}(-j\beta t_{13})]\} +$$

$$\frac{2j}{\beta(1+\cos\vartheta)} \{ \text{Ei}[-j\beta(r_{14}+s_1'+s_4'')] - \text{Ei}[-j\beta(r_{24}+s_2'+s_4'')] +$$

$$\text{Ei}[-j\beta(r_{23}+s_2'+s_3'')] - \text{Ei}[-j\beta(r_{13}+s_1'+s_3'')]\}.$$

To evaluate this integral we introduce a new variable of integration,

$$t = r + s'' - s'\cos\vartheta, \qquad \frac{ds''}{r} = \frac{dt}{t} \cdot$$

This enables us to reduce the double integral to a simple integral. The latter is integrated by parts and then another variable of integration,

$$\xi_4 = r_4 + s' - s_4'' \cos \vartheta, \qquad \frac{d\xi_4}{\xi_4} = \frac{ds'}{r_4},$$

is introduced. It should also be noted that

$$r_4 + r_4'' - r' = \frac{2r_4'' t_4}{r_4 + r_4'' + r'}.$$

The integral involving $r - s' + s''$ is obtained from the above integral if we change the sign of the variable of integration $s'$ and replace $\vartheta$ by $\pi - \vartheta$. The integral involving $r - s' - s''$ is obtained by changing the signs of both variables of integration without changing $\vartheta$.

# APPENDIX II

## Inverse Radiation Impedance of a Thin Cone,

$$Z_{11} = R_{11} + jX_{11}$$

$$R_{11} = 30(\text{Cin } 2L - \sin^2 L), \qquad L = \frac{2\pi l}{\lambda}$$

$$X_{11} = 30 \text{ Si } 2L - 15 \sin 2L$$

| $l/\lambda$ | $R_{11}$ | $X_{11}$ | $l/\lambda$ | $R_{11}$ | $X_{11}$ | $l/\lambda$ | $R_{11}$ | $X_{11}$ |
|---|---|---|---|---|---|---|---|---|
| 0.00 | 0.0000 | 0.000 | 0.34 | 44.8031 | 64.668 | 0.67 | 55.0500 | 35.989 |
| 0.01 | 0.0001 | 1.887 | 0.35 | 47.7434 | 64.555 | 0.68 | 54.2315 | 37.453 |
| 0.02 | 0.0012 | 3.783 | 0.36 | 50.6233 | 64.201 | 0.69 | 53.5958 | 39.064 |
| 0.03 | 0.0064 | 5.699 | 0.37 | 53.4173 | 63.624 | 0.70 | 53.1591 | 40.791 |
| 0.04 | 0.0197 | 7.643 | 0.38 | 56.1013 | 62.826 | 0.71 | 52.9343 | 42.607 |
| 0.05 | 0.0479 | 9.624 | 0.39 | 58.6521 | 61.816 | 0.72 | 52.9313 | 44.491 |
| 0.06 | 0.0985 | 11.649 | 0.40 | 61.0475 | 60.613 | 0.73 | 53.1562 | 46.412 |
| 0.07 | 0.1808 | 13.723 | 0.41 | 63.2674 | 59.232 | 0.74 | 53.6121 | 48.337 |
| 0.08 | 0.3051 | 15.852 | 0.42 | 65.2932 | 57.689 | 0.75 | 54.2981 | 50.244 |
| 0.09 | 0.4830 | 18.037 | 0.43 | 67.1085 | 56.012 | 0.76 | 55.2101 | 52.097 |
| 0.10 | 0.7263 | 20.276 | 0.44 | 68.6997 | 54.218 | 0.77 | 56.3402 | 53.875 |
| 0.11 | 1.0477 | 22.577 | 0.45 | 70.0556 | 52.338 | 0.78 | 57.6773 | 55.547 |
| 0.12 | 1.4599 | 24.930 | 0.46 | 71.1680 | 50.396 | 0.79 | 59.2071 | 57.089 |
| 0.13 | 1.9754 | 27.327 | 0.47 | 72.0319 | 48.416 | 0.80 | 60.9123 | 58.476 |
| 0.14 | 2.6065 | 29.768 | 0.48 | 72.6454 | 46.429 | 0.81 | 62.7727 | 59.693 |
| 0.15 | 3.3647 | 32.243 | 0.49 | 73.0097 | 44.462 | 0.82 | 64.7658 | 60.713 |
| 0.16 | 4.2605 | 34.734 | 0.50 | 73.1296 | 42.546 | 0.83 | 66.8670 | 61.526 |
| 0.17 | 5.3031 | 37.234 | 0.51 | 73.0129 | 40.702 | 0.84 | 69.0500 | 62.118 |
| 0.18 | 6.5003 | 39.730 | 0.52 | 72.6706 | 38.960 | 0.85 | 71.2872 | 62.482 |
| 0.19 | 7.8581 | 42.202 | 0.53 | 72.1168 | 37.345 | 0.86 | 73.5498 | 62.611 |
| 0.20 | 9.3806 | 44.634 | 0.54 | 71.3684 | 35.878 | 0.87 | 75.8090 | 62.502 |
| 0.21 | 11.0696 | 47.008 | 0.55 | 70.4450 | 34.584 | 0.88 | 78.0356 | 62.163 |
| 0.22 | 12.9248 | 49.309 | 0.56 | 69.3685 | 33.475 | 0.89 | 80.1993 | 61.588 |
| 0.23 | 14.9435 | 51.509 | 0.57 | 68.1630 | 32.572 | 0.90 | 82.2765 | 60.796 |
| 0.24 | 17.1205 | 53.602 | 0.58 | 66.8542 | 31.888 | 0.91 | 84.2385 | 59.850 |
| 0.25 | 19.4483 | 55.557 | 0.59 | 65.4694 | 31.428 | 0.92 | 86.0593 | 58.598 |
| 0.26 | 21.9168 | 57.365 | 0.60 | 64.0366 | 31.205 | 0.93 | 87.7171 | 57.230 |
| 0.27 | 24.5135 | 59.002 | 0.61 | 62.5848 | 31.217 | 0.94 | 89.1917 | 55.709 |
| 0.28 | 27.2237 | 60.458 | 0.62 | 61.1427 | 31.464 | 0.95 | 90.4654 | 54.054 |
| 0.29 | 30.0306 | 61.715 | 0.63 | 59.7386 | 31.944 | 0.96 | 91.5239 | 52.292 |
| 0.30 | 32.9153 | 62.760 | 0.64 | 58.4013 | 32.648 | 0.97 | 92.3557 | 50.456 |
| 0.31 | 35.8574 | 63.587 | 0.65 | 57.1574 | 33.566 | 0.98 | 92.9531 | 48.571 |
| 0.32 | 38.8348 | 64.184 | 0.66 | 56.0324 | 34.686 | 0.99 | 93.3116 | 46.664 |
| 0.33 | 41.8244 | 64.544 | | | | 1.00 | 93.4307 | 44.766 |

# APPENDIX III

## Inverse Mutual Radiation Impedance of Two Arms
## of a Thin Biconical Antenna

| $l/\lambda$ | $R_{12}$ | $X_{12}$ | $l/\lambda$ | $R_{12}$ | $X_{12}$ | $l/\lambda$ | $R_{12}$ | $X_{12}$ |
|---|---|---|---|---|---|---|---|---|
| 0.00 | 0.0000 | 0.000 | 0.34 | 34.0367 | 13.694 | 0.67 | −11.8799 | −0.655 |
| 0.01 | 0.0001 | 0.729 | 0.35 | 35.4562 | 11.804 | 0.68 | −11.9102 | +2.604 |
| 0.02 | 0.0012 | 1.467 | 0.36 | 36.6873 | 9.739 | 0.69 | −11.5482 | 5.863 |
| 0.03 | 0.0063 | 2.221 | 0.37 | 37.7065 | 7.458 | 0.70 | −10.7940 | 9.073 |
| 0.04 | 0.0197 | 2.999 | 0.38 | 38.4922 | 5.094 | 0.71 | −9.6535 | 12.187 |
| 0.05 | 0.0476 | 3.806 | 0.39 | 39.0258 | 2.698 | 0.72 | −8.1386 | 15.158 |
| 0.06 | 0.0978 | 4.649 | 0.40 | 39.2912 | 0.177 | 0.73 | −6.2669 | 17.941 |
| 0.07 | 0.1792 | 5.531 | 0.41 | 39.2759 | −2.440 | 0.74 | −4.0615 | 20.492 |
| 0.08 | 0.3017 | 6.453 | 0.42 | 38.9710 | −5.049 | 0.75 | −1.5510 | 22.771 |
| 0.09 | 0.4760 | 7.417 | 0.43 | 38.3716 | −7.642 | 0.76 | +1.2311 | 24.741 |
| 0.10 | 0.7134 | 8.420 | 0.44 | 37.4770 | −10.182 | 0.77 | 4.2469 | 26.369 |
| 0.11 | 1.0251 | 9.459 | 0.45 | 36.2906 | −12.634 | 0.78 | 7.4544 | 27.627 |
| 0.12 | 1.4222 | 10.527 | 0.46 | 34.8204 | −14.964 | 0.79 | 10.8080 | 28.493 |
| 0.13 | 1.9154 | 11.618 | 0.47 | 33.0789 | −17.136 | 0.80 | 14.2579 | 28.949 |
| 0.14 | 2.5144 | 12.720 | 0.48 | 31.0827 | −19.117 | 0.81 | 17.7592 | 28.984 |
| 0.15 | 3.2277 | 13.822 | 0.49 | 28.8528 | −20.875 | 0.82 | 21.2548 | 28.592 |
| 0.16 | 4.0622 | 14.910 | 0.50 | 26.4143 | −22.382 | 0.83 | 24.6944 | 27.773 |
| 0.17 | 5.0231 | 15.967 | 0.51 | 23.7957 | −23.612 | 0.84 | 28.0260 | 26.541 |
| 0.18 | 6.1136 | 16.982 | 0.52 | 21.0293 | −24.541 | 0.85 | 31.1988 | 24.903 |
| 0.19 | 7.3345 | 17.931 | 0.53 | 18.1503 | −25.150 | 0.86 | 34.1636 | 22.883 |
| 0.20 | 8.6840 | 18.799 | 0.54 | 15.1962 | −25.424 | 0.87 | 36.8739 | 20.309 |
| 0.21 | 10.1579 | 19.567 | 0.55 | 12.2068 | −25.354 | 0.88 | 39.2866 | 17.610 |
| 0.22 | 11.7492 | 20.216 | 0.56 | 9.2232 | −24.933 | 0.89 | 41.3625 | 14.814 |
| 0.23 | 13.4482 | 20.728 | 0.57 | 6.2874 | −24.161 | 0.90 | 43.0673 | 11.580 |
| 0.24 | 15.2423 | 21.085 | 0.58 | 3.4414 | −23.044 | 0.91 | 44.3718 | 8.147 |
| 0.25 | 17.1165 | 21.272 | 0.59 | 0.7272 | −21.590 | 0.92 | 44.2525 | 4.564 |
| 0.26 | 19.0530 | 21.274 | 0.60 | −1.8146 | −19.815 | 0.93 | 45.6922 | 0.884 |
| 0.27 | 21.0319 | 21.079 | 0.61 | −4.1452 | −17.739 | 0.94 | 45.6804 | −2.837 |
| 0.28 | 23.0312 | 20.676 | 0.62 | −6.2278 | −15.250 | 0.95 | 45.2130 | −6.547 |
| 0.29 | 25.0269 | 20.058 | 0.63 | −8.0288 | −12.645 | 0.96 | 44.2930 | −10.186 |
| 0.30 | 26.9938 | 19.220 | 0.64 | −9.5182 | −9.977 | 0.97 | 42.9304 | −13.701 |
| 0.31 | 28.9054 | 18.161 | 0.65 | −10.6700 | −6.991 | 0.98 | 41.1418 | −17.036 |
| 0.32 | 30.7346 | 16.883 | 0.66 | −11.4627 | −3.869 | 0.99 | 38.9505 | −20.142 |
| 0.33 | 32.4540 | 15.390 | | | | 1.00 | 36.3864 | −22.967 |

# APPENDIX IV

## The Inverse Radiation Resistance, $R_a$, and Reactance, $X_a$, of a Thin Biconical Antenna with Equal Arms Making a 90° Angle, and the Mutual Radiation Resistance, $R_{12}$, between Its Arms

| $l/\lambda$ | $R_a$ | $X_a$ | $R_{12}$ | $l/\lambda$ | $R_a$ | $X_a$ | $R_{12}$ | $l/\lambda$ | $R_a$ | $X_a$ | $R_{12}$ |
|---|---|---|---|---|---|---|---|---|---|---|---|
| 0 | 0 | 0 | 0 | 0.34 | 94.955 | 143.103 | 2.6743 | 0.67 | 135.324 | 59.256 | 12.612 |
| 0.01 | 0.0002 | 4.041 | 0 | 0.35 | 101.586 | 143.340 | 3.0495 | 0.68 | 132.497 | 60.724 | 12.017 |
| 0.02 | 0.0024 | 8.093 | 0 | 0.36 | 108.157 | 143.068 | 3.4551 | 0.69 | 129.887 | 62.581 | 11.348 |
| 0.03 | 0.0128 | 12.188 | 0 | 0.37 | 114.616 | 142.292 | 3.8909 | 0.70 | 127.535 | 64.794 | 10.608 |
| 0.04 | 0.0394 | 16.342 | 0 | 0.38 | 120.914 | 141.020 | 4.3556 | 0.71 | 125.478 | 67.327 | 9.8048 |
| 0.05 | 0.0960 | 20.575 | 0.0001 | 0.39 | 126.999 | 139.268 | 4.8473 | 0.72 | 123.750 | 70.143 | 8.9439 |
| 0.06 | 0.1974 | 24.897 | 0.0002 | 0.40 | 132.825 | 137.059 | 5.3652 | 0.73 | 122.376 | 73.194 | 8.0316 |
| 0.07 | 0.3624 | 29.324 | 0.0004 | 0.41 | 138.348 | 134.417 | 5.9064 | 0.74 | 121.380 | 76.435 | 7.0778 |
| 0.08 | 0.6120 | 33.864 | 0.0009 | 0.42 | 143.521 | 131.373 | 6.4674 | 0.75 | 120.776 | 79.820 | 6.0898 |
| 0.09 | 0.9694 | 38.524 | 0.0017 | 0.43 | 148.308 | 127.964 | 7.0457 | 0.76 | 120.575 | 83.297 | 5.0776 |
| 0.10 | 1.4590 | 43.306 | 0.0032 | 0.44 | 152.673 | 124.231 | 7.6367 | 0.77 | 120.781 | 86.820 | 4.0504 |
| 0.11 | 2.1068 | 48.210 | 0.0057 | 0.45 | 156.585 | 120.219 | 8.2368 | 0.78 | 121.395 | 90.336 | 3.0202 |
| 0.12 | 2.9386 | 53.231 | 0.0094 | 0.46 | 160.019 | 115.973 | 8.8415 | 0.79 | 122.405 | 93.799 | 1.9954 |
| 0.13 | 3.9808 | 58.360 | 0.0150 | 0.47 | 162.952 | 111.547 | 9.4440 | 0.80 | 123.803 | 97.159 | 0.9890 |
| 0.14 | 5.2590 | 63.582 | 0.0230 | 0.48 | 165.372 | 106.992 | 10.041 | 0.81 | 125.566 | 100.376 | 0.0100 |
| 0.15 | 6.7980 | 68.883 | 0.0343 | 0.49 | 167.268 | 102.362 | 10.624 | 0.82 | 127.673 | 103.403 | −0.9294 |
| 0.16 | 8.6202 | 74.240 | 0.0496 | 0.50 | 168.640 | 97.714 | 11.190 | 0.83 | 130.092 | 106.205 | −1.8208 |
| 0.17 | 10.746 | 79.630 | 0.0700 | 0.51 | 169.489 | 93.102 | 11.731 | 0.84 | 132.795 | 108.748 | −2.6525 |
| 0.18 | 13.194 | 85.024 | 0.0967 | 0.52 | 169.825 | 88.579 | 12.242 | 0.85 | 135.746 | 110.998 | −3.4140 |
| 0.19 | 15.978 | 90.389 | 0.1309 | 0.53 | 169.665 | 84.200 | 12.716 | 0.86 | 138.902 | 112.939 | −4.0990 |
| 0.20 | 19.109 | 95.694 | 0.1740 | 0.54 | 169.029 | 80.017 | 13.146 | 0.87 | 142.225 | 114.542 | −4.6965 |
| 0.21 | 22.595 | 100.905 | 0.2278 | 0.55 | 167.943 | 76.075 | 13.526 | 0.88 | 145.668 | 115.797 | −5.2014 |
| 0.22 | 26.437 | 105.981 | 0.2938 | 0.56 | 166.441 | 72.423 | 13.852 | 0.89 | 148.186 | 116.692 | −5.6061 |
| 0.23 | 30.634 | 110.884 | 0.3737 | 0.57 | 164.560 | 69.099 | 14.117 | 0.90 | 152.744 | 117.227 | −5.9043 |
| 0.24 | 35.180 | 115.573 | 0.4694 | 0.58 | 162.341 | 66.140 | 14.316 | 0.91 | 156.291 | 117.401 | −6.0930 |
| 0.25 | 40.061 | 120.016 | 0.5823 | 0.59 | 159.829 | 63.577 | 14.445 | 0.92 | 159.781 | 117.224 | −6.1690 |
| 0.26 | 45.263 | 124.169 | 0.7148 | 0.60 | 157.073 | 61.438 | 14.500 | 0.93 | 163.174 | 116.707 | −6.1302 |
| 0.27 | 51.764 | 127.997 | 0.8683 | 0.61 | 154.123 | 59.743 | 14.476 | 0.94 | 166.431 | 115.870 | −5.9764 |
| 0.28 | 56.537 | 131.461 | 1.0449 | 0.62 | 151.031 | 58.505 | 14.373 | 0.95 | 169.514 | 114.731 | −5.7082 |
| 0.29 | 62.554 | 134.534 | 1.2465 | 0.63 | 147.851 | 57.732 | 14.187 | 0.96 | 172.392 | 113.322 | −5.3277 |
| 0.30 | 68.781 | 137.185 | 1.4750 | 0.64 | 144.637 | 57.429 | 13.917 | 0.97 | 175.033 | 111.669 | −4.8390 |
| 0.31 | 75.177 | 139.385 | 1.7311 | 0.65 | 141.444 | 57.590 | 13.564 | 0.98 | 177.413 | 109.807 | −4.2466 |
| 0.32 | 81.701 | 141.116 | 2.0157 | 0.66 | 138.322 | 58.204 | 13.129 | 0.99 | 179.509 | 107.772 | −3.5570 |
| 0.33 | 88.308 | 142.360 | 2.3298 | | | | | 1.00 | 181.308 | 105.602 | −2.7765 |

# APPENDIX V

## Inverse Radiation Impedance, $Z_a = R_a + iX_a$, of Two Thin Cones Making an Angle $\vartheta$

### $R_a$

| $l/\lambda$ | $\vartheta = 40°$ | 60° | 80° | 100° | 120° | 140° | 160° | 180° |
|---|---|---|---|---|---|---|---|---|
| 0 | 0 | 0 | 0 | 0 | 0 | 0 | 0 | 0 |
| 0.01 | 0.000 | 0.000 | 0.000 | 0.000 | 0.000 | 0.000 | 0.000 | 0.000 |
| 0.02 | 0.001 | 0.001 | 0.002 | 0.003 | 0.004 | 0.004 | 0.005 | 0.005 |
| 0.03 | 0.003 | 0.006 | 0.010 | 0.015 | 0.019 | 0.022 | 0.024 | 0.025 |
| 0.04 | 0.009 | 0.020 | 0.033 | 0.046 | 0.059 | 0.070 | 0.076 | 0.079 |
| 0.05 | 0.022 | 0.048 | 0.079 | 0.112 | 0.143 | 0.169 | 0.185 | 0.191 |
| 0.06 | 0.046 | 0.099 | 0.163 | 0.231 | 0.295 | 0.347 | 0.381 | 0.393 |
| 0.07 | 0.085 | 0.182 | 0.300 | 0.425 | 0.542 | 0.637 | 0.699 | 0.720 |
| 0.08 | 0.144 | 0.307 | 0.506 | 0.717 | 0.914 | 1.074 | 1.178 | 1.214 |
| 0.09 | 0.229 | 0.487 | 0.803 | 1.136 | 1.446 | 1.698 | 1.861 | 1.918 |
| 0.10 | 0.345 | 0.734 | 1.208 | 1.708 | 2.174 | 2.550 | 2.795 | 2.879 |
| 0.11 | 0.499 | 1.062 | 1.746 | 2.466 | 3.134 | 3.674 | 4.024 | 4.145 |
| 0.12 | 0.698 | 1.484 | 2.436 | 3.437 | 4.365 | 5.113 | 5.597 | 5.764 |
| 0.13 | 0.948 | 2.013 | 3.303 | 4.653 | 5.903 | 6.908 | 7.557 | 7.782 |
| 0.14 | 1.256 | 2.665 | 4.366 | 6.144 | 7.784 | 9.100 | 9.949 | 10.242 |
| 0.15 | 1.629 | 3.452 | 5.648 | 7.936 | 10.041 | 11.726 | 12.811 | 13.185 |
| 0.16 | 2.072 | 4.387 | 7.167 | 10.055 | 12.704 | 14.819 | 16.177 | 16.645 |
| 0.17 | 2.593 | 5.483 | 8.942 | 12.525 | 15.800 | 18.406 | 20.078 | 20.653 |
| 0.18 | 3.197 | 6.749 | 10.989 | 15.364 | 19.349 | 22.511 | 24.533 | 25.228 |
| 0.19 | 3.888 | 8.196 | 13.321 | 18.588 | 23.368 | 27.147 | 29.558 | 30.385 |
| 0.20 | 4.671 | 9.831 | 15.948 | 22.208 | 27.865 | 32.322 | 35.157 | 36.129 |
| 0.21 | 5.551 | 11.662 | 18.877 | 26.229 | 32.844 | 38.035 | 41.328 | 42.455 |
| 0.22 | 6.529 | 13.692 | 22.113 | 30.654 | 38.302 | 44.277 | 48.057 | 49.348 |
| 0.23 | 7.608 | 15.923 | 25.656 | 35.474 | 44.225 | 51.031 | 55.321 | 56.783 |
| 0.24 | 8.789 | 18.356 | 29.502 | 40.686 | 50.596 | 58.267 | 63.086 | 64.726 |
| 0.25 | 10.072 | 20.990 | 33.644 | 46.267 | 57.387 | 65.951 | 71.310 | 73.130 |
| 0.26 | 11.457 | 23.819 | 38.069 | 52.198 | 64.565 | 74.037 | 79.940 | 81.940 |
| 0.27 | 12.941 | 26.838 | 42.764 | 58.450 | 72.088 | 82.471 | 88.913 | 91.091 |
| 0.28 | 14.523 | 30.038 | 47.709 | 64.990 | 79.907 | 91.193 | 98.160 | 100.510 |
| 0.29 | 16.198 | 33.408 | 52.881 | 71.779 | 87.968 | 100.131 | 107.603 | 110.115 |
| 0.30 | 17.963 | 36.936 | 58.254 | 78.775 | 96.210 | 109.213 | 117.155 | 119.818 |
| 0.31 | 19.811 | 40.606 | 63.798 | 85.930 | 104.567 | 118.355 | 126.728 | 129.526 |
| 0.32 | 21.737 | 44.404 | 69.482 | 93.192 | 112.968 | 127.474 | 136.225 | 139.138 |
| 0.33 | 23.734 | 48.310 | 75.270 | 100.507 | 121.340 | 136.480 | 145.549 | 148.557 |
| 0.34 | 25.794 | 52.305 | 81.126 | 107.817 | 129.607 | 145.283 | 154.600 | 157.678 |
| 0.35 | 27.910 | 56.370 | 87.011 | 115.064 | 137.692 | 153.791 | 163.279 | 166.399 |
| 0.36 | 30.073 | 60.482 | 92.886 | 122.188 | 145.516 | 161.915 | 171.489 | 174.621 |
| 0.37 | 32.274 | 64.621 | 98.709 | 129.128 | 153.004 | 169.566 | 179.135 | 182.248 |
| 0.38 | 34.505 | 68.762 | 104.442 | 135.825 | 160.080 | 176.659 | 186.127 | 189.187 |
| 0.39 | 36.757 | 72.886 | 110.042 | 142.222 | 166.673 | 183.115 | 192.383 | 195.356 |
| 0.40 | 39.021 | 76.968 | 115.472 | 148.262 | 172.716 | 188.861 | 197.826 | 200.677 |
| 0.41 | 41.288 | 80.989 | 120.694 | 153.894 | 178.147 | 193.831 | 202.391 | 205.087 |
| 0.42 | 43.550 | 84.927 | 125.671 | 159.069 | 182.911 | 197.968 | 206.022 | 208.528 |
| 0.43 | 45.798 | 88.762 | 130.371 | 163.743 | 186.960 | 201.227 | 208.676 | 210.960 |
| 0.44 | 48.025 | 92.477 | 134.762 | 167.878 | 190.254 | 203.570 | 210.321 | 212.353 |
| 0.45 | 50.225 | 96.053 | 138.818 | 171.441 | 192.763 | 204.975 | 210.940 | 212.692 |
| 0.46 | 52.390 | 99.477 | 142.515 | 174.405 | 194.465 | 205.429 | 210.529 | 211.977 |
| 0.47 | 54.516 | 102.734 | 145.833 | 176.753 | 195.350 | 204.933 | 209.098 | 210.222 |
| 0.48 | 56.597 | 105.815 | 148.758 | 178.471 | 195.418 | 203.501 | 206.674 | 207.456 |
| 0.49 | 58.629 | 108.709 | 151.277 | 179.556 | 194.677 | 201.160 | 203.296 | 203.725 |
| 0.50 | 60.611 | 111.409 | 153.385 | 180.011 | 193.150 | 197.949 | 199.018 | 199.088 |

198

## APPENDIX V (*Continued*)

# Inverse Radiation Impedance, $Z_a = R_a + iX_a$, of Two Thin Cones Making an Angle $\vartheta$

$R_a$

| $l/\lambda$ | $\vartheta = 40°$ | 60° | 80° | 100° | 120° | 140° | 160° | 180° |
|---|---|---|---|---|---|---|---|---|
| 0.51 | 62.539 | 113.913 | 155.080 | 179.847 | 190.867 | 193.922 | 193.908 | 193.617 |
| 0.52 | 64.413 | 116.217 | 156.366 | 179.081 | 187.869 | 189.143 | 188.047 | 187.400 |
| 0.53 | 66.232 | 118.322 | 157.249 | 177.741 | 184.209 | 183.687 | 181.527 | 180.534 |
| 0.54 | 67.997 | 120.230 | 157.743 | 175.860 | 179.947 | 177.642 | 174.451 | 173.129 |
| 0.55 | 69.710 | 121.947 | 157.864 | 173.477 | 175.152 | 171.101 | 166.932 | 165.304 |
| 0.56 | 71.374 | 123.480 | 157.632 | 170.638 | 169.900 | 164.169 | 159.091 | 157.183 |
| 0.57 | 72.990 | 124.836 | 157.073 | 167.395 | 164.275 | 156.955 | 151.053 | 148.901 |
| 0.58 | 74.564 | 126.028 | 156.214 | 163.806 | 158.366 | 149.575 | 142.950 | 140.591 |
| 0.59 | 76.100 | 127.066 | 155.087 | 159.930 | 152.267 | 142.146 | 134.915 | 132.393 |
| 0.60 | 77.603 | 127.966 | 153.724 | 155.833 | 146.072 | 134.790 | 127.082 | 124.444 |
| 0.61 | 79.078 | 128.742 | 152.163 | 151.582 | 139.881 | 127.626 | 119.582 | 116.879 |
| 0.62 | 80.532 | 129.409 | 150.441 | 147.245 | 133.792 | 120.774 | 112.544 | 109.829 |
| 0.63 | 81.969 | 129.984 | 148.595 | 142.891 | 127.901 | 114.347 | 106.090 | 103.420 |
| 0.64 | 83.397 | 130.484 | 146.667 | 138.590 | 122.305 | 108.455 | 100.336 | 97.766 |
| 0.65 | 84.821 | 130.926 | 144.694 | 134.410 | 117.093 | 103.202 | 95.387 | 92.975 |
| 0.66 | 86.247 | 131.326 | 142.716 | 130.417 | 112.353 | 98.680 | 91.338 | 89.139 |
| 0.67 | 87.681 | 131.701 | 140.770 | 126.674 | 108.163 | 94.974 | 88.271 | 86.340 |
| 0.68 | 89.128 | 132.066 | 138.893 | 123.239 | 104.596 | 92.157 | 86.253 | 84.643 |
| 0.69 | 90.593 | 132.436 | 137.119 | 120.169 | 101.716 | 90.289 | 85.337 | 84.095 |
| 0.70 | 92.079 | 132.824 | 135.480 | 117.510 | 99.575 | 89.417 | 85.560 | 84.730 |
| 0.71 | 93.592 | 133.243 | 134.003 | 115.308 | 98.218 | 89.571 | 86.940 | 86.562 |
| 0.72 | 95.133 | 133.702 | 132.716 | 113.597 | 97.677 | 90.770 | 86.480 | 89.585 |
| 0.73 | 96.705 | 134.212 | 131.639 | 112.408 | 97.972 | 93.015 | 93.164 | 93.779 |
| 0.74 | 98.309 | 134.778 | 130.792 | 111.763 | 99.114 | 96.292 | 97.959 | 99.101 |
| 0.75 | 99.946 | 135.406 | 130.187 | 111.674 | 101,097 | 100.572 | 103.813 | 105.494 |
| 0.76 | 101.615 | 136.100 | 129.836 | 112.148 | 103.908 | 105.811 | 110.660 | 112.882 |
| 0.77 | 103.314 | 136.860 | 129.744 | 113.184 | 107.518 | 111.948 | 118.417 | 121.174 |
| 0.78 | 105.042 | 137.685 | 129.912 | 114.772 | 111.889 | 118.911 | 126.986 | 130.263 |
| 0.79 | 106.796 | 138.574 | 130.338 | 116.894 | 116.970 | 126.615 | 132.256 | 140.030 |
| 0.80 | 108.571 | 139.521 | 131.015 | 119.524 | 122.702 | 134.962 | 146.105 | 150.344 |
| 0.81 | 110.363 | 140.520 | 131.932 | 122.633 | 129.013 | 143.843 | 156.400 | 161.064 |
| 0.82 | 112.167 | 141.563 | 133.076 | 126.179 | 135.827 | 153.142 | 167.001 | 172.041 |
| 0.83 | 113.976 | 142.641 | 134.429 | 130.120 | 143.056 | 162.736 | 177.760 | 183.123 |
| 0.84 | 115.785 | 143.743 | 135.971 | 134.406 | 150.608 | 172.496 | 188.529 | 194.152 |
| 0.85 | 117.585 | 144.856 | 137.677 | 138.982 | 158.387 | 182.289 | 199.155 | 204.972 |
| 0.86 | 119.371 | 145.969 | 139.523 | 143.791 | 166.291 | 191.981 | 209.488 | 215.427 |
| 0.87 | 121.134 | 147.069 | 141.483 | 148.771 | 174.219 | 201.440 | 219.380 | 225.366 |
| 0.88 | 122.867 | 148.141 | 143.527 | 153.861 | 182.066 | 210.534 | 228.690 | 234.644 |
| 0.89 | 124.561 | 149.171 | 145.626 | 158.996 | 189.732 | 219.139 | 237.283 | 243.127 |
| 0.90 | 126.210 | 150.147 | 147.752 | 164.114 | 197.115 | 227.134 | 245.035 | 250.690 |
| 0.91 | 127.806 | 151.055 | 149.875 | 169.150 | 204.121 | 234.408 | 251.833 | 257.221 |
| 0.92 | 129.341 | 151.882 | 151.966 | 174.044 | 210.658 | 240.861 | 257.579 | 262.624 |
| 0.93 | 130.810 | 152.617 | 153.999 | 178.738 | 216.643 | 246.402 | 262.189 | 266.819 |
| 0.94 | 132.206 | 153.250 | 155.948 | 183.176 | 222.000 | 250.955 | 265.595 | 269.744 |
| 0.95 | 133.524 | 153.771 | 157.789 | 187.308 | 226.662 | 254.459 | 267.750 | 271.357 |
| 0.96 | 134.759 | 154.173 | 159.500 | 191.089 | 230.571 | 256.866 | 268.622 | 271.634 |
| 0.97 | 135.907 | 154.450 | 161.064 | 194.478 | 233.683 | 258.145 | 268.200 | 270.572 |
| 0.98 | 136.965 | 154.597 | 162.465 | 197.441 | 235.962 | 258.283 | 266.494 | 268.190 |
| 0.99 | 137.932 | 154.613 | 163.691 | 199.950 | 237.385 | 257.282 | 263.530 | 264.524 |
| 1.00 | 138.805 | 154.497 | 164.733 | 202.041 | 237.942 | 255.162 | 259.357 | 259.634 |

## APPENDIX V (*Continued*)

### Inverse Radiation Impedance, $Z_a = R_a + iX_a$, of Two Thin Cones Making an Angle $\vartheta$

$$X_a$$

| $l/\lambda$ | $\vartheta = 40°$ | 60° | 80° | 100° | 120° | 140° | 160° | 180° |
|------|--------|---------|---------|---------|---------|---------|---------|---------|
| 0    | 0       | 0       | 0       | 0       | 0       | 0       | 0       | 0       |
| 0.01 | 2.219   | 3.059   | 3.746   | 4.292   | 4.708   | 5.001   | 5.175   | 5.232   |
| 0.02 | 4.444   | 6.129   | 7.509   | 8.608   | 9.445   | 10.034  | 10.385  | 10.501  |
| 0.03 | 6.680   | 9.222   | 11.306  | 12.969  | 14.238  | 15.132  | 15.664  | 15.841  |
| 0.04 | 8.932   | 12.346  | 15.153  | 17.398  | 19.114  | 20.325  | 21.045  | 21.284  |
| 0.05 | 11.206  | 15.514  | 19.065  | 21.914  | 24.096  | 25.637  | 26.556  | 26.861  |
| 0.06 | 13.506  | 18.732  | 23.056  | 26.533  | 29.204  | 31.094  | 32.221  | 32.596  |
| 0.07 | 15.836  | 22.008  | 27.135  | 31.271  | 34.454  | 36.712  | 38.059  | 38.507  |
| 0.08 | 18.200  | 25.349  | 31.312  | 36.137  | 39.860  | 42.503  | 44.083  | 44.609  |
| 0.09 | 20.600  | 28.760  | 35.592  | 41.138  | 45.426  | 48.475  | 50.299  | 50.906  |
| 0.10 | 23.037  | 32.242  | 39.979  | 46.277  | 51.154  | 54.626  | 56.705  | 57.396  |
| 0.11 | 25.515  | 35.798  | 44.472  | 51.550  | 57.040  | 60.950  | 63.292  | 64.071  |
| 0.12 | 28.031  | 39.425  | 49.069  | 56.952  | 63.071  | 67.432  | 70.043  | 70.912  |
| 0.13 | 30.587  | 43.123  | 53.763  | 62.471  | 69.233  | 74.050  | 76.932  | 77.892  |
| 0.14 | 33.179  | 46.885  | 58.543  | 68.091  | 75.501  | 80.775  | 83.928  | 84.977  |
| 0.15 | 35.806  | 50.704  | 63.396  | 73.789  | 81.846  | 87.571  | 90.990  | 92.126  |
| 0.16 | 38.465  | 54.573  | 68.307  | 79.541  | 88.233  | 94.396  | 98.068  | 99.288  |
| 0.17 | 41.151  | 58.481  | 73.255  | 85.317  | 94.623  | 101.200 | 105.110 | 106.407 |
| 0.18 | 43.859  | 62.415  | 78.218  | 91.083  | 100.969 | 107.930 | 112.056 | 113.421 |
| 0.19 | 46.584  | 66.362  | 83.172  | 96.802  | 107.225 | 114.528 | 118.840 | 120.264 |
| 0.20 | 49.318  | 70.306  | 88.089  | 102.433 | 113.336 | 120.930 | 125.394 | 126.864 |
| 0.21 | 52.055  | 74.230  | 92.940  | 107.935 | 119.247 | 127.073 | 131.647 | 133.150 |
| 0.22 | 54.788  | 78.118  | 97.694  | 113.262 | 124.903 | 132.890 | 137.527 | 139.045 |
| 0.23 | 57.508  | 81.951  | 102.321 | 118.369 | 130.246 | 138.313 | 142.962 | 144.477 |
| 0.24 | 60.207  | 85.709  | 106.788 | 123.211 | 135.217 | 143.278 | 147.880 | 149.373 |
| 0.25 | 62.877  | 89.374  | 111.062 | 127.743 | 139.762 | 147.719 | 152.213 | 153.661 |
| 0.26 | 65.509  | 92.927  | 115.112 | 131.920 | 143.825 | 151.578 | 155.897 | 157.278 |
| 0.27 | 68.094  | 96.347  | 118.906 | 135.699 | 147.357 | 154.797 | 158.874 | 160.165 |
| 0.28 | 70.625  | 99.619  | 122.416 | 139.042 | 150.311 | 157.327 | 161.091 | 162.269 |
| 0.29 | 73.093  | 102.722 | 125.612 | 141.911 | 152.644 | 159.124 | 162.505 | 163.546 |
| 0.30 | 75.490  | 105.642 | 128.469 | 144.274 | 154.322 | 160.152 | 163.082 | 163.963 |
| 0.31 | 77.809  | 108.362 | 130.964 | 146.105 | 155.317 | 160.384 | 162.796 | 163.495 |
| 0.32 | 80.044  | 110.869 | 133.077 | 147.379 | 155.606 | 159.803 | 161.634 | 162.130 |
| 0.33 | 82.189  | 113.152 | 134.792 | 148.080 | 155.178 | 158.403 | 159.594 | 159.868 |
| 0.34 | 84.239  | 115.199 | 136.096 | 148.199 | 154.027 | 156.185 | 156.684 | 156.721 |
| 0.35 | 86.189  | 117.003 | 136.981 | 147.729 | 152.158 | 153.165 | 152.928 | 152.714 |
| 0.36 | 88.035  | 118.559 | 137.442 | 146.675 | 149.585 | 149.369 | 148.360 | 147.884 |
| 0.37 | 89.776  | 119.862 | 137.479 | 145.045 | 146.330 | 144.833 | 143.027 | 142.283 |
| 0.38 | 91.410  | 120.912 | 137.096 | 142.856 | 142.427 | 139.604 | 136.987 | 135.972 |
| 0.39 | 92.936  | 121.710 | 136.303 | 140.130 | 137.916 | 133.742 | 130.310 | 129.027 |
| 0.40 | 94.355  | 122.259 | 135.112 | 136.899 | 132.847 | 127.315 | 123.079 | 121.532 |
| 0.41 | 95.667  | 122.567 | 133.541 | 133.197 | 127.279 | 120.399 | 115.381 | 113.582 |
| 0.42 | 96.877  | 122.640 | 131.613 | 129.067 | 121.276 | 113.081 | 107.381 | 105.281 |
| 0.43 | 97.986  | 122.489 | 129.352 | 124.558 | 114.911 | 105.453 | 98.995  | 96.740  |
| 0.44 | 98.998  | 122.128 | 126.788 | 119.723 | 108.263 | 97.616  | 90.525  | 88.075  |
| 0.45 | 99.919  | 121.569 | 123.953 | 114.618 | 101.414 | 89.672  | 82.024  | 79.409  |
| 0.46 | 100.754 | 120.830 | 120.884 | 109.305 | 94.451  | 81.729  | 73.611  | 70.863  |
| 0.47 | 101.509 | 119.928 | 117.617 | 103.848 | 87.464  | 73.896  | 65.406  | 62.560  |
| 0.48 | 102.191 | 118.880 | 114.192 | 98.314  | 80.545  | 66.281  | 57.530  | 54.627  |
| 0.49 | 102.807 | 117.708 | 110.652 | 92.769  | 73.784  | 58.992  | 50.097  | 47.175  |
| 0.50 | 103.363 | 116.431 | 107.037 | 87.283  | 67.271  | 52.135  | 43.219  | 40.324  |

## APPENDIX V (*Continued*)

# Inverse Radiation Impedance, $Z_a = R_a + iX_a$, of Two Thin Cones Making an Angle $\vartheta$

$$X_a$$

| $l/\lambda$ | $\vartheta = 40°$ | 60° | 80° | 100° | 120° | 140° | 160° | 180° |
|------|---------|---------|---------|---------|---------|---------|---------|---------|
| 0.51 | 103.868 | 115.071 | 103.391 | 81.922 | 61.095 | 45.808 | 37.004 | 34.180 |
| 0.52 | 104.329 | 113.647 | 99.756 | 76.753 | 55.340 | 40.107 | 31.546 | 28.840 |
| 0.53 | 104.753 | 112.181 | 96.174 | 71.839 | 50.084 | 35.116 | 26.935 | 24.391 |
| 0.54 | 105.148 | 110.693 | 92.685 | 67.240 | 45.401 | 30.914 | 23.247 | 20.911 |
| 0.55 | 105.521 | 109.202 | 89.327 | 63.014 | 41.357 | 27.567 | 20.545 | 18.460 |
| 0.56 | 105.878 | 107.728 | 86.138 | 59.212 | 38.009 | 25.131 | 18.881 | 17.087 |
| 0.57 | 106.225 | 106.288 | 83.151 | 55.879 | 35.407 | 23.648 | 18.290 | 16.824 |
| 0.58 | 106.568 | 104.897 | 80.396 | 53.058 | 33.589 | ·23.149 | 18.791 | 17.689 |
| 0.59 | 106.911 | 103.571 | 77.901 | 50.779 | 32.584 | 23.648 | 20.390 | 19.679 |
| 0.60 | 107.259 | 102.322 | 75.689 | 49.070 | 32.408 | 25.148 | 23.074 | 22.779 |
| 0.61 | 107.615 | 101.160 | 73.778 | 47.950 | 33.067 | 27.636 | 26.815 | 26.954 |
| 0.62 | 107.981 | 100.095 | 72.184 | 47.428 | 34.556 | 31.085 | 31.568 | 32.153 |
| 0.63 | 108.360 | 99.133 | 70.917 | 47.509 | 36.857 | 35.452 | 37.273 | 38.309 |
| 0.64 | 108.750 | 98.279 | 69.982 | 48.185 | 39.942 | 40.682 | 43.856 | 45.341 |
| 0.65 | 109.154 | 97.534 | 69.381 | 49.445 | 43.770 | 46.708 | 51.228 | 53.153 |
| 0.66 | 109.569 | 96.900 | 69.110 | 51.267 | 48.292 | 53.447 | 59.286 | 61.634 |
| 0.67 | 109.993 | 96.373 | 69.162 | 53.623 | 53.445 | 60.808 | 67.918 | 70.666 |
| 0.68 | 110.424 | 95.951 | 69.523 | 56.478 | 59.162 | 68.689 | 77.000 | 80.118 |
| 0.69 | 110.858 | 95.628 | 70.180 | 59.788 | 65.363 | 76.980 | 86.403 | 89.852 |
| 0.70 | 111.292 | 95.395 | 71.110 | 63.508 | 71.964 | 85.563 | 95.988 | 99.725 |
| 0.71 | 111.720 | 95.243 | 72.292 | 67.582 | 78.874 | 94.316 | 105.614 | 109.590 |
| 0.72 | 112.137 | 95.163 | 73.700 | 71.953 | 85.996 | 103.113 | 115.139 | 119.298 |
| 0.73 | 112.538 | 95.143 | 75.304 | 76.561 | 93.233 | 111.826 | 124.419 | 128.702 |
| 0.74 | 112.916 | 95.169 | 77.074 | 81.339 | 100.482 | 120.327 | 133.313 | 137.658 |
| 0.75 | 113.265 | 95.229 | 78.978 | 86.224 | 107.642 | 128.491 | 141.687 | 146.027 |
| 0.76 | 113.580 | 95.309 | 80.982 | 91.146 | 114.612 | 136.197 | 149.409 | 153.677 |
| 0.77 | 113.854 | 95.396 | 83.053 | 96.039 | 121.295 | 143.329 | 156.360 | 160.488 |
| 0.78 | 114.080 | 95.475 | 85.156 | 100.837 | 127.595 | 149.780 | 162.428 | 166.349 |
| 0.79 | 114.253 | 95.533 | 87.258 | 105.475 | 133.424 | 155.451 | 167.518 | 171.164 |
| 0.80 | 114.367 | 95.558 | 89.327 | 109.891 | 138.699 | 160.255 | 171.544 | 174.853 |
| 0.81 | 114.418 | 95.538 | 91.331 | 114.029 | 143.346 | 164.116 | 174.438 | 177.350 |
| 0.82 | 114.400 | 95.462 | 93.242 | 117.833 | 147.297 | 166.972 | 176.149 | 178.609 |
| 0.83 | 114.311 | 95.321 | 95.033 | 121.256 | 150.497 | 168.777 | 176.643 | 178.602 |
| 0.84 | 114.146 | 95.106 | 96.680 | 124.255 | 152.900 | 169.497 | 175.904 | 177.319 |
| 0.85 | 113.904 | 94.812 | 98.161 | 126.794 | 154.473 | 169.117 | 173.935 | 174.771 |
| 0.86 | 113.583 | 94.433 | 99.460 | 128.843 | 155.193 | 167.638 | 170.756 | 170.988 |
| 0.87 | 113.183 | 93.967 | 100.562 | 130.381 | 155.049 | 165.075 | 166.409 | 166.018 |
| 0.88 | 112.704 | 93.414 | 101.457 | 131.394 | 154.045 | 161.461 | 160.951 | 159.929 |
| 0.89 | 112.146 | 92.773 | 102.139 | 131.873 | 152.195 | 156.845 | 154.457 | 152.806 |
| 0.90 | 111.514 | 92.049 | 102.604 | 131.820 | 149.526 | 151.290 | 147.020 | 144.751 |
| 0.91 | 110.809 | 91.245 | 102.855 | 131.244 | 146.077 | 144.875 | 138.746 | 135.882 |
| 0.92 | 110.035 | 90.370 | 102.896 | 130.160 | 141.898 | 137.690 | 129.755 | 126.327 |
| 0.93 | 109.198 | 89.431 | 102.735 | 128.592 | 137.050 | 129.839 | 120.180 | 116.229 |
| 0.94 | 108.303 | 88.438 | 102.385 | 126.569 | 131.602 | 121.435 | 110.162 | 105.738 |
| 0.95 | 107.357 | 87.404 | 101.861 | 124.127 | 125.635 | 112.601 | 99.851 | 95.013 |
| 0.96 | 106.365 | 86.341 | 101.181 | 121.309 | 119.234 | 103.467 | 89.401 | 84.217 |
| 0.97 | 105.337 | 85.264 | 100.365 | 118.160 | 112.493 | 94.166 | 78.971 | 73.514 |
| 0.98 | 104.279 | 84.186 | 99.437 | 114.732 | 105.508 | 84.836 | 68.720 | 63.070 |
| 0.99 | 103.201 | 83.124 | 98.420 | 111.080 | 98.382 | 75.617 | 58.805 | 53.045 |
| 1.00 | 102.110 | 82.093 | 97.340 | 107.259 | 91.217 | 66.646 | 49.377 | 43.596 |

# APPENDIX VI

## The Inverse Mutual Radiation Resistance of Two Inclined Cones

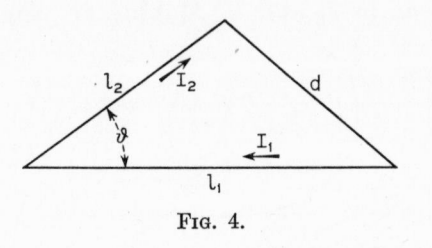

FIG. 4.

The mutual radiation resistance of two inclined wires (Fig. 4) with reference to the maximum current amplitude is

$$
\begin{aligned}
R_{12} = {} & 15 \cos(L_1 - L_2)(\operatorname{Cin} x_1 + \operatorname{Cin} x_2) - \\
& 15 \cos(L_1 + L_2)(\operatorname{Cin} x_3 + \operatorname{Cin} x_4) + \\
& 15 \sin(L_1 - L_2)(\operatorname{Si} x_1 - \operatorname{Si} x_2) + \\
& 15 \sin(L_1 + L_2)(\operatorname{Si} x_3 + \operatorname{Si} x_4) + \\
& 30 \sin L_1 \sin L_2 (1 - \operatorname{Cin} 2L_1 - \operatorname{Cin} 2L_2) - \\
& 30 \sin L_1 \cos L_2 \operatorname{Si} 2L_2 - 30 \sin L_2 \cos L_1 \operatorname{Si} 2L_1,
\end{aligned}
$$

where

$$
L_1 = \beta l_1 = \frac{2\pi l_1}{\lambda}, \qquad\qquad L_2 = \beta l_2 = \frac{2\pi l_2}{\lambda},
$$

$$
d^2 = l_1{}^2 - 2l_1 l_2 \cos \vartheta + l_2{}^2,
$$

$$
x_1 = \beta(-l_1 + l_2 + d), \qquad\qquad x_2 = \beta(l_1 - l_2 + d),
$$

$$
x_3 = \beta(l_1 + l_2 - d), \qquad\qquad x_4 = \beta(l_1 + l_2 + d).
$$

# APPENDIX VII

## The Inverse Mutual Radiation Resistance of Two Thin Cones, of Lengths $l_1$ and $l_2$, Making an Angle 180°

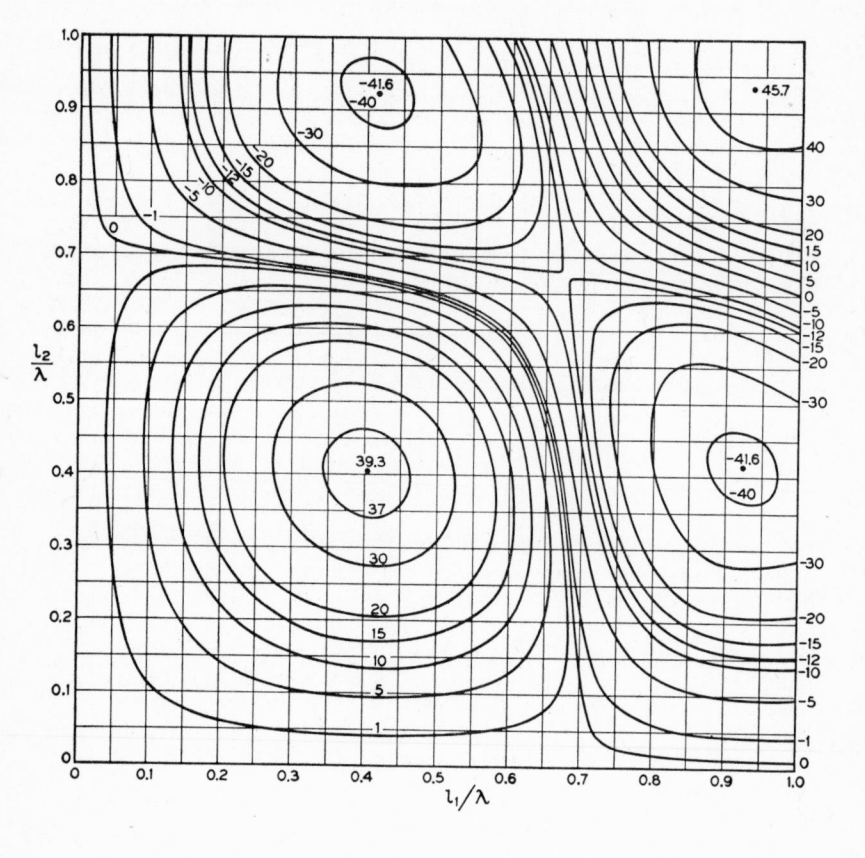

# APPENDIX VIII

## $M(\beta l)$ and $N(\beta l)$ for Cylindrical Antennas, for Use in Equation 1–136

| $l/\lambda$ | $M(\beta l)$ | $N(\beta l)$ | $l/\lambda$ | $M(\beta l)$ | $N(\beta l)$ | $l/\lambda$ | $M(\beta l)$ | $N(\beta l)$ |
|------|--------|--------|------|--------|--------|------|--------|--------|
| 0 | 0 | 0 | 0.34 | 46.83 | 156.48 | 0.67 | 64.02 | 46.65 |
| 0.01 | −0.2364 | 0.01322 | 0.35 | 56.22 | 157.64 | 0.68 | 59.34 | 51.79 |
| 0.02 | −0.9399 | 0.1054 | 0.36 | 65.63 | 157.87 | 0.69 | 55.32 | 57.59 |
| 0.03 | −2.094 | 0.3542 | 0.37 | 74.95 | 157.19 | 0.70 | 52.05 | 63.95 |
| 0.04 | −3.671 | 0.8339 | 0.38 | 84.09 | 155.59 | 0.71 | 49.58 | 70.76 |
| 0.05 | −5.634 | 1.615 | 0.39 | 92.93 | 153.10 | 0.72 | 47.97 | 77.94 |
| 0.06 | −7.934 | 2.761 | 0.40 | 101.37 | 149.76 | 0.73 | 47.26 | 85.36 |
| 0.07 | −10.516 | 4.331 | 0.41 | 109.31 | 145.61 | 0.74 | 47.46 | 92.91 |
| 0.08 | −13.31 | 6.373 | 0.42 | 116.66 | 140.71 | 0.75 | 48.60 | 100.49 |
| 0.09 | −16.26 | 8.929 | 0.43 | 123.34 | 135.14 | 0.76 | 50.66 | 107.96 |
| 0.10 | −19.28 | 12.03 | 0.44 | 129.27 | 128.97 | 0.77 | 53.62 | 115.21 |
| 0.11 | −22.28 | 15.68 | 0.45 | 134.38 | 122.31 | 0.78 | 57.46 | 122.14 |
| 0.12 | −25.20 | 19.92 | 0.46 | 138.63 | 115.24 | 0.79 | 62.12 | 128.63 |
| 0.13 | −27.93 | 24.72 | 0.47 | 141.96 | 107.87 | 0.80 | 67.55 | 134.59 |
| 0.14 | −30.41 | 30.07 | 0.48 | 144.35 | 100.32 | 0.81 | 73.68 | 139.92 |
| 0.15 | −32.54 | 35.95 | 0.49 | 145.78 | 92.68 | 0.82 | 80.41 | 144.54 |
| 0.16 | −34.25 | 42.32 | 0.50 | 146.26 | 85.09 | 0.83 | 87.66 | 148.38 |
| 0.17 | −35.47 | 49.14 | 0.51 | 145.79 | 77.64 | 0.84 | 95.33 | 151.38 |
| 0.18 | −36.12 | 56.34 | 0.52 | 144.40 | 70.46 | 0.85 | 103.30 | 153.50 |
| 0.19 | −36.15 | 63.86 | 0.53 | 142.13 | 63.65 | 0.86 | 111.48 | 154.69 |
| 0.20 | −35.51 | 71.63 | 0.54 | 139.03 | 57.31 | 0.87 | 119.73 | 154.95 |
| 0.21 | −34.15 | 79.56 | 0.55 | 135.16 | 51.53 | 0.88 | 127.95 | 154.26 |
| 0.22 | −32.04 | 87.57 | 0.56 | 130.61 | 46.42 | 0.89 | 136.02 | 152.65 |
| 0.23 | −29.17 | 95.56 | 0.57 | 125.45 | 42.03 | 0.90 | 143.83 | 150.12 |
| 0.24 | −25.52 | 103.44 | 0.58 | 119.78 | 38.45 | 0.91 | 151.25 | 146.73 |
| 0.25 | −21.10 | 111.12 | 0.59 | 113.71 | 35.71 | 0.92 | 158.19 | 142.53 |
| 0.26 | −15.93 | 118.49 | 0.60 | 107.34 | 33.88 | 0.93 | 164.56 | 137.57 |
| 0.27 | −10.031 | 125.47 | 0.61 | 100.79 | 32.96 | 0.94 | 170.25 | 131.95 |
| 0.28 | −3.446 | 131.96 | 0.62 | 94.17 | 32.99 | 0.95 | 175.20 | 125.74 |
| 0.29 | +3.771 | 137.88 | 0.63 | 87.59 | 33.95 | 0.96 | 179.34 | 119.04 |
| 0.30 | 11.560 | 143.16 | 0.64 | 81.18 | 35.83 | 0.97 | 182.61 | 111.96 |
| 0.31 | 19.85 | 147.71 | 0.65 | 75.04 | 38.60 | 0.98 | 184.96 | 104.60 |
| 0.32 | 28.55 | 151.48 | 0.66 | 69.29 | 42.23 | 0.99 | 186.39 | 97.09 |
| 0.33 | 37.57 | 154.42 | | | | 1.00 | 186.86 | 89.53 |

# APPENDIX IX

## $M(l)$ and $N(l)$ for Tapered Antennas

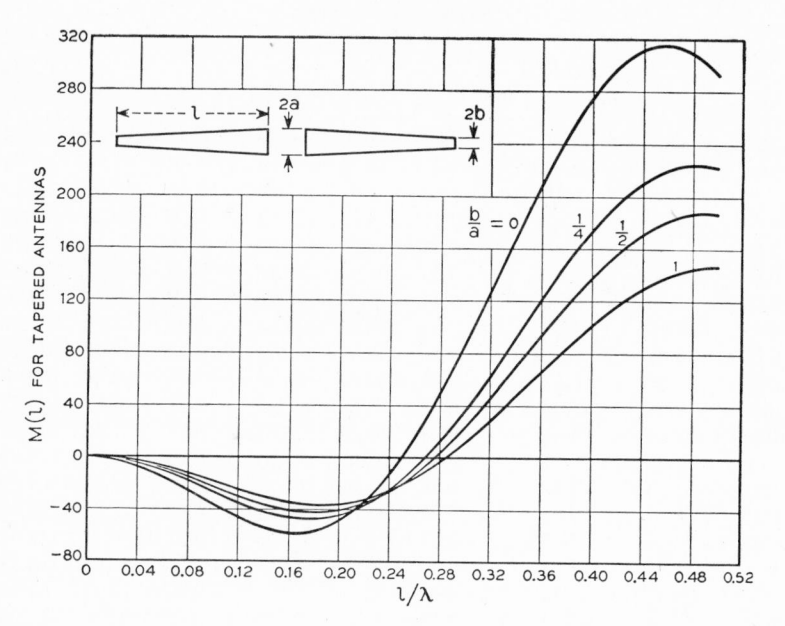

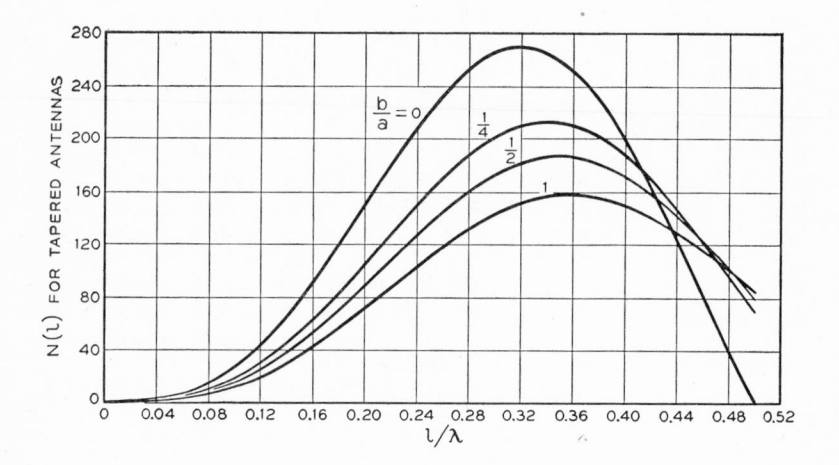

# INDEX

207